I'M GOOD

I'M GOOD

OLIVIA GAYNOR

NEW DEGREE PRESS

I'M GOOD

ISBN   978-1-64137-968-7   *Paperback*

978-1-64137-798-0   *Kindle Ebook*

978-1-64137-799-7   *Ebook*

CONTENTS

ACKNOWLEDGMENTS

———

I'd like to thank everyone who listened to me talk about living with chronic illnesses. Thank you for providing that first platform to explore my thoughts and feelings that led me to writing this book. I had the amazing opportunity to talk with some of my favorite chronic illness influencers like The Disabled Hippie & Lady of Lyme who took time out of their busy schedules to share their lives with me. Thank you to my amazing family and my amazing publishing family. I could not have created something so beautiful inside and out without the help from Eric Koester, Brian Bies, Karina Agbisit, and John Chancey.

Abigail Dodds	Alisa DeLuca	Allie Kunen
Alyssa Hanel	Andrew Ryder	Anna Evenosky
Annemarie Hayes	Ariana Aguero	Arlene Starr
Brenna Sherrer	Brianna Howland	Brooke Freeburg
Caroline MacKeen	Catherine McEachern	Chelsea Spell
Cheyenne Tang	Chloe Buergenthal	Christina Costa
Christina Flamporis	Christina Kovacs	Cindy Derrow
Cindy Shera	Dana Rubenstein	Danielle deBairos

Debbie & Ed Gaynor	Debra Samel	Diana Conroy
Dina Yyson	Ella Houlihan	Emily H Reith
Eric Koester	Fallon Keane	Gabrielle Feuer
Hadar Re'em	Harli Starr	Helen Donadio
Ingrid Hjerpe	Irene Chien	Isabel Kaufman
Jacqueline Miller	Jennifer Bosworth	Jennifer Moscovitch
Jodi Sokoloff	Julia Termine	Kammie Takahashi
Katharine Stuppi	Katherine Paul	Laura Cole
lizaburkin	Louis Braver	Lynn H Slotkin
Maddy Giles	Madeleine Vaver	Madeline Basirico
Maia Brint	Margo Libre	Mariah Prosansky
Mary Fitzhugh	Marygrace Pier	Matthew Athanas-Linden
Meghan Palumbo	Melissa Elizabeth	Melissa Gralitzer
Meriel Conroy	Miki Lazowski	Mina Yazdanian
Miranda Salters	Molly A. Plotkin	Nancy P Collins
Nellie Fagan	Olivia Garcia	Pam Postrel
Pamela Moschini	Paula Derrow	Portia Alleyne
Quentin Daniel Bernhard	Raimi Marx	Rasleen Grewal
Rebecca Donadio	Reed Schmidt	Renee Heller
Renee Levine	Sarah Evenosky	Sarah Goldman
Sarah Vetesi	Savanna Frazier	Susan Luth Leahey
Sydney Baron		

For June, my forever best friend. You know what? I love you.

"I encourage you all to recognize that disability is a family you can join at any point in your life."[1] — Judy Heumann

---

1   *TED, Our fight for disability rights — and why we're not done yet* | TED, October 2016, video, 15:58.

PART ONE

INTRODUCTION

———

Here I am, twenty-one and unable to get out of my own bed. My body is weak. My mind is strong, but it has great moments of weakness. Right now, it is feeling quite weak. When you're living with chronic illnesses, there are times where your brain does not want to fight. That's where I am now. My diseases have no timeline. They come and go at whatever strength and time they please. I have very few things that I have power over in my life since my diagnoses. They take over every aspect of my life and often make me feel helpless and alone. Writing is something that I can control. It gives me power.

To outsiders, my life is absurd and people are unsure of how I function day to day. Honestly, I'm unsure of how I function too. Somehow, I make it work. My story is my own, but it isn't so different. Through my many interviews, time on Twitter, and support groups, I've found that my story is almost average.

This whole world of people may have different diagnoses but are going through the same struggles and finding their own ways to make it work. We are chronic illness warriors who often fight invisible battles. These battles are physical as well as mental. We fight to wake up in the morning, get dressed, take our pills, and simply survive. We fight perceptions that people have about us. Seemingly, we have it better off because people do not know we're sick; we "don't look sick," which able-bodied people see as a perk. However, this lack of obvious illness causes all sorts of problems because we have to fight for both accommodations and for people to believe us. I've spent my whole life explaining my struggles to people, but I never get to speak in-depth about my lived experience.

Although I can't control the diseases that live inside of me, I can control how I look at them and how I talk about them with others. I can frame my life in the way that I want to frame it. Many things are more difficult for me, but I manage it all well. I've learned how to balance my anxieties, fears, hopes, dreams, and reality. I'm writing this book because I think that my insights on how to cope with chronic illness can help other people. I purposely wrote this book in an accessible way because I want family members, friends, and anyone who knows anyone with a chronic illness to better understand what it's like to live in a body like mine. A guest on the *Invisible Not Broken* podcast, Nitika Chopra once said, "I'm a patient and I've built enough courage to try and push through all of my fears to see if I can help someone."[2] I am also a patient and I want to try and help others like me,

---

2   Nitika Chopra, Interview by Eva Minkoff, Invisible Not Broken, podcast audio, August 18, 2019

but I also want to create something that even able-bodied people want to read.

People with chronic illnesses often face extreme isolation and loneliness. I, and others throughout this piece, will be here to continually remind you that you're not alone. Statistically, six in ten American adults have a chronic illness and four in ten have multiple.[3] You are not alone, even if it may feel like it at times. Chronic illnesses are complex and hard to explain, but my goal is to help you feel loved and cared for, while also helping you to explain your situation to those around you. Maybe you're a loved one, and I'm here to support you too. This book is meant to give advice on a wide range of topics while also realizing that sometimes there is no right answer or right thing to say. Just know that there are so many people out there who understand what you're going through and know the toll it takes on your body. You are not alone.

I want you to feel a sense of security as you read this. Whether you're a patient, a parent of a patient, a best friend, or a significant other, I want this book to be there for you. You should read this book if you're chronically ill, curious, or have a loved one who you want to better understand. Together, we will walk through my own journey with incredible stories from disability influencers, friends, and celebrities who are all struggling with us. We will talk about the intersectionality of disability, love, self-worth, mental illness, choices, the idea

3   "National Center for Chronic Disease Prevention and Health Promotion," Center for Disease Control and Prevention, U.S. Department of Health & Human Services, October 23, 2019

of "good days," autonomy, and disclosure of disability. We will talk about these little moments that may seem insignificant to an able-bodied person but impact a chronically ill person in a large way. I can't wait to share these stories with you.

BACKGROUND

———

I was born on January 21, 1998. I was supposed to be born in February. Honestly, nothing too exciting came from my birth. Well, that's somewhat of a lie. All the doctors on staff that night were betting on me because my mom had previously had a c-section with my older brother. Once you have one c-section, you're bound to have another. I decided I wanted to come out the old-fashioned way: straight from my mother's vaginal canal. For the first time in my life, I fooled a lot of doctors. Unknowingly, this would be a recurring theme throughout my entire existence.

From there, things were kind of fine. I feel like every baby has some issues. As long as it isn't cancer or organ trouble, it's usually okay that the baby isn't perfect. My baby issues were definitely second-tier problems. I had a little cornea surgery where, according to my family, I received banana scented anesthesia. I believe that banana anesthesia fueled my hatred for the fruit. I refused to eat bananas throughout my entire childhood. In kindergarten I was praised for bringing a banana as a healthy snack, but after receiving that compliment I threw it in the trash. Nothing could make me eat that dreaded thing.

After the cornea issue, I was diagnosed with baby colitis. From day one my stomach was having issues and the nightly suppositories and I became closer than close. At least after the diagnosis it was confirmed I was allergic to milk. Unfortunately, my mom was unable to produce breast milk to feed me. She had almost killed my brother from her lack of milk three-and-a-half years prior so I don't even think she gave it a shot. However, my mom was reassured that this was just a phase and that I would grow out of baby colitis.

In this same period of infancy my grandmother, and future best friend, came for a visit. I seemed very happy lying on my back, not moving. I believe her exact words were, "What's wrong with her?" Her tone was harsh but ultimately saved me. It turned out I had no muscle tone in my left leg. I used to drag that bad boy wherever I went. That gangly thing didn't stop me from exploring the great wide world of my confined house. I was then started on my first physical therapy regiment at only ten months old. It would not be my last.

You're probably thinking, "This girl was messed up! Of course, she has all of these problems! Of course, she is chronically ill! It all makes sense." Apparently, it didn't make any sense. Apparently, doctors couldn't look at my charts and see that I was not a normal baby. No, I wasn't cancer ridden or born with my organs outside of my body. In their eyes, I was okay. I wasn't an emergency. But believe me, I wanted nothing more than to be okay and fit in.

Throughout my childhood, I played every sport imaginable. I played basketball on the boys' team because they didn't have one for the girls. I played baseball until fourth grade when my dad forced me to switch over to softball. When I look back, through all of my athletic endeavors, those moments were filled with fear. If I had to slide in softball, I would fall into a panic. Everyone else could do it, but for some reason I feared that if I slid the wrong way my body would shatter.

These moments should have been filled with pure excitement, but I was living with this anxious mind that wasn't anxious for no reason. I was anxious to keep myself safe. I was anxious because my mind knew that something was wrong with my body even if the outside world didn't. As much as anxiety deteriorated my mental health, it saved me from hurting myself even more. My brain was telling me that I needed to be more careful than other kids my age. I tried as hard as I could to balance this relatively muddy and unclear information with the societal expectations for children to be playful and adventurous.

In the end, I probably pushed myself too much. I played softball throughout my high school years but if I had known that the extensive and rigorous exercise was hurting more than it was helping me, I would have quit sooner. I pushed myself far too much, and by junior year I could barely walk around school. My left hip would send shooting pains down my leg. Looking back, my hip was most likely subluxated which is just a step down from dislocated. I couldn't walk normally for months, but I still played softball my junior year.

My young life was filled with hospital visits and questions, but all of these questions typically ended up at dead ends. My knowledge of my body was never taken into serious consideration and I was often deemed too sensitive. I was emotional and distraught because my body was betraying me in small ways. I often wonder what my life would be like now if doctors had listened to my complaints and fears earlier on in my life.

During junior year of high school when my hip was throbbing and sending shooting pains down my side, I went to see a doctor. It had gotten so bad that I couldn't wait to be seen by my usual orthopedic doctor. The physician who saw me treated me like an idiot. He chewed bubble gum in my face and called me "sweetie" in a clearly demoralizing way. I couldn't walk properly and the pain was constant and intense. He basically said nothing was wrong and that I was fine. I knew both of those things were not true. I felt invalidated and infantilized. I was talked down to and my lived experience was minimized. So, I kept pushing myself. I knew that I was sick, but his demeaning tone said otherwise. The sad part is, I will never know how things could have turned out. This is why I work every day to make my current life the best one possible. After all, it is the only life I have.

FIRST DIAGNOSIS

———

Many procedural things happen when you're admitted to the hospital, but I don't remember any of them from the day I received my first diagnosis. I'm sure they took my height and weight and blood pressure, but I don't recall any of that. I don't remember saying anything to my new doctor or even giving my medical history, which I'm sure was something we went over. What I do remember is the feeling of utter joy that filled me when I was being diagnosed in Dr. P's office. My chest hurt, not because something was wrong with it, but because my insides were finally smiling. They were heard, and even thinking about it now I can close my eyes and feel at ease. I was not crazy. I was so incredibly proud to be right. I spent my entire childhood knowing that I was different and that I didn't feel well. I had to explain myself to adults who didn't take my pain or worries seriously. Once you get a diagnosis, people care and start to listen.

I flipped over onto my side so he could look at my butt. He pulled my cheeks apart and stated, "yep, that's Crohn's," and closed my cheeks back up. There was no need for further inspection. My doctor was looking for key signs of outer inflammation. I had hemorrhoids and fissures that he could visually see. On top of that, the symptoms I described to him added confidence to his diagnosis. He did say that I still needed a colonoscopy and endoscopy to see what was going on with my insides. I was so over the moon and just wanted to tell the entire world what was going on with my body.

To my surprise, my mom advised me not to say anything until the results of the colonoscopy and endoscopy came back. My heart sank. How could she say that to me? I think that there are many reasons why my mom reacted this way. One, no parent wants their kid to be sick. Part of her worries regarding my announcement could have come from that fear. If you tell the world then it has to be true. Another reason was that we didn't have the final results from the test. She did not want me to give out false information. When you've spent your whole life being told "oh you're so dramatic" and "it's not possible to be in so much pain," having a name is key for validation.

I had waited twelve years to hear that all of my symptoms were real and I was indeed very sick. Now all of a sudden, we didn't want to spread information that was potentially false. I had been spreading wrong information my whole life. I was told that I was healthy, so I tried my best to perform as such. I had always tried my hardest to appear healthy even when I knew it was the furthest from the truth. The toll that pretending wellness takes on a person is beyond draining, and at that moment I was done pretending. I would walk around faking a smile because all of the other kids my age were smiling. Have you ever had someone take too many pictures of you and your face hurts from smiling? It's like that, but that feeling of discomfort isn't just on your face but in your heart. I'd soon learn that a name and a diagnosis does not mean the pretending is over.

I don't remember if I actually cried in front of my mom, but I recall begging her to let me share this news with the world. I just wanted to tell one person, like my best friend or something. She insisted on waiting until everything was 100 percent confirmed. The high of finally receiving a diagnosis was quickly followed by the defeat and continuous silence I would have to face.

The two tests ended up not being pretty. You spend the entire day starving yourself. On top of that, you end up drinking an entire bottle of MiraLAX, which is an over the counter laxative. You mix it with Gatorade to keep yourself hydrated with electrolytes. I always drink some with iced tea, and for my first test they allowed me to drink root beer. If you've ever wondered what drinking an entire bottle of laxative is like, by the end you're pooping out pure liquid. You have nothing left in your system. The preparations made me hate Gatorade for the rest of my existence, but that wasn't even the worst part. After my procedures, I was officially diagnosed with Crohn's disease. To no one's surprise, the colonoscopy came back and was an actual shit show. My insides were ruined with cuts and blown up with extreme inflammation. I spent an entire day out of my sixth-grade classroom and in the hospital. We met with nutritionists, dermatologists, rheumatologists, social workers—anyone that could possibly have a hand in my case work.

I remember nothing about these meetings. Nothing except the comic book I was handed which went over how to explain Crohn's disease to other kids. I knew kids weren't known for being the kindest so I wanted to educate myself on Crohn's as best I could. I wanted to be ready with the right information and comebacks for any rude comments. I read the comic over and over, holding it tight like it was the instruction manual that held all of the most important information I would ever need to know about Crohn's. I was convinced this terribly written comic book would allow me to change the world, starting with my classmates.

Later in my life, I met another person who is living with Crohn's. Her name was Anna and we met by pure luck. Her sister was in my sorority in college and she brought Anna to formal. I met Anna right before I was diagnosed with Complex Regional Pain Syndrome (CRPS) and Ehlers-Danlos Syndrome (EDS). She was able to help me cope with those initial experiences down the line. She was able to do so because she has many of the same diseases I have. We are similar in many, many ways.

Anna, a twenty-one-year-old chronic illness warrior, also felt drawn to become an advocate. She described it as "a gut feeling and came on right after my first diagnosis," similar to me. We both believed with all of our hearts that we could "educate others, be a mentor and friend to fellow chronic illness sufferers, and advocate for the rights we deserve." All we wanted to do was help and advocate.

So as a twelve-year-old, I figured the first step was to educate everyone I knew on Crohn's. I've always had a big imagination and drive to do things. I would become obsessed with a topic and learn absolutely everything I could about it. It was the same with Crohn's. I had been hurting for so long, and now that I had a diagnosis, I needed to share it with the world. My parents wanted to educate themselves, but the rest of the world didn't seem as interested. That did not stop me from wanting to learn and advocate at a young age. I figured that if more people knew about it, maybe I could inspire or change what someone thought about it. For the most part, I really just wanted to share my story. I wanted someone who would listen and the best way to find that someone is to throw your ideas out to a giant group and hope at least one person gets back to you.

Once I was allowed to share my diagnosis, I immediately began researching to find out if I could raise money for it. I came across the Crohn's & Colitis Foundation of America, now just the Crohn's & Colitis Foundation. I created a team named "Olivia's Crohn's Crushers," which I thought was original until I saw a ton of other teams with the exact same name. My aunt, a fabulous lady who does commercials for Disney/Pixar, photo-shopped my head onto a green body stepping onto the team name. I added that graphic to a flyer which explained my disease and why I was raising money for it.

I vividly remember the anxious butterflies in my stomach as I put the flyers about the Take Steps Walk in the pick-up bin in front of my sixth-grade classroom. If there was paper in there, it was mandatory that you brought it home to your parents. I stood up against my locker and watched as my classmates came out of the room and picked up my papers.

I watched some of them read it and some of them toss it. I looked at their faces, hoping to get some sort of reaction. It was relatively lackluster and an overall disappointment. I quickly learned that twelve-year-old boys and girls are not super excited about bowel diseases.

It is already hard enough to fit in during middle school and here I was purposely standing out. As I should have expected, I didn't have many takers for kids who wanted to stand out with me. A few girls walked up and said that they'd try to come to the walk and would ask their parents about donating. I wearily nodded.

Every day I would check in with the people who had expressed some interest, but by the time the event rolled around everyone said they couldn't go to the walk. They would follow that up excitedly with "but I donated!" At this moment in time, I wasn't really on a mission for some cure. I was early on in my treatment and the options seemed endless. All I wanted was support from my friends and family. The money was the least of my problems; the connections were my most important goal. So, I was less than thrilled when my classmates happily declared, "but I donated!" Their words rang hollow and were the furthest from what I needed to hear.

Then came the day of the walk. I was so full of excitement as I put my shirt on that had the "no/do not" sign with Crohn's in the middle and my face with our team name on the back. I thought that I was unstoppable. At this point in my treatment, I was chock full of prednisone, a common steroid, and I had blown up like a balloon. My mom was even calling me "moon face," which I think was a sweet attempt at trying to normalize my extreme weight gain. Before steroids, I could have three shrimp and be full until breakfast the next morning. On steroids, I could eat a bacon, egg, and cheese croissant from Dunkin Donuts, a medium iced tea, and a Boston creme donut. About twenty minutes after finishing it all up, I would yell at my mom that I was hungry. I think you can now picture the insane amount of weight I gained in a very short period of time. Although steroids are a great rescue drug, meaning that they'll save you from danger which in this case was Crohn's, they have harmful side effects. One of those side effects includes extreme weight gain. This was both good and bad. I was finally eating, but I could not stop.

When I got to the walk, my name was on a sign as one of the top fundraisers. I had raised around two thousand dollars, which was more money than I had seen in my entire life. The top team tent had free donuts awaiting me and I couldn't contain my pudgy self and I waddled over as fast as I could. "Free donuts!" I exclaimed, and then proceeded to explain why I received a donut even though my parents are very good at reading signs and didn't need an explanation; I was simply proud.

After this initial bout of excitement, I looked around and saw several other teams and They were all huge. They were all laughing, taking pictures, and supporting someone that they loved. I looked around and had my family. My best friend at the time also came for a little bit. My heart sank and I wondered why no one wanted to come and support me. Why wasn't I good enough to receive love from others?

The walk should have been simple. The route went around a pond in Boston and I doubt it was even a mile long. My knees were full of rheumatoid arthritis, though, which didn't help in terms of walking. I had a limp and braces on my legs to help. After a few hundred feet, I couldn't walk anymore and groaned, "I can't do it anymore." My parents supported me, said that was fine, and we went and sat down.

I sat there in despair, I couldn't beat this disease. I couldn't "walk to end Crohn's," and I didn't have anyone there to help me walk for a cure either. I was filled with so much disappointment by my lack of supporters that the rest of the day was an unmemorable blur. Twelve-year-old me got free donuts, but there was no one to share them with. If there was no one to even share a sweet treat with, there certainly wasn't anyone there to support me in my battle against Crohn's in the years to come.

CHRISTINA'S FIRST DIAGNOSIS

———

My first diagnosis of Crohn's was not rare in the fact that I had to endure a lot of pain and waiting. These stories that come from the chronically ill community are far too common, and when I started writing this book I wanted to reach out and hear from others within the community. For Lady of Lyme, Christina, her diagnosis followed a similar pattern. She learned to live with her symptoms while she struggled to get the right diagnosis. This is Christina recounting her own illnesses. Her story is unique in some ways, but in others it matches up quite nicely with a majority of chronically ill lives.

Her journey to finding out she had Lyme disease started all the way back in 2006. She spent her summer days playing spotlight tag outside with friends to pass the time. Christina lived in extremely wooded areas which are typically associated with an abundance of ticks. After one particular night of playing outside, she came down with flu-like symptoms. She was sick all summer and no one could figure out what was wrong. As she bounced around from doctor to doctor, no one mentioned Lyme disease. Looking back, she recalled that no one ever seemed to think, "oh gosh, it could be Lyme disease or a tick-borne illness." Not only did the local doctors fail to consider a tick-borne illness, but no one in her community considered it a possibility either. According to her experiences, the mentality was "hmm, it's elsewhere, not here" when it came to Lyme disease.

For me, Lyme disease was something that I knew of from a very young age. Hearing her story and learning that other parts of the country weren't as aware of this illness was a bit shocking. I know the hurt and heartbreak of being sick without knowing why. Living like this is far from easy.

Over the years, Christina was prescribed a variety of antibiotics which helped make her feel a little bit better, but never managed to make her feel like her old self. Before she knew it, she was off to college. Her freshman year was difficult, but not the kind of difficult that many freshmen experience. She wasn't having trouble adjusting to classes or figuring out time management, but she faced this constant feeling of fatigue. She was "tested for mono numerous times that first semester" because her symptoms seemed to match with mono, a very common college illness. According to the Cleveland Clinic, "about 85 percent to 90 percent of American adults have developed antibodies to the Epstein-Barr virus by the time they are forty years old, which means that they have been infected with the virus at some point in their lives."[4] (3)

---

4   Mononucleosis (mono): Symptoms, Cleveland Clinic, Cleveland Clinic, November 24, 2015

People discredited her pain and fatigue by normalizing it. They claimed that college was just more strenuous than high school, but that type of reaction hurts undiagnosed and chronically ill people. It makes them doubt their symptoms or second-guess their own body. For Christina, she continued to fight and said, "I just don't feel right." This is something that I have personally dealt with. I spent twelve years complaining of stomach pain and bleeding only to be dismissed by doctors. My parents were following what a so-called expert said, so I don't blame them for not knowing. How could they? But I too persisted. I didn't feel right and as I got older, I could not only better explain my symptoms but would also stick up for myself and fight for my medical needs.

As she continued to get sicker and find little-to-no relief from her symptoms, she did what a lot of sick people do—she visited a variety of specialists. She went to a gastroenterologist for her stomach issues, a neurologist for her neurological issues, and a cardiologist for her heart palpitations. Everyone assumed these issues were all separate, so these specialists only focused on their area of expertise and didn't ever think to connect her problems together. Christina's health ebbed and flowed, her doctors would "put a band-aid on things here and there, but it was a solid five years" where she suffered greatly. Five years of no answers. I know it's hard, but try to imagine walking through life, crippled from pain year after year. Second after second can feel like years within itself. The process of diagnosing is painful and long. It's not like what you see in TV shows and movies, where doctors think outside of the box. Doctors are wonderful and important people, but they're also human which means they'll miss the mark sometimes.

It wasn't until after college, and her entrance into the working world, that she was finally diagnosed. She was not diagnosed in a typical way. She was working at a school for children who have different disabilities varying from autism to ADHD. She was told that she had to give her kids a visual acuity test and her boss thought it would be a good idea if she "did the test as one of the students" because that would be the best way Christina could learn. Christina failed the test. Her manager was terrified and said, "you know, I have to tell you, something is obviously not right because you really, really should not fail that." This manager encouraged her to see a neurological ophthalmologist who ultimately found brain damage during a scan. This brain damage could only be from an accident or from an infectious and internal source.

This doctor sent her off to one final doctor who did a simple blood test. It came back positive for Lyme disease. Unlike myself, Christina wasn't thrilled with this diagnosis. She didn't believe him. When you're suffering for any extended period of time, it's normal to not believe the answer you're given. If there was actually an answer, why wasn't it given sooner? The diagnosis of Lyme disease just didn't make sense to her, especially after she googled the disease and found that it effects people who spend a lot of time outdoors, like those who go hiking and camping. Christina had never been hiking before, but here she was being diagnosed with Lyme disease. There are just so many variables, and as Christina and her mother learned, medicine isn't so cut and dry. Finding out any sort of weakness can be shocking, even if you've been searching for an answer for a while.

Christina's story of searching is similar to my own and to many other chronically ill people. Each story has unique moments, but overall, they tend to follow similar trajectories.

"YOU KNOW YOUR BODY BEST"

"You know your body best."

All doctors have started telling me this. They started to say this around the age of nineteen but I knew my body at eighteen, seventeen, and sixteen. Hell, I knew my body at the age of four in preschool. Yet, it wasn't until I was almost out of my teens that I was given respect and honor over knowing my own body which had been sliding into ruin for years.

You need some more background on my medical journey toward my first diagnosis which, yes, is long and difficult but necessary to fully grasp living with a chronic illness. These diseases have slowly ruined my emotional health, but they have given me a sense of humor about life that very few people share. My medical history has also given me this book where I have had the amazing opportunity to talk to people who are very influential within the disabled community. I learned from them and their experiences and had the pleasure of entering into their world. Listening to each of them talk about their diseases and the impacts they've had was touching, and I connected to their words. Now, I can share those words with you and give you a glimpse into their world.

Warning: Things are about to take a gross medical turn.

Every year I would go for my physical exam. During the exam, my height and weight would be measured and recorded. I was always within the first percentile. I was short and very skinny. I complained all the time of what my parents' thought were "growing pains." I had to take Tylenol or Motrin every night as a child or else I would cry out in pain. Besides my legs, which from the beginning seemed to fuck me over, I was having stomach problems. Not just typical tummy troubles— serious life-debilitating trouble. I would try to go to the bathroom and have pools of blood beneath me. I used to sit on the toilet, crying for my parents because it was overwhelming. I didn't know why my body was doing this. The answer I was given for the first twelve years of my life was hemorrhoids.

I wasn't growing and I wasn't gaining weight. I was always in pain at night and I bled every time I used the bathroom. Still, according to my pediatrician, everything was fine.

The doctor was nice, but she thought of me as a kid. I've found that when doctors judge you based on your age, they make assumptions such as, "Oh, well kid just exaggerates their pain levels." Sure, some kids do, but you can't look at all kids with the same lens. If you do that, either all of your patients have cancer and are dying, or they are all perfectly fine. I've always been very articulate, and my parents have let me run my doctor's appointments as long as I have been able to talk. They did that because I knew what I was going through and I could explain it. It was my body after all. But for most of my early life, the doctors I visited didn't see it the same way.

Later in life, I was diagnosed with Complex Regional Pain Syndrome after I had my wisdom teeth removed. All of a sudden, I couldn't seem to walk, I was in constant pain, and I was very tired. My body became weaker almost instantly. The pain from my mouth was constant and I continued to bleed from my incision areas for around five months. Because of the pain and now more prevalent dislocations that seemed to be occurring, I visited my rheumatologist. On the spot, he diagnosed me with both Complex Regional Pain Syndrome (CRPS) and Ehlers-Danlos Syndrome (EDS). I've had CRPS symptoms almost my entire life, but before my wisdom teeth I hadn't had a terrible flare. To give you an idea, my CRPS symptoms include burning sensations, full musculoskeletal pain, sensitivity to temperatures, sensitivity to human touch, sweating, and swelling. CRPS is complicated but it is basically, "damage to, or malfunction of, the peripheral and central nervous systems."[5]

Although most CRPS diagnoses come from a single injury (ex: a broken foot or sprained ankle), mine stemmed from the constant subluxations and dislocations my body endured

---

5   Complex Regional Pain Syndrome Fact Sheet, National Institute of
     Neurological Disorders and Stroke, National Institute of Neurological
     Disorders and Stroke & National Institutes of Health, March 13, 2020

because of EDS. EDS is a connective tissue disorder and affects almost anything with tissue, but for me, mostly my joints and their almost constant subluxations were affected. Because my joints are almost never fully in the socket, they're loose. My body combats that by tightening up the muscles around the area which causes extreme pain. EDS also impacts my ability to heal. The inability to heal properly affected my wisdom teeth removal post-op.

Although I was diagnosed with these conditions at this moment in 2017, he claimed that I had been diagnosed with hypermobile issues previously. Because it was just referred to as being extra flexible, it didn't cause concern. If I had been told that the constant dislocations and subluxations were bad for me, I would have stopped playing sports long ago. I wouldn't have tried so hard to fit this mold of what an able-bodied person should be able to do. I would have been more careful and actually had a real diagnosis so that people would take me seriously. I wasn't just "bendy," I had a disorder. I was living with something that apparently caused my CRPS and yet no one seemed to think it was important to inform me. I had spent my whole life complaining to doctors that I was in a ton of pain and everything hurt. My body moved differently and I should have been told earlier that these symptoms I was sharing mattered. They should have been validated right on the spot.

For example, I cried of growing pains every night of my life. I lived off of chewable Tylenol and Motrin. Everyone just said that they were growing pains, and I believed them. I was told that they were normal and that they were a part of growing up. Later, I learned that growing pains are often a sign of

EDS. EDS can also affect your digestive tract, so it could have easily been interfering with my Crohn's symptoms as well. I was born without muscle tone in my left leg Lack of muscle tone is also very common with EDS. You can see that there are all of these signs that doctors missed. No one was putting the puzzle together, and because of that I had to suffer. I was deemed too sensitive, too dramatic. I was deemed too young. Because of those traits, I was deemed as an unreliable source and thus my concerns were not taken seriously.

After interviewing a few people, I learned that not being listened to wasn't just a childhood phenomenon. Christina was in her early twenties as she searched for a diagnosis for five years. Ultimately, she was diagnosed with Lyme disease. Only after her mother, who happens to be a doctor, came to the appointments did she notice a change in how she was treated. She emphasized how her own doctors were treating her with higher regard simply because she was the daughter of a medical doctor.

For Christina there were "so many things I mean, obviously going through trying to get diagnosed, if I would go to an appointment and I would be there alone without my mom, I would be treated completely different than if my mom was there and they knew she was a medical doctor, like completely different and that really upset me because I was like, 'What the heck! How would this doctor treat someone who didn't come with someone who was a medical doctor?' That made me really upset." As someone who was the child of a non-medical doctor, I'd say that the treatment matches up with Christina's worries.

Although it was always my body, although it was always my pain, I never seemed to be the expert. When you spend all of this time trying to find the perfect doctor, most people would expect to find someone who would actually listen to their patient's concerns. At first Christina expected that "they're going to listen to patients, and they're going to listen to their concerns and piece them together. So, it really kind of upended I think, a lot of what, you know, a lot of us, you know, thought about the way medicine working in the medical community or anything in general." After years of desperately wanting to be listened to about what was happening in our own bodies, Christina and I stopped looking for miracles. We just wanted to be treated with respect.

These actions seem so simple because that's what the healthy world thinks happens when you enter a doctor's office. People who go for their yearly physical assume you go into the office and you leave with answers and a feeling of respect. However, most of the time you have to fight to be heard and you have to fight and prove that you know your body.

Why is this concept of self-knowledge so difficult for medical professionals to grasp? Honestly, I'm not sure, but the more time I spend in hospitals and waiting rooms, the more time I have to think and reflect on what is going on around me. I think that a lot of the time, the onus is on the parents. If parents believe their kids like my parents did, they will be in a better place. I see patients who I know are over eighteen years old and yet their parents are sitting there filling out their paperwork as if they don't know how to do anything for themselves. This discredits what young people have to say. Putting yourself into a position against world renowned doctors isn't easy, but it is something that I believe needs to be done. The child has to speak as much as they can. The teenager needs to speak as much as they can. The young adult needs to speak as much as they can. The patient knows themselves best.

MAYBE BEING DIFFERENT ISN'T GOOD

———

Living with chronic invisible illnesses comes with its own set of distinct challenges. For those who don't know, invisible illnesses are ones that people can't see. I have Crohn's disease which is a form of inflammatory bowel disease (IBD), meaning I have inflammation and other complications in my digestive tract as well as the Crohn's that has moved to other parts of my body. That being said, looking at me you wouldn't know I had Crohn's because I look normal to the average person. Even when I gained all that weight while on steroids, people just saw it as me gaining weight and didn't understand that medical side effects caused the gain.

Other invisible and chronic illnesses include diabetes, CRPS, EDS, and rheumatoid arthritis. Because invisible illnesses are unseen, most people assume you're well and able-bodied. People don't really believe that you're sick. People don't think that you need any support (i.e., ambulatory wheelchair user, handicap parking pass, etc.). People think that you're healthy and you just complain a lot. People don't understand that you're sick all of the time, you don't have control over flares, and you can't be putting other people before your own needs. My whole life, including this exact moment in time, I have struggled listening to ableists speak their mind on the matter of my body. Every day, even with some of my good friends, I have to explain myself. I shouldn't have to, but I often do. Few people in my life fully accept me, and I'm waiting for that to happen more often as this world becomes a more inclusive place.

The first time someone actually pointed out my disease, I felt my face flush in embarrassment and my voice go silent. My throat became dry and I didn't have anything to say. In that moment I couldn't find the words, but I did afterwards. I kept this secret from my family for years because my parents loved this girl's parents and I didn't want to bring it up. I was embarrassed that I stood out and was called out for something I couldn't control. The girl laughed as she said, "you have arthritis," as I struggled down the three steps in her house. I just stood there on the second step confused, concerned, and called-out.

Previously, I was publicizing my illnesses because I thought that awareness was important and that I, an individual, could make a difference. In that exact moment, publicizing my diseases felt like the worst decision I could have ever made.

Pretty early on I started to question things about my disabilities. Although this was the first time that it was deliberately pointed out, I did think about it on my own. At this point in my life, I didn't refer to them as disabilities. I just said that

I had Crohn's and I had arthritis, but I didn't label myself beyond that because I didn't know there were other labels. I didn't have a computer. I had a regular flip phone. I didn't have the access that young people now have to communities that they see themselves within. I didn't see myself as disabled. I think seeing myself as able-bodied hurt me because I often pushed myself to reach able-bodied standards. I also didn't have the vocabulary and knowledge about disability theories and studies that I now have. Back then, I was living in a world where I thought I was just going to get better. I thought that if I was on the right medication, I'd live a pretty normal life. I had a very positive, and honestly very naive, outlook on my future.

After I got my wisdom teeth removed in college and my CRPS flared and basically shut down my nervous system, while at the same time being diagnosed with EDS, I started to see I was different. Not only did I see I was different, but I wanted to educate and inform others. As a college student, I now had access to Instagram and Twitter and connected to these other people who were also suffering. I met my best friend, who also has these same diseases, months before I was diagnosed. Now I have Anna and we can talk about our struggles together. Between the internet, chronically ill Twitter users such as Christina, Instagram disability influencers such as Julian, and my friend Anna, I have people who get it.

The dangerous part of my naivety and lack of connection to the chronically ill community was that I didn't refer to myself as disabled and didn't think I had limitations. I didn't start identifying as disabled until college. So, in middle school, I thought that I could continue doing all of the things I did before I was diagnosed because, well, I was doing them before. I was still playing sports and doing normal things, so I wasn't fully comprehending the gravity of the situation at hand. Sports were my life, and although I was struggling, my dad signed me up for our town basketball league at age twelve.

I was a huge tomboy growing up, I only wore boy's clothes, and I refused to participate in anything that could be classified as feminine. As a sociology major, I learned how ingrained societal norms were within my personhood. To be fair, I started dressing myself at the age of two. I always knew what I wanted and what I liked, and what I didn't.

Sports were always a good outlet for me. I had a team, I had a coach, and I had a schedule. One day my dad called me into the bonus room, the room over the garage, to make sure he had filled out all of the information correctly. The medical section was completely blank.

"Dad, you have to put that I have Crohn's and arthritis in the medical spot." I thought that was completely absurd. Had he forgotten about that new part of my life? I realized I had only been recently diagnosed, but it was a huge change.

"Oh, they don't need to know that." I didn't know it then, but this was one of my first experiences with my dad not being able to properly cope with a new diagnosis. This would happen many more times in the future, and his anger and sadness would come out in different ways. He was in denial.

"Yes, they do," I said adamantly.

Was he embarrassed that something was wrong with me? I didn't understand at all. The next day, I talked to my babysitter about it and she said that the old family she worked for had a child with a disability. The dad always made him play sports and be a part of things despite having a more prominent and physically limiting disability. She told me that he probably didn't accept it. Yet, I had accepted it so quickly.

SEEKING SUPPORT
In my dad's mind, when there was no name to my problems, he could easily ignore them. Now, these diagnostic names came with a sense of reality that he wasn't ready to face. If my dad had trouble seeing it, how could I possibly hope that other kids would understand it? As my conditions advanced and more diseases were added to the list overtime, my dad's denial became more of an issue. I didn't agree with my father in terms of ignoring the problem, but I decided to do all of the things I wanted to do in spite of my diseases. These early experiences shaped me and taught me how to persevere. I was determined to do everything I wanted to do. I wanted to show people that you can still do a lot of wonderful things in this world, even if you're struggling. I didn't want to have limitations. At this stage in my disease, I had some limitations but I also managed to overcome a lot of them. The same cannot be said for my future diagnoses.

For this type of passion to continue on, even when you're in the midst of dealing with your own chronic struggles, is not unique. Julian, or @thedisabledhippie as he's better known on Instagram, is a disability influencer. He recounted his disease progression during our interview.

For Julian, his illnesses started at a young age and since the age of five he has spent a lot of time in and out of hospitals. At one point he was "housebound for a couple of years," which sent him into a mental illness spiral. Although he was depressed and no longer in school, he started to ask himself important questions such as, "What am I going to do with my life?" This is a question that so many chronically ill people have to face, but Julian looked at his obstacles with a different mindset. Eventually he realized that "this is a really unique opportunity to self-reflect and figure out where my life is going. It's almost like hitting rock bottom." Sometimes hitting bottom can be good, and for Julian, it started his journey on Instagram and his advocacy work. Being stuck inside of a hospital is terrible and painful, but Julian looks at these hospital visits as growing periods.

Like Julian, I too take these depressing and heartbreaking experiences to try and improve. After my Crohn's diagnosis, I went away to summer camp as I had many years prior. My mom was worried because I couldn't really do much, but I wanted to be social. I loved my camp and all I wanted to do was be normal and spend time with my friends. I saw myself as the same as them. Yes, I was facing some struggles due to my diseases, but I also saw myself becoming a better person. I was already empathetic, but that summer I went above and beyond to help with the girl in my bunk who was bipolar and often isolated from the rest of us. I couldn't do a lot of physical activities, so I cheered for everyone and I did my best to make everyone feel important.

Looking back, I decided to take on the role of supporting my peers for two reasons. One, I really do love helping people.

I found my knack for that right around the time of my first diagnosis. I realized that I was able to take what made me different and make other people feel comfortable about their differences. That feeling of accomplishment with relationship building meant the world to me.

The second reason was that I wanted that effort to be reciprocated. I believed that if I gave my whole heart and listened and cared that someone would do that for me in return. However, that didn't seem to work out in my favor very often. I wasn't getting the friendly support that I wanted and needed, and I craved it. I'm not even talking about support regarding my disability, I simply mean a solid friendship. Throughout high school, I was just used as peoples' therapist and friend in a pinch. If I was struggling with normal high school issues, I didn't have anyone my own age who would listen. If I was struggling with my health, I was in the same boat. The only person who I could always confide in was my mom. She was struggling too, and we could do it together.

That method of loving and supporting others worked enough to get me awarded the "All Around Camper" award, which I was so excited about. Everyone was so proud of me and in that moment, I was thrilled. I didn't think anything could bring me down. Honestly, nothing really did.

Sadly, I couldn't stay this elated forever. Life kept going in the same manner it always had. I didn't get more support from friendships or the love that I craved. I got a cheap fake wooden frame and a thin piece of paper with a certificate clearly made from a Microsoft Word template. I guess all that hard work just made me a better person, but once that initial moment of excitement passed it felt like nothing had truly changed. Julian found a lot of happiness in his darkest moments. He was finding himself and bettering himself, and overtime found his new happiness. At the age of twelve with my Crohn's diagnosis, and even through high school, I gained happiness from helping others but lost happiness when the kindness wasn't returned. I wanted a support system and was relying on others to help lift me up. I was seeking outer approval instead of internal approval.

CHOICES

When you're chronically ill you have to make all of these choices, yet you don't get a say. This weird idea can be hard to grasp. All of these choices you have to make with yourself that the majority of society doesn't have to even think about. For most people, their decision-making process comes from a totally different place, oblivious to many of the thoughts that those who are chronically ill have to face.

Every little action has an impact on chronically ill people. Every choice you make, such as if you want to make dinner that night, go out, or order in, takes a toll. If you decide you want to make dinner, it is economically a great choice. You also get to customize what you make to your specifications. However, standing for long periods of time can be problematic for people with chronic pain. Lifting the pots and pans and putting them in the oven can be a lot of work. Washing dishes or even simply placing them in the dishwasher can be quite the burden. So, it might be a healthier meal than a burger from a fast food chain, but it is unhealthy at the exact same time.

While you have to make constant deals with yourself, deciding what to do and what not to do, many times the decision isn't truly yours to make. Even if it feels like you are making the choice, your body is making it for you. The other day my mom asked if I was feeling good enough to go shopping. It wouldn't have been an outrageous trip, but it would involve standing, trying things on, and being an active member during the outing. My brain and upper body were raring and ready to go. However, my lower half was throbbing, and when it wasn't in pain there was this overall weakness that felt as though I could topple at any second. Ultimately, I decided that it wouldn't be a good idea for me to go out, in part because I had my first day at my internship the very next day. Yes, I made the decision not to go out shopping, but it wasn't truly my choice. If I had gone, I would have regretted every second of it. I have no control over what my body does and doesn't do.

Christina struggled with the same issue when it came to choices. Living in a college environment, it's common for most students to go out, drink, and have fun. Christina was often referred to as a "flake" by some of her college friends who didn't understand why she would tell them "yeah, I'm coming out!" and then bail later on. She struggles with migraines, along with many other symptoms that are beyond her control. Christina couldn't make definitive plans in advance to go out with her friends simply because she didn't know how her body would react at a future date. She didn't get to experience the idealized college dream of living fearlessly.

I have never had the luxury of fearlessness. Even before I was ever diagnosed with anything, I was always so careful. I knew that something was wrong inside of my body, but I didn't know what it could be. My yearly complaints of sitting in my own blood weren't enough for my pediatrician to recommend I see a gastroenterologist (GI), who recommended that I see someone for my "growing pains." If doctors didn't see the blood as a problem, then they wouldn't be able to see the invisible pain I felt throughout my entire person—my small, underweight person. If the doctors didn't see it, how can I expect other people to?

When I would go to softball practice, they had us practice sliding. The coaches told me that if I overthought it, I would hurt myself; I just had to trust my body and let things flow. I watched as each girl before me got a running start and quite literally threw themselves into a fall, which allowed them to slide right into second base A lot of the girls thought this was all so exciting and fun, but I kept going to the back of the line in fear that my body would just break.

I was more fragile than them and I had to be more careful. Even if no one else knew, I knew my fragility. Growing up you hear how kids, especially teenagers, believe that they are invincible. I have never, not once in my life, thought of myself as invincible. I saw myself as breakable, fragile, and overall wrong. Something was hurting me all of the time and my family thought I was too sensitive and complained too much. My nighttime routine throughout my entire childhood always included chewable Tylenol for my "growing pains," which were later part of my hypermobile EDS (hEDS) diagnosis. These choices that undiagnosed children deal with impact the entire trajectory of their lives.

In this moment, my coaches acted as if I had a choice. I could either let go and slide, or I could worry and hurt myself. My fear was that if I didn't worry, if I didn't pay attention, I would hurt myself. The way in which people whipped their bodies around when playing sports frightened me. I wanted to be aggressive and dive for the basketball on the court. I wanted to slide into home plate. I wanted to be able to run faster than everyone else around the lacrosse field. There were a million things that I wanted to do. There were choices that I wanted to make, but I knew in my heart that I couldn't.

The choices that young people make are often scrutinized. They are not right, or they could have gone about their decision making better. No one stops and thinks about why a young person makes a certain choice. In our society we respect adults, as we should. We do so because they have more life experience and thus, know more than us. However, a suburban dad turned town-league-softball-coach does not know more about my body. As it was my own body, obviously I knew more about it than he did. However, not having a name for all of my problems made them difficult to communicate, even more so when the one name I did have—Crohn's—was an invisible illness.

I would have never told a coach that I was afraid my body would break because at first glance I look healthy. If I had said anything to the contrary, he would have laughed and dismissed my concerns. He would have given me reasons why, and I bet the first one would be that I'm young and young people bounce back and all of this bullshit that adults project onto children. You can't lump all children together because everyone is an individual with their own unique needs and limitations.

People naturally use their lived experiences as the norm. However, everyone is different and thus, their lived experiences are quite different as well. Having a forty-three-year-old man tell you that sliding won't hurt you if you just relax because he played sports and knows what it's like, doesn't mean he knows what it's like to be a little girl with constant pain. He doesn't know what it's like to be a child in this era. He doesn't know how you are feeling on the inside. The inside is telling you that you shouldn't do what you are about to do. No one fully understands the daily sacrifices that chronically ill people make. Each choice, even the smallest ones, have a larger consequence. For Christina, it was the choice of whether or not to go out with friends and risk feeling weak and sick later on. For me, it was the choice to play sports or not. At this age, I was at a disadvantage because I didn't have the words for my issues. I didn't have any diagnoses, I only had my gut.

WHICH DO YOU CHOOSE?

———

When you're sick, you lack a great deal of autonomy. For almost two years, I have been on Prednisone. Prednisone is a type of steroid that helps make you feel better when you're really, really sick, but at the same time makes you sick in other ways. Your mind makes you feel hungry all the time, and as expected you gain weight almost instantly. The feeling of always being hungry leads to weight gain fairly quickly.

Even before the actual weight sets in, your face blows up like a balloon and does not deflate unless you are completely off the medication or on a low dose for many months. You're tired, but all the while your mind is racing so you can't seem to focus on anything. Back when I was first diagnosed, I participated in a study to help doctors determine how steroids affect the minds of young people. The side effects can be very confusing and complex and still need more in-depth analysis. I wanted to be in this study because, like I said early on in the book, I had this urge to tell people about my illness, learn about my illness, and help raise money for it. I figured a good way to give back would be to give the data from my body and my experience to help kids in the future.

When you first start steroids, you have all this energy. It's like being hopped up on stimulants. You can't stop tapping your pen and your mind is going all over the place. It can be hard to focus, but I got used to those side effects pretty quickly. It was the intense feeling of always being hungry and having no control that lasts the entire time you're on steroids, at least in my case. This was the most prominent effect that stuck with me for the rest of my life. This drug is not one you want to be on.

For this study, they were testing my memory and my brain activity. I wore this crazy octopus-like cap that had little electrodes on it. I had to remember lists and pictures. I'd say the hardest part was understanding the person who was asking me all these questions. She had a thick Russian accent and I thought that made the experience a bit more difficult. I was paid two hundred dollars, which felt like a million dollars to me at the age of twelve. So, I decided to give that money to the Crohn's & Colitis Foundation (previously the CCFA). The one hundred dollars from the second part of the study I kept for myself.

For me, the immense weight gain has been the hardest part this time around. I have stretch marks all over my body, mostly focused on the sides of my stomach and my thighs. Due to my EDS, I have very sensitive skin and I heal poorly. The results are dark red and purple streaks along my body as my skin stretches to accommodate the weight gain.

When I was eleven, I didn't like how Prednisone made me feel. I was not able to concentrate as well when I first started the meds. That took some getting used to. I didn't like how I always felt hungry. I just didn't fully feel like myself in terms of how my brain was functioning on a day-to-day basis. However, my weight didn't really bother me. Looking back at photos of me during this Prednisone period was hard, and I saw myself in a very different way. I didn't like how I looked. This drug makes you hate yourself, at least that's what it did for me.

Although I was never formally diagnosed, I'd say that Prednisone caused me to have body dysmorphia tendencies, which causes a dissonance to occur between your brain and your body. I would feel one way in my head, then look at myself in the mirror and feel disgusted. That person looking back isn't me. She doesn't have a jaw line. She is this round lump of a person. Clothes weren't fitting how they used to and I was getting fat deposits, a very common side effect where you get lumps of fat in random places. No matter how much I tried to exercise or how well I tried to eat, my body was holding on to water and lumping random fat deposits throughout. I couldn't look at the size of my pants without wanting to cry. I hated trying on new clothes because if they didn't fit, I felt bad about myself. In my head I was still me, but these photos taken of me looked like another being, almost like a monster.

A few months ago, I was finally weened down to three milligrams of Prednisone. I was doing alright at five milligrams, so we went to four and then inevitably to three. After around three months on three milligrams, I could start to see my face again. I wasn't this clumpy ball of fat lumps, instead,

I was seeing Olivia again. My face was beginning to have a shape and a jawline, instead of being extremely round. I already have a round face, so the addition of steroids blows it out of proportion. One thing that my hairdresser always marvels at is the fact that I have all of my hair. Between the different types of chemotherapies, other medications, and stress, I still had my long, brown hair. My hair is this part of me that has always been the same. No matter my weight, the medications, or the situation my health was in, my hair was exactly the same. Little in my life has stayed true over time. My diseases and symptoms have changed, my meds have changed, my life has changed from middle school to college, but my hair hasn't.

The drugs were giving me this dysmorphic feeling every day. My clothes no longer fit. I felt ashamed and hated looking in the mirror, something I used to love. As I decreased the dosage, my appetite began to go down. With my appetite lessened, I finally lost some weight and my clothes felt looser. I have a long way to go until I'm back to my old size. They said it could be five or six months until the drug is fully out of my system. However, starting to see my face again felt wonderful. I finally saw a glimpse of a jawline which had been hidden by my doughy face. I could fit in more clothes. I didn't love my body as much as I used to, but I was starting to again. I'd been missing the person that I once knew.

One would think that seeing oneself in the mirror and starting to like what they see would help mellow me out. However, as my face has gone down, my Crohn's has come back full throttle. I don't know what I expected to happen when I decreased the steroids. It was something that I really wanted to do. There is no way to know if the meds are truly working if you have Prednisone covering everything up. However, I didn't realize that the new drug wasn't really working at all. We tried adding in an oral chemo which made me feel worse, and since going off of that medication the infusion seems to be doing its job even less.

I'm in aching pain as I write this and on the verge of tears because I am alone in my dorm room, once again. My Crohn's has taken over my life. I feel too sick to go to the senior toast, the pregame, or really any social event. I am isolated. I'm isolated from this world I so badly want to be a part of. I'm missing out on final college experiences because my body is in charge. I'm nauseous, and pains from cramps and gas are wreaking havoc on my stomach. I fell violently ill around noon and haven't bounced back.

It feels impossible for me to have it all. If I stay on the steroids, then my pain is theoretically less in all areas. If I decrease my dose, then I risk the lack of control over my diseases. I would also get my face back with the lower dosage. This decision is not an easy one but the long-term effects of steroids are brutal, and I found out that my bone density is not very good, which is a side effect of long-term use. All of these choices have implications. None of these choices are risk-free. By lowering my dose, I start to look like myself, but feel terrible. The other option is I can look like someone else, a person I don't recognize and cringe when I see myself in the mirror, but feel slightly okay with my Crohn's. Neither of these options feel fair. In this moment, nothing seems fair and giving up seems like the simplest answer. All I want is a hug from my mom and for her to whisper in my ear that everything will be okay.

"It is just a moment in time. It is just a moment in time."

I tell myself this over and over whenever I feel overwhelmed. This phrase is the mantra that pulls me through very tough times. Chronic illnesses are terrible and unreliable, but that unreliability is what makes it bearable. I might feel like death now, but in twenty minutes from now I could start to feel better. I know in my head that this will pass just like all of the terrible moments have passed before. Even with this knowledge, it can be hard to believe when I am in such awful pain right now.

The "now" is harder. The "now" feels like you're standing in the eye of a hurricane, painfully alone. Now I need someone. Now I need my mom. Now I need my dad. Now I'm scared that I can't do this. Now I'm scared that I can't finish college. I can't be here. Even when my mind is ready, my body seems to continually fail me.

I seemingly always have to choose. I have to choose medication. I have to choose which side effects are worth it. I have to choose to think in a way that is not detrimental to my mental health or my physical health. I have to realize that things are unreliable, which sometimes works out in my favor. These choices inevitably aren't really choices at all. They're options that are forced upon me if I want to try and live a normal life.

Which would you choose?

PART TWO

THIS WEIRD PART

After sixth grade, things kind of got better for me but my mom ended up in a coma.

After sixth grade, I lost all of that steroid weight and quickly became malnourished. I went back to weighing around seventy pounds. I was so tiny and pre-pubescent that I needed to get cups in my bat mitzvah dress because I had no chest.

My mom was trying to avoid the start of chemotherapy at all costs. Chemotherapy is not just used for cancer patients, but also for autoimmune diseases. We were told that I would be on this drug for the rest of my life. I would need infusions every six-to-eight weeks, and that terrified my parents. In an attempt to avoid chemotherapy, I was put on this holistic diet to try and put my Crohn's in remission naturally. This diet prevented me from eating gluten, wheat, yeast, sugar, dairy, anything fermented, and some fruits and vegetables. I hated this diet, but there was one day in particular that I absolutely abhorred it.

It was raining, and not that pleasant warm summer rain, but that weird cold rain that rarely happens during the summer months. We planned to go to the movies with our friends and decided to go out for lunch beforehand. I couldn't eat anything on the menu, so while those around me had French onion soup to warm them up, I ate some sliced deli turkey out of the plastic bag it came in. I was so incredibly angry. I was mad at my body for not being well and mad at my parents for putting me on this diet.

I was mad at my mom who forced me to try this final option before going on to chemotherapy. This diet had worked for her, and so she thought that it could really help me. She suffered from chronic sinus infections and things of that nature and eating healthy seemed to benefit her. However, I sat there on the verge of tears because not only was I suffering in terms of what I could and could not consume, but I was still very, very ill. My mom began to cheat on her diet, but mostly stuck to it. However, a few months after my bat mitzvah my mom got sick. She got really, really sick. She was never the picture of health, but this time period of her hospital visits kicked my anxieties about illness into full gear.

I was in the seventh grade when my mom went to the hospital. I didn't use an alarm clock since my dad always came in to wake me up, but one morning I just woke up on my own. One of the hallway lights was on but the rest of the house was dark. I left my room with a pit in my stomach. I found my dad at the end of the hallway. He said to me, "Mom isn't feeling well and we're just going to get her checked out at the hospital." I did not want to hear those words. I just wanted to find my mom. I went to her room and found my mom putting on her shoes. In what seemed like mere seconds, I heard the ambulance coming up our driveway and the red lights flashing.

"I'll be back later," she whispered.

I was quivering at this point. I hugged her as tightly as I could, and hated to let her go. I had this urge to hold on forever. I watched her go in the back of the ambulance from the window above the garage, tears pouring down my face. My brother and my dad told me I should just relax and that everything was fine. They disregarded my intense feelings, as I was deemed overly sensitive from a young age, but I knew it wasn't alright.

That night we went over to the hospital to visit her. She was still sitting in the bay at the ER and was having trouble breathing. She wore an oxygen mask and her eyes were glazed over. I tried to talk to her, but she wasn't speaking. Suddenly the area was flooded with doctors and nurses rushing to fix whatever was happening in front of me. She was going septic. My mom was wheeled away as they continued working on her. As they began to close the doors she said, "I'll be okay, Lucy." Lucy is her nickname for me.

I don't cry in public, but in this moment, I couldn't hold back the tears. They closed the glass door and a nurse told my dad to take me away. The doctor, a tall man with gray hair and rectangular glasses, walked over to speak with us.

"I promise I'll take good care of her."

Everyone continued to reassure me that things were fine. They reassured me that she was just going there to get checked out. They reassured me that this was temporary, but just like my own continuing issues, nothing in our lives was temporary. The thing is, illness doesn't discriminate. People of all ages, races, genders, sexualities, and religious backgrounds get sick. It is something that can't always be controlled, no matter how healthy you eat or how much sleep you get. All of those little things can help, but at the end of the day sickness can swing by for a visit and turn that visit into a lifetime stay.

This one-night stint at the hospital turned into a coma. It turned into a breathing tube in the ICU. It turned into me being "too young" to see her. The hospital claimed that I had to be fifteen to see my own mother because of the state she was in. When we finally convinced them to let me in to the ICU, I looked at her through glass doors. I stood back a few feet and just gawked at this woman I barely recognized. The air smelled of latex-free gloves, yellow gowns, and paper-thin masks that make your skin itch. She laid there like a seemingly lifeless being.

A few days later, I was finally allowed into her room. I held her hands that were so swollen I thought they were going to pop. I talked to her and hoped that she could hear me. I sang to her and let her know how much she was loved. One day I was holding her hand and she squeezed mine back. It was such a light squeeze that if you weren't paying attention, you might have missed it. That little squeeze meant the world to me, and it was easily one of the happiest moments of my life. After our visits, I had to go back home where all I thought about was her. I thought about how much I loved her and cared for her. I thought about how unfair this all was, that she was sick, and I was sick. Now when I went to birthday parties, parents were always asking about my mom and then finished up by asking me how I was doing. Overall, it was a very depressing birthday conversation.

After about a week, they removed the breathing tube and she was lifted from her medically induced coma. She was back, but in another sense, she was far, far gone. She had no voice. She couldn't communicate or eat. She didn't know how to walk, and she hallucinated a lot. I needed to get my best friend back. I needed to talk to her and tell her how I was feeling. I wanted to visit her every day after school, but that wasn't always an option since neither my older brother nor myself could drive. We had to rely on a babysitter or a friend to help us see our mom. For the first few weeks, my aunt from California came out to help us adjust.

I thought my body was bad, but this poor woman's body completely disowned her. This threw my mind into a panic. On top of it all, I was still sick. My Crohn's was active and I continued to sit in pools of blood. I wasn't digesting my food and I was always in pain. My sickness, my thoughts, and my feelings took a backseat to it all. There was too much going on in our house. I knew that chemotherapy was in my future. Honestly, and weirdly, I didn't mind. I don't think that I fully understood the concept. I did, however, understand that this drug could make me feel better, and at this point that's all I wanted.

One day my dad lost it. He is a man who holds things in. He denies reality to keep moving forward. What he doesn't realize is that you aren't moving forward if you don't accept the circumstances you're in.

One night, we were riding home from visiting my mom and I was becoming emotional and started to cry. My emotions were very uncontrollable at this time. My brother and I were yelling about something and my dad pulled over on the side of the road and told me to walk home. He meant it. I could feel hyperventilation begin deep down in my chest. It rose through my brain. Eventually, it sprung out by way of a wail. My brain and my body were out of control and my emotional state was shaken up. The intense crying and emotion managed to change my dad's mind, and he pulled back onto the road and continued to drive home.

I just wanted my mom. I just wanted to hug her and hold her and sit in her lap like a small child. Instead, I was facing difficult choices with my own health while watching my family make difficult choices about my mom's health.

This period of time fueled the flames of anxiety regarding sickness. I was no longer afraid of not only my own body, but my mother's as well. I was learning that not only could I not control my own body, but I couldn't control the bodies of the people I loved. This need for control encouraged the development of not only my anxiety, but also my OCD. After her near-death experience, we both seemed to only get worse.

Our symptoms matched up a lot of the time and we were struggling together. We began to worry about each other's health while often neglecting our own. I feared for myself. I feared for my mother. Her visits to the hospital repeatedly turned into panic attacks and my own hospital visits had me on edge. I was always scared of the next thing, the unknowns our bodies chose to throw at us. This weird part of our lives, this part where no one was totally okay, screwed up my brain in a way that has taken years of therapy to slowly unravel. It's hard to imagine having two very sick people in one house, but this weird part, the part where we just never got well again, is happening right now. For me, this weird part is seemingly a never-ending loop of sickness for my mom and me. I think that anyone who gets sick, or has a family member who gets sick, finds themselves in their own "weird part." This space in time where they don't know what the next steps are or what the future holds.

The unpleasant part is that you need to learn to be okay with the unknown. I'm not saying that this is an easy task. It's something that I work on every day of my life. It's hard working on getting better, going with the flow, and waiting, but they're important skills to learn when coping with illness. Just take baby steps. You can have moments of sadness and frustration, but you can't let those feelings overwhelm you every day. Just remember to breathe and give yourself a mental break.

CHEMO AND INFUSION ETIQUETTE

My mom lost her hair due to the stress of almost dying. I wasn't losing my hair, but I was starting chemo right when she got out of rehab. It's called Remicade and it saved my life. I was flaring and weighed around eighty pounds in the seventh grade, maybe less. It was a medicine that was pumped into me through an IV. In 2011, there weren't many options for treatment and it was either chemo or I would have my entire rectum removed and have an ostomy bag for my entire life. Although neither was an appealing offer, my family went for lifelong chemo.

I felt better almost right away. It fixed my skin issues, arthritis, and Crohn's. It was the best drug I could have ever asked for. It was my miracle drug. I didn't even mind spending hours at the hospital after school because I knew that I could sit back, relax, and enjoy the medicine entering my veins and keeping me from slowly deteriorating. I made *Bridesmaids* my film of choice and watched it just about every infusion.

At the infusion center, I was special. I wasn't different in the sense that I was sick; everyone was there for some sort of infusion. What made me different at the infusion center was purely my humor. In terms of my illness, here I was normal. The nurses never made rude comments or made me feel like I was a burden on them. Here, we were both just following orders. I was getting my medicine and they were told to put it in. In a weird way, we were kind of in the same situation unlike a doctor/patient relationship. It wasn't like a relationship with other kids my age for many obvious reasons, and it wasn't like the relationship I had with my family. The connections I made at the hospital were different and I felt so special.

I was unique because of my weird impressions that I could do on command. I sat there and nurses came over and asked me to produce comedy routines, and I was more than happy to accommodate their requests. Any opportunity to make other people happy brought me extreme joy. For a long time, I thought that was what I was meant to do. I used to act and perform, but eventually my anxiety of crowds became too much. What scared me the most was the idea of failing in front of a large group of people. One or two nurses I could handle, but more than that was too much.

Allow me to paint the picture of my typical chemo session in Waltham or Boston. First, they take your height and weight because the amount of drugs they give you depends on your weight. Then, you enter into your bay. I always had my own little bay with a TV and an automatic reclining chair. I was attached to monitors to document my heart rate, and my vitals were checked every thirty minutes by one of the many nurses on staff. I did have a nurse assigned to me for the session, but everyone helped out over the course of my treatment. Before any intravenous medicines made their way into me, I took some pre-meds consisting of Benadryl and Tylenol, which help prevent an allergic reaction to the treatment itself. The nurses go over your medications every single time you come because all knowledge of your person is important. During this session they ask about your symptoms. For me, this meant I was publicly asked the amount of times I poop and what it looks like.

I honestly don't mind these questions when they come from the nurses at Boston Children's Hospital. I have such close relationships with medical staff that I actually look forward to my infusions. They've watched me grow up from an awkward middle schooler to a twenty-one-year-old woman. I've made them sit through my comedy reels and my incessant questions about medications and procedures. In a medical system that can be cruel and difficult to work in, the infusion center was the one place where I always felt welcomed and safe. I didn't have to worry about saying or doing the right thing or being professional. I was able to be a kid.

Going back to the technical parts of the infusion, once all of the basic procedures are over, I get hooked up to an IV, which in turn is attached to a machine that regulates the speed at which I get my infusions. Different infusions need to go at different speeds, which is relatively common. Over the course of the day, the infusion usually speeds up and they do so with a click of a button. After the main bag of drugs is slowly injected into your bloodstream, you get something called a "flush." A "flush" is a bag of fluid that helps you get every bit of the med and it cleans you out. You sit for maybe another fifteen minutes to let that happen. The "flush" signals that you are at the end of your appointment.

If you are not someone who has been to one of these sessions, there might seem like there is a lot of things going on. Truly, there are a lot of moving parts. I think it's actually harder for the nurses than the patients who have to sit there and let the nurses know if anything feels off. Now that you have a nice picture of this individualized and safe environment, allow me to tell you about my experience in Pennsylvania.

Once I started school, it became clear that I would need to get my infusions while I was down there. I go to school in Pennsylvania and obviously I need to get my juice every month. This "infusion center" is far from what I expected. When I told my nurses at home this tale, one asked, "Is this in the United States?"

First you walk into an office building, and before you enter the main center you open up this side door that looks as if it leads to the trash receptacle. You walk through these long hallways where medical staff are strewn about. After two right turns, you've made it to the final corner where the nurse is stationed. Only one nurse exists. Now, it's important to mention that this nurse is extremely kind and sweet, but that does not change the standard of care that I'm used to.

There is no privacy. There are no bays. We sit in a circle as if we are at a campfire with other sick people that we don't know. Because this infusion center is for adults, I am stuck with middle-aged men who think that the world was made for them and that their word is the word of God. But before I delve deeply into the people who reside there for those few hours, let me talk to you about the technology.

There is no technology. There are no machines. I am not plugged into anything. In fact, during my last infusion I had to share a pole with the guy next to me. That means that there is absolutely no scientific way that I am getting these medicines into me. The first time I went, it was like I was a queen for the day because I had my very own pole. The luxury of my own pole meant that about halfway through Nurse Carol raised it so the infusion went faster via gravity, as if we were in the 1800s. On this second appointment, I not only had to share my pole with a man I will call Glenn, but I had to listen to Glenn talk ad nauseam.

Basic protocols are simply thrown out the window here. I don't get weighed before my infusion. I don't have my height taken. They also don't do pre-meds before giving me my specific drug. When I told them that I take a Benadryl and Tylenol before the infusion, they had a slight hissy fit because they had to go out and buy these drugs. They didn't have them on hand. What medical facility does not have basic pain and allergy medication?

I mentioned I was allergic to Tegaderm. It's a type of film that goes over the IV to keep it stable. She would have known this if she took down my list of medicines and allergies like a normal infusion center, however, she did not. She then told me that I was "lucky" because they have a patient who doesn't like tape and gauze after the IV is taken out. I was lucky because they went out of their way to purchase band-aids for this other patient. Yes, I was told that I was "lucky" that they had band-aids to cover my IV instead of the Tegaderm.

This day seemed to last forever in my mind. All of my expectations about what an infusion center is supposed to do completely changed. I had no idea that this is what it was like outside of an elite children's hospital. When I told this to my nurses at home, they were all pretty appalled and it helped to know that I was not in fact crazy, but a person with very normal expectations. However, one nurse said, "well, that's why we're the number one children's hospital in the world." Honestly, I wish that I could stay at the best facility for the rest of my life. The care at the infusion center is simply wonderful. When I walk in, I know I'm loved. Sadly, as I come up on what might be my last infusion at Boston Children's Hospital as I'll be transferring over to an adult doctor, my heart aches. I don't want to give up the one place that makes having all of these issues seemingly okay. I wish I could stay there forever.

"I'M GOOD"

My diseases have no timeline. They come and go at whatever strength and time they please. They ruin trips and outings, and they manage to ruin the day-to-day life that I attempt to lead. However, I don't look sick. Not looking sick is one of those things that all chronically ill people will tell you is this weirdly terrible burden. You're told by able-bodied people that you are lucky, as if looking like you actually have a disability is something to be ashamed of. You look normal, so that should be enough. The issue with that mentality is that I am not normal. The way in which my body functions is far from normal, and the more time I spend with friends and family the more I notice how truly different I am. Although I accept my difference and my close friends and family know what I need, there is a whole world out there passing judgment all of the time.

Society has this idea of how people are supposed to act in public. In American society, if you are out and about it is important that you look put together. Especially if you're at a nice event, you want to show people your best self, your highlight reel if you will. You smile and dress up. You're putting on the best act you can and then someone goes, "and how are you doing?"

I pause for a second because my heart is pulling and stretching and begging me to tell the truth:

"Actually, I'm super sick. Some days I lose my fine motor skills and my parents have to cut my food for me even though I'm twenty-one. I've been pooping nonstop but have also been constipated which is so weird. My joints keep dislocating and it feels like no position is ever going to feel comfortable. I'm always worrying about my health and whether the drugs are working. I wonder why I'm like this. It's really hard and I'm just doing the best I can."

Instead I reply, "I'm good." That is the response that is expected. Everyone wants to hear that response because it makes them feel okay. But your feelings shouldn't be about making others feel okay. As people with disabilities, we are taught to make others comfortable around us. This embarrassment within and accommodation of the able-bodied world is what kept Christina from showing the world how disabled she was.

She said that "I didn't want them to see how sick I was. I was really, really good at hiding it from people. I would suffer silently." Christina lived a double life for such a long time, but during college it was much easier to live that way. She explained it as a "benefit" of college because "it's easier, a little bit, to live that double life." In front of her college friends, she would act brave and tough, but once she was alone, she would call her mom and cry to her on the phone. I've done this too. So much goes on when you're in college that people aren't focused on every little thing you do. When you're living a double life, lack of focus from others allows you to continue this behavior. It's an awful behavior. In reality, it's terrible needing to fake how you're really doing in front of people who are supposed to be your friends and care about you, but it's hard knowing how much to show and when to show it. Chronic illnesses are complicated and extremely messy. Living this double life isn't fair but it's often a part of living with a chronic illness.

We shouldn't have to hide it from people. It is already hard to live in our own bodies, so the added pressure of putting on a brave face every time we go out in public is absurd. If you are a person with invisible diseases, it's common and normal to not talk about your suffering because if other people can't see it, it must not be real. If you are a caretaker or friend of someone with an invisible illness, you should ask about specifics regarding their disabilities. However, be mindful when it comes to the casual "how are you?" If there are other people around, your friend might be hesitant to express what's actually been going on with their body. Such a simple question can send me into a loop of self-despair. I feel like I'm lying. I'm lying to these extended family members and distant friends, and it makes me feel like total shit. When I hide my illnesses, I feel like I am hiding myself because these daily experiences have shaped my life in every way. They have shaped my humor and how deeply I love those around me.

My parents always tell me not to be bothered by what other people think. That is an impossible task when you're trying to juggle who you look like and who you are. For example, we went to an adorable adult bat mitzvah for twenty or so ladies above the age of eighty. It was so cute, and I wanted to adopt all of them. These women were not given the right to read Torah when they were of age, which is typically twelve or thirteen. Even my own mother was not allowed to read directly from the Torah. So, this moment was more than seventy years in the making for most of them. This was their special day and they all had the opportunity to give a little speech about why this event was special for them. These moments made the congregation's heart swell. However, during Shabbat services there are parts where it is customary to stand. They say to only do so if you can, but the only people who don't stand are over eighty years old and even some of them suck it up and do it.

Imagine if you were in services and looked over to see a twenty-something-year-old just sitting there when she looks perfectly able. She can stand. You think she can stand. She knows that you think that, so you know what she decides to do? She stands and she is holding on to the pew in front of her with all of her being. When one hand starts to tremble, she redistributes her weight, but then her knee feels like it's going to give out and she shuffles over to a new position.

All this time she is suffering. She is suffering because society expects things of her that they shouldn't, but these ideals are ingrained deep into her psyche. This standing, which continued as people schmoozed after the service, caused her pain in that moment. Unable to bend her right leg which is locked, stuck from standing in that one position makes walking down steps at the end of the service nearly impossible.

Worse than that, she woke up the next day weak and unable to move in the way she had hoped. By the end of the next night, she couldn't clear the table off from Mother's Day dinner because her legs felt like 100 pound weights. Her dad had to help her get off her chair.

These norms and assumptions that we all naturally make are literally hurtful. I'm not sure how people are supposed to change their assumptions, but I think a big part of it all is understanding what disability looks like. It's similar to gender. You can't assume people's gender anymore, and the same should be said for disability because it also comes in many variations. This will be hard for many people to grasp because when they think of a disability, all they imagine is a wheelchair. They are stuck in this mindset that disability signifies an inability to live and enjoy life. Disability can change how surrounding people see you. For Christina, she struggled with showing her boyfriend how sick she was. She told me that "I just didn't want him to see me that sick. I felt like if he was seeing me that sick, he would never be able to see me any other way." I'm sure that's how a lot of chronically ill people feel. I find it hard to balance embracing my sickness in my relationships while not letting it be the only thing that we talk about.

People can have many different kinds of disabilities. Even using a wheelchair is policed by able-bodied people. Ambulatory wheelchair users like myself struggle with assumptions made such as, "well, if you can walk, you don't need a chair." These statements come from ignorance. If they are not spoken, they are conveyed through disapproving looks as if you're in this life for all of its "perks."

This world is not made for us. The chronically ill are a brave, strong-willed, and bad-ass community that will never back down from the worst ableism. But it's hard to have to fight ourselves every day to live, and then also fight for our rights on the side. We fight for this acceptance that can be so hard to get. Most people, at least those I've met or seen on the internet, want you to ask questions. They're curious about your life and your lived experience. So, ask questions. Learning is the type of work that needs to be done for there to be strides in understanding the broad spectrum of disability.

YES, THIS PART IS
INVISIBLE TOO

———

When I was a freshman in college, my mental health meds stopped working. I was crying on the floor, convulsing, and had no control over my body. Everyone was getting the flu around me and common illnesses always made me anxious. However, this was too much. My parents hopped in the car and drove six hours to get me, turned around, and drove six hours home. During the second semester freshman year I took my first of three medical leaves.

Mental health is a hot topic of today. Everyone seems to be talking about the importance of talking. Mental health with athletes, mental health for postpartum women, mental health for veterans—mental health is important for everyone. There is great evidence about talking with a friend or a professional and how that simple act can save a life. A study from the American Psychological Association (2004) found that out of fifty-nine million people who sought out therapy, 80 percent of those people found it helpful.[6] That being said, mental health for the chronically ill is an entirely different beast.

Isolation can be a serious problem for people with chronic illnesses. Isolation can be self-induced like in Christina's case where, when the onset of symptoms began while out with friends, she would go out to her car and sob by herself. Christina chose to suffer alone because she worried about others seeing her sick. Julian was brought up in a very Italian household where illness was something shameful for a family. His family would not let him talk about his illnesses with friends or anyone else, and this kept him isolated from the world. Later in his life, he was housebound and fell into a depression, as one might expect.

My parents are always looking out for me, and as I start my post-grad job search, they worry about me disclosing my disabilities. Yes, there is a very good chance that my application would be tossed to the side, but I can't omit information they ask for on the application. My parents are not ashamed of me in the least. On the contrary, they are so proud. They are proud of everything that I've done despite my illnesses. That being said, they worry that I will share too much. My feelings are all over the place, and I've been very anxious throughout this job-hunting process. I worry if I'm enough. I worry if I can prove myself. I'm worried that I won't even get the chance. I'm not worried about finding a job like able-bodied people do, I'm worried because my disability will impact

6   J. Chamberlin, Survey says: More Americans are seeking mental health treatment (American Psychological Association, 2004)

their decision and choosing to openly talk about it is risky. That being said, not disclosing would make me more anxious.

Something that not many people realize is that those who have invisible illnesses suffer from medical PTSD. This is the idea that the medical community has hurt you with their systems and misdiagnoses that have then caused trauma. Regular anxiety comes with being sick. You don't know when you're going to get a flare. You don't know if your medications are going to stop working. You don't know when the next medical situation is going to pop up.

New symptoms in particular can be quite scary because sick people know what they know. When you live in pain with certain symptoms, you almost get used to them. For example, if I'm having pain in my leg, I can usually deduce that the pain is coming from my arthritis or maybe a subluxation from my EDS. My stomach area will most likely be Crohn's related, although CRPS can creep in there during a flare as my neurons are misfiring. When a new pain or ache comes up, it can really mess with your mind. You don't know this sensation. You don't know this pounding. You don't know, and when you're always listening to your body, not knowing is scary.

When you have Crohn's long enough, you know what foods bother you and which ones don't, but there was a time when you didn't know that. Imagine you are suddenly unable to do anything. You have pain everywhere and you are chronically fatigued. You feel so weak and sick, but you're told that you're fine. You are not fine, and you know your body, but you have to fight the system and try to convince people that you're as sick as you say. Once given a diagnosis, some of that stress dissipates. When I was diagnosed with CRPS and EDS on that same visit, I understood myself better. At least I wanted to, and I decided I wanted to read studies and the blogs of people who have been going through this for much longer than I have. I couldn't do anything with my body, and I thought that I was crazy, but I wasn't. It was gaslighting at its finest.

This specific situation had an impact on my mental health. I finally had names for the unknown pain and dislocations, but these names came with more sporadic behavior than before. Your mind gets tired of figuring things out; how one disease is affecting the other nine. It was almost as if I had to relearn my entire body. Honestly, I'm still learning about it two years after these diagnoses. You're always worrying about tripping, falling, or moving in the wrong way. You make one wrong move and your body basically explodes with signals. Recently, I fell on the ice at home. I had the initial pain from the fall, but the after-effects were brutal. It sent my body into a CRPS flare and my body dislocated in many spots. I lost some hand function because of the way I fell. My brain would not stop harping on the pain, which is something that is really difficult to overcome.

When you live with chronic illnesses, the flares come out of nowhere and the pain has a life of its own. It's often so hard to figure out what's hurting, why it's hurting, and where it's all stemming from. It wears you down and your brain feels like it's on fire. On top of trying to understand your own body, you're trying to explain it to other people. This is mentally exhausting and confusing, especially when you're talking to your family who is clearly upset by your constant suffering.

These chronic illnesses deteriorate the mental health of these patients. Even Sarah Hyland, one of the stars of *Modern Family*, has opened up about her struggles with illness and mental health. The constant feeling of "being too much" or "being a burden" is extremely common. According to Hyland, "At that time, I was very depressed for a long time. I was contemplating suicide. I had gone through twenty-six years of always being a burden, of always having to be looked up after, having to be cared for 'cause I've always had health issues, and it's a really helpless feeling."[7]

These feelings are all too common for chronically ill people, and the pain, isolation, and anxieties of a chronically ill person are extremely complex. Anna, a fellow chronic illness sufferer, told me that her mental health has gone through highs and lows and she has "hit rock bottom," and in spite of all that she has "worked [her] ass off to get an extremely stable state." Anna helps to show us that even if we have different illnesses, obstacles with our mental health are very common. Everyone with chronic illness struggles with their mental health.

I've been officially diagnosed with generalized anxiety disorder, OCD, an OCD related tic disorder, and trichotillomania. Trichotillomania is a hair pulling disorder. Like a tic, as you often don't know you're even doing it to yourself. I spent a

---

7   *SELF*, Sarah Hyland on Her Two Kidney Transplants | SELF, December 10, 2018, video, 2:12.

large part of my high school career without a left eyebrow. It's a manifestation of OCD, part of the compulsion aspect of it. Like my other illnesses, I speak openly about my mental health. I found that when I started to do that, people reached out and thanked me because they had that disease too or they were always anxious. They realized that they were not alone. Most of my anxiety stems from my health and my diseases. That makes sense because "what normal twenty-one-year-old has been through the medical system as often as me?"

On top of that, my mother's hospitalization was extremely traumatizing for me and contributed greatly to my anxieties about the medical field. The hospital is this place where everything is skewed. You are surrounded by so many other sick people that the illness population seems huge. When you leave and go back into the real world, you notice you're the only one with this or that condition. You realize that you're different. You realize that this difference pushes you toward isolation.

I get anxious about change. I love stability because I don't have any with my health. Because of that, I tend to control as many situations or as many of the outcomes as I possibly can. When I don't have this control, my OCD and trichotillomania worsen. When people around me get sick, I panic because I can't get sick. I have a weakened immune system due to all of the drugs I'm on. I don't fight anything off naturally, so I rely heavily on antibiotics. Also, I can't get my infusions if I'm sick, which can really set me back as that's my main treatment for my Crohn's.

Looking back at high school, it was rough. Mental illness was mentioned all of the time in my high school and we had days devoted to learning about it. But because no one ever talked about their personal experiences, there was also a lack of real talk about mental illness. I still felt alone even though the statistics tried to tell me otherwise.

My deteriorating mental state hit its worst point in junior year of high school when I watched a TV show where a girl tried to kill herself. I ended up on the floor of my parent's room crying, in a full-blown panic attack, rocking on the floor because I thought that the character's actions reflected my own. I thought that I wanted to kill myself. This scared me, and as I cried and convulsed on the floor I squeaked out, "I think I want to see a therapist now."

These panic attacks had been going on for almost a year before the realization in my parent's room. I was living in a constant state of panic. I would go to all of my high school classes, but at the end I would leave without remembering anything that was said. One day, I took a test in science, turned it in, and had no recollection of what I just produced. That scared me. The more on edge I became the less in control I became, and that cycle continued.

My parents were thrilled to hear that I now wanted to see a therapist because they had spent months encouraging me to go. I had always thought that I could handle it on my own. I finally realized that I could not. They picked me up, both physically and emotionally. I knew my parents were on my side.

It wasn't until I was far from home at college that I had a relapse.

Freshman year of college I had what most people would call a mental breakdown. It was to the point that my school actually called my parents to come and get me. They drove six hours, got me, and turned the car around to drive back home that day. I was out of control. My mind was betraying me so much that it was affecting my body in a physical way. I would sit frozen for hours or rock on the floor. I was taking several Lorazepam a day to help, but I got anxious taking it because I know how addictive it can be. Everything seemed scary to me. Every new thing created a sense of panic. This panic stemmed from something so simple: the flu. My roommate at the time had the flu, and I truthfully couldn't handle it while living in the world's smallest dorm. The flu created this spiral of anxious thoughts and panic attacks.

I was out of control.

So just as they did in high school, my wonderful and amazing parents picked me up. This time, they picked me up from college a week before spring break. I couldn't be left alone. Sleeping by myself scared me and I dreaded going to bed every night. My mom stayed with me for a couple of days, but eventually she had to go back to work. I didn't want her to leave me. I didn't think that I could make it through the day without her. I set up my living situation for the day. I sat on my parent's bed and put HGTV on. This is where I fell in love with the channel. I didn't eat. I didn't even like the idea of going to the bathroom by myself. I would only eat when my mom or dad came home at the end of the day, but nothing even appealed to me. I had to force it down my throat.

My therapist, who I've been seeing for five years now, and I have developed a good relationship and he knows me well. When I saw him that week I came home from college, he mentioned putting me in an outpatient program. I'm honestly not 100 percent sure of what one of these programs entails because I refused to go. To be frank, I lost my shit. I pleaded with him that I could do better and refused to go to a program all at the same time. I could do this with him, on my own, no program needed. I thought that only crazy people went to programs. I wasn't crazy. I wouldn't fit in there. I had this stigma of mental health and, until my return to school after this incident, I was silent about the mental part of my disabilities. I've only ever cried a couple of times in those four years, but this day I was bawling. I couldn't be stopped. Turns out, all I needed was a little more Zoloft, my miracle drug. This was my first experience needing to leave school due to medical needs. It was a short medical leave, but it was one that would prepare me for the following two.

I truly don't believe that you can be chronically ill and have no mental health issues. These types of forever diseases are like terminal cancer, but you never die. You have these things that you carry with you that are out of the ordinary. Yes, everyone has baggage, but to say that people with disabilities' baggage is the same as an able-bodied person would be a blatant lie.

Anna knows all about mental health and chronic illness. She understands how hard it is to live in a body that does what it wants, when it wants. Anna told me that a good day "is a day which I have some level of control over my illness, even the small victories feel huge when you're been stripped of control over your own body...They say mental health is just as important as physical health which is why I believe that when I look back at my best days, they are jam packed with enjoyable activities that calm my body from inside out." Focusing on your mental health is important but, when you're physically suffering, it can be an easy thing to ignore. Try your best to remember your mental health.

As difficult as living with mental health issues and chronic illness issues is, it makes you so tough. I love how my brain works. Yes, it irritates me and frustrates me to no end, but at the end of the day I've learned to be content with it. OCD comes with many different perks. My OCD pushes me to stay on top of things, get ahead of things, and think strategically to make the most efficient decision possible. The OCD, paired with my extreme sense of empathy that somewhat stems from my anxiety, helps me to emotionally relate to others. This combination of traits is often quite wonderful and sets me apart from my peers. It isn't an easy mix, but it's what I've learned to live with and continue to learn to live with.

When you're looking at someone with a chronic illness, just know that their mental health matters just as much as their physical health.

MY TICS

My tics are new elements of my diseases. Tics are these abrupt movements or little sounds that people make to satisfy themselves in some way. It's a need to do the tic. It is almost like you don't control when they happen or why they happen. I was diagnosed with OCD when I was sixteen years old, but it mostly revealed itself in pretty typical forms. I checked the oven and the stove and made sure everything was always turned off. I wouldn't use an electric toothbrush for years because I was afraid that if it got wet that it would explode or catch on fire. I was always a very cautious child. Around sixteen my OCD turned into trichotillomania, which is basically a fancy name for hair-pulling. I had no idea that I was doing it because it was a compulsion to help me overcome whatever issue I was experiencing in the moment. That being said, I was left without an eyebrow for the majority of junior year of high school and sophomore year of college.

According to my parents, I've always had some sort of tic. More recently my tics are directed toward my eyebrow, but around the third grade I developed this coughing tic. My parents made a deal with me. They told me that if I went a couple of months without ticking then they would get me a new skateboard, something I wanted badly.

I am, and always have been, a very anxious person. Even though I wasn't diagnosed until high school, I have been fighting a lifelong battle with anxiety. I can't lie, and if I do it eats me up inside. My brain replays entire conversations over and over again until I crack. Until I can't handle my own mind anymore. Now, illness tends to bring me a lot of anxiety and induces tics. When everyone at school is ill with the flu or a sinus infection, I automatically get worried. I have to take extra precautions because I'm on chemotherapy and immunosuppressed. However, I continue to worry about falling ill.

Sometimes I'll get anxious from my own illnesses. If I can't digest food for a few days, meaning that after I eat, it basically comes right out and usually with a pool of blood, I don't want to eat. I get very scared to put food into my body because I don't want to get sick. In theory, this makes sense but I can't not eat, which I know. So, I'll sit for hours at a time looking at a menu online, deciding if I should eat or not. I'm always replaying the aftermath and working myself up over it.

Determined to get that new skateboard, I did everything possible to hold in my coughing tics when I was around my parents. I trained myself to hold them in around the people who mattered, but I would tic when alone or at school or really anywhere else. When I finally got to that three-month mark, my parents were happy and proud of me. I was happy, but I also had this feeling deep inside that wanted to vomit up my secret. I lied to them and felt horrible about it. I had not quit ticking; I had quit ticking in front of them.

My dad and I went to the skateboard shop called Eastern Boarder on Route 9 in Framingham, Massachusetts to pick out my reward for supposedly eliminating my coughing tic. The skateboard was completely customized, so I went through and picked out all the parts for the skateboard. I had a fully designed brand new skateboard, but I couldn't even be happy about it. I felt like I didn't deserve this gift because I didn't follow the rules. I didn't truly earn this. I just remember thanking my parents constantly and looking at that skateboard, knowing I couldn't bear to ride it. I got it under terrible circumstances, and I was ashamed that I had hid my tics.

I never really used the board. I used it around my friends at the time who were all boys that loved to skateboard and snowboard and do extreme sports. I wanted to be like them. I wanted to play football, skateboard, and do everything tough guys did. I was infatuated with extreme sports, with physical sports. I wanted to fit in and show the boys that I was just as tough as them and that I wasn't some girly-girl who couldn't hang.

However, I was not only upset because I got this skateboard for the wrong reasons, but I had this fear in the back of my mind. It was once again this unknown, later explained by the diagnoses of EDS and CRPS, but nevertheless this constant worry was in the back of my head. It was this fear that if I fell off of the board something bad would happen to me. Even if I watched all my friends ride and fall, I knew I couldn't fall. I wanted to be like them and act like them, but I was too scared of my own body. I would only try tricks on grass and only wanted to ride my board on carpet. I knew that my body was different, and I couldn't take risks like everyone else. I didn't know exactly why yet, but I knew that my body was too fragile for skateboarding.

Moving forward to today, I have many different tics. I still have a tendency to pull at my eyebrow, but I've gotten much better at redirecting my hands to my service dog or other parts of my body where I can't rip anything out. I still struggle, but after five years I have a better handle on it. I also make a clicking sound where my mouth is typically closed but others can hear it. I tested it on my brother because I wasn't sure if it was a loud tic that others would notice, and he could hear it. I have another one where I kind of half swallow and make my ears pop. This tic only bothers me and no one else because I'm the only one who can actually hear it. Then there is my new tic, the biggest of them all.

My new tic involves stomach twitching. I pull in the left side of my upper stomach over and over again. When I do this, my entire torso shifts and jiggles around in an uncomfortable way. The abrupt movements impact my whole body and sometimes push my body in an uncomfortable direction. The strain of pulling my upper stomach where it does not want to go puts stress on places like my shoulder and ribs. Often times my shoulder muscles will spasm or my ribs will even shift and subluxate. On top of that, if I do this tic for a long time my stomach will start aching. This is not good for someone with EDS. The amount of times that I tic and push my rib and shoulder out are insane and cause spasms and more pain than I ever want. The issue is I just can't seem to stop. These tics, the more dramatic ones in my stomach, seem to tell me things. I get them when I'm in a situation that makes me uncomfortable or when I'm very anxious.

For example, I'm not a good test taker. This week I had a quiz, and in the five days leading up to it I could not stop ticking. They were out of control. I couldn't focus on other classes because my mind was always worrying about this sociology quiz. In doing so, my body was reacting to my anxieties with aggressive and painful stomach tics. My insides were quite literally shifting beneath my skin and pulsing without warning, all in reaction to an upcoming quiz.

I've found that, for me, tics come with new experiences. "New" is terrifying and is often accompanied by crippling anxiety. It makes it a lot harder to enjoy the new and savor special experiences when my brain thinks too much, too fast, and my body reacts in an aggressive manner through ticking. A wonderful example of "new" being not so great happened this past summer. Over the summer I got a new-to-me car. My other car was absolutely terrible and run down. I didn't worry too much when driving the old car because it was beat up anyway. Lately, I've been ticking while driving which is incredibly annoying. I'm assuming it's because I'm scared of ruining my nice new car. When I drive, I'm only in as much control as I can be. I can't control the other people on the road and the choices that they make. This makes me feel ultra-paranoid and leads to stomach tics. If I'm singing a song or distracting myself in another way, I can some-times take my mind off of it. But overall, my tics are telling me something.

Tics are still kind of new to me. They're fresh territory and I'm still learning how to deal with them and figuring out what they all mean. This is one of the areas of my body and my illnesses that I don't know too much about. Most of the time people don't even notice that I'm doing anything, so out of all my issues, my tics tend to move to the back burner. I still need to learn more, but I'm getting a better understanding every day.

CRYING INTO THE VOID

———

Most of the time, living this life, I feel like I'm crying into a void. I'm yelling for help and the only people who hear me cry out have no power but all the love. My parents tell me how they wish there was some magic pill they could give me. When I call them on the phone, crying in my dorm room alone because of the pain and fatigue, they want to help. My ninety-four-year-old grandma and I chat on the phone, commiserating at our ailments that are far too similar for the age gap. My parents and family tell me all the things they'd do for me to make me healthy, but they lack these resources.

The people keeping me on mute have all the power and none of the love. I can't describe what it feels like to live in a world of let downs. Imagine the time you wanted something so incredibly badly and it didn't work out. Your heart was completely shattered and you didn't think you would be able to get through this moment in time. For me, this moment is a repetitive thing. It's so repetitive, it has become a trauma that is never ending. Whenever I get prescribed a new med, I get excited. I think that this could really be it and that I could go back into remission. The thing with biologics, the kind of medicine that I take for my Crohn's, is that they don't know which meds work for which people. It's all just one big guessing game. It's a game I've now lost over ten times. Combination therapies, singular therapies, steroids—all the medicines I've tried have now failed me. It's like a really shitty blooper reel that's an hour long, and your computer freezes so you can't forcibly quit Google Chrome.

With this territory there comes an innate loneliness. You can join all of the support groups and hear from others who are battling the same thing, but no story will completely match yours. A person's story can help guide you to a better treatment plan, but when you're living in a world where the medicines work for less than half of the suffering population, you're at a loss. Most of the time, people post questions that you could easily google. They want to know if they can get tattoos while on certain medications or if they can take pro-biotics or if they can drink or smoke. These types of posts are not there for any kind of connection, but are used as a dumping ground for information.

New people in the group ask how long it took for the drug to work for everyone else. This is hard because every person varies. People ask about the dosage and how often people get infusions and if this new regimen helped. It's the same questions every single day. Support groups are great for when you're first starting a med or are first diagnosed, but eventually they become too much. Some days, your whole life feels like this constant loss. In these groups, people often post when they're leaving the group because the drug no longer works for them. It's sad watching other people go through this cyclical and terrifying pattern.

Part of this loss is your team. Most people with complex medical issues have a team of people who are ideally supposed to work together. Yet, many times the patient ends up playing phone tag and begging for better communication between the physicians. Some doctors don't like to collaborate out of pride. Some of them just don't like to collaborate with each other. Not all people work well with each other, and sadly that also goes for doctors.

This situation happened to me. One of my doctors, my very kind gastroenterologist, wanted to put me on two very strong drugs and the other, my very experienced rheumatologist, refused because he thought that the risks were too high. The one looking at the risks claimed that the only way he'd allow me to be on both drugs was if I was an elderly woman on my deathbed and I wanted my last few months to be pleasant. Yes, there would be potential for harmful side effects as with all my complex drugs, but his answer was still disheartening. Obviously, I want to be safe, but with drugs nothing is ever truly safe. I was at a low point with my health and just wanted some relief.

These two doctors struggled to communicate to find a solution and it became my problem. I begged over email for my gastroenterologist to talk to my rheumatologist, but things never seemed to work out. Because of their inability to agree, I've been on a constant dose of steroids for the past two years. The toll that this attempted facilitation took was emotionally draining for me. No patient is thinking about your pride and how your colleagues will see you. They are only thinking of themselves and what they can do to better their lives. By refusing to communicate with the rest of the patient's team, the doctor is only making their patient's life worse.

Sadly, people pleasing is a big part of this game with your supposed team. You need to smile at your appointments and put on this act of bravery. You need to make jokes and seem appealing because the more they like you the more willing they will be to help you. The lesson I have learned is that I must always be "on" when I'm at appointments. It doesn't seem to really matter that I am a very knowledgeable patient with the ability to articulate twenty-one years of medical history and complications. The important thing is I am a fun patient to care for, cracking jokes and trying to lighten the mood. I'm thanking my doctors ten times over for doing the jobs they are being paid to do.

I've found that if your doctors like you, they're more willing to help. So instead of being a really sick patient that has left school because of the worsening conditions, I have to smile and laugh and make the appointment enjoyable—for the doctor, not myself. I'm the one struggling just to complete daily tasks, but it is up to me to make the doctor feel good about themselves. That's pretty terrible, isn't it?

This is the sad truth of the medical world. The skills I have learned from being a sick kid are honestly wild. I know how to work through one of the most complicated systems around. Many young adults don't even want to call their primary physician to make an appointment. When you're like me, like us, you basically have a superpower. You learn how to talk to so many different kinds of people and figure out how to work best with them. You know the steps needed to change medications and work with insurance. You know how to make nurses laugh until they can't see straight. You can list off your twenty-seven daily medications on their dosage with ease, and you even know the generic name as well as the brand. Adults don't always know how to navigate it, but when you grow up within its trenches it becomes a world that you can maneuver through with ease, even if that ease is painful.

If you're not crying into the void, you are screaming into it. You are screaming into it because you need these people to help you. You scream because you don't know what else you can do, and you can see that your options are slimming. You scream because being quiet and polite didn't work. You scream because the male doctors overlook your wants, needs, emotions, and thoughts. You scream because clearly the other options didn't work out and you desperately need attention and care.

You scream because it is the best chance you have for making sense of all of it. For me, I'm lucky enough to have found a new doctor who seemingly wants to help. The other day, she called to check in on me and the issues I was having. I've never had such direct communication that was both kind and fruitful. Although this medical field is incredibly hard to deal with and it might seem like there are more bad doctors than good, there will be wonderful healthcare professionals out there. Don't think that this is the end for you because, somewhere out there, there is someone who is yearning to help. Even nurses can make your life easier. I've become quite close to the billing department and administrative assistants who make me feel cared for. Sometimes you have to look around that dark void, and you may have to look way too hard, but if you do there will be someone who is willing to help.

EVEN WHEN THE GOOD DAYS ARE BAD

———

When you're healthy, you don't think about the good days. You aren't thinking about how lucky you are that you made it to all of your classes today and that you won't have to do any makeup work. You aren't thinking about how your body doesn't feel like it's going to collapse as you're going on your afternoon stroll. When you're healthy, your idea of a bad day is different than someone who has chronic illnesses. Sure, if you have a test and you aren't ready for it you might look at that day as bad, but then the rest of your day is probably okay. If you're running late for work and realize you forgot about that important meeting, you probably think that's a bad day. However, you can make up for that part of the day by staying late or doing a little extra work and helping out your team. The difference is that able-bodied people don't specifically look at the good days. Sick people try to hold on to them for all of eternity because they don't know if they'll ever return.

Although I have always been sick to some degree, I haven't always been this sick. As each year of college has passed by, I have gotten sicker. That is the reality of the situation and what makes it truly terrifying. You always think that it can't get worse than it is in this exact moment, but chronically ill bodies love a good old "Eff you!" to remind you how delicate and out of control you truly are.

This brings me back to good days. Sick people love good days. I don't know any sick person who isn't so extremely grateful for these good days that occasionally grace us with their presence. That being said, they are also some of the saddest days. Some days I'll wake up in a positive mindset, in a minimal amount of pain, and I know that the day will be good. When I recognize that a day is going well, I try my best to enjoy and appreciate every second of it. I don't know when I'll get another one, so I try and do all of the things I want to do while at the same time trying to make sure I don't do too much. That is another one of our constant struggles.

When you've gone a really long time without a good day, you want to do everything. For some people, it's going on a nice long walk with minimal pain. For other people, it's working as hard as they can to live out this wonderful day. Some chronically ill people choose to conserve their energy when they have good days. They'll use it sparingly. Other chronically ill people will take that day to do everything that they've been missing out on, which often means that they'll push themselves too hard. People who push themselves will go on a long walk, go to the store, shop for hours, visit a friend, go out to dinner, and basically use their entire battery life. Early on in my chronically ill life, I would push myself until I couldn't function the next day. Now, I typically try and reign it in and do a couple smaller activities.

It's just human nature to pursue all of the good in the world. For example, yesterday was a good day. I was super productive in the morning and got a lot of my work done for the upcoming week. I was able to relax with my service animal Keller, who was content on hanging around with me and taking it slow. My school hosted their annual farmer's market and I got a freshly brewed sweet tea from the tea truck with a sweetness level rating of seven. I got to sit out in seventy-degree weather in shorts and a t-shirt without profusely sweating (classic temperature regulation problems). I got to sit on a bench for hours, people watching and making people smile simply by hanging out with my pup. I even had a chiropractor appointment, which always makes me feel good and loved because she is one of the few doctors who listens. After my appointment, I spent the rest of the evening at a new dog park where I met a lot of nice people and dogs, and Keller got the chance to just roam free. Yesterday was certainly a good day.

All of those wonderful things from my good day yesterday give me a bad taste in my mouth because now I don't have them. Now I'm sitting in bed, bleeding, hungry, nauseous, and sad. I've been sick for two years with a Crohn's flare. The Crohn's works with my CRPS to increase my pain levels, which makes the day even harder than it needs to be. I'm bleeding a lot and I cry when I try and go to the bathroom. I text my mom in fear that I'm getting worse which only makes her anxious as well. Today I am crying and screaming and pounding my angry fist at the void.

To a healthy person, this will sound silly. They'll say that I should just be grateful for that good day, and I am grateful for that day. However, that day is now painful. Yesterday I knew what it was like to be okay again, even if it was only for a moment, and knowing that feeling is now so far out of reach physically pains me. Since I was less sick earlier in my life, I know what a good day or week looks and feels like. Those times are long gone, so having that single moment taken away now is even more painful. I never truly know how long that good moment will last and my heart hurts knowing that every future moment is unknown. Humans shouldn't be expected to jump from one extreme to the other, but that is how chronic illness functions. It functions on a system of insanity and disorder. It pushes my OCD out into the open and the tics come flooding in.

Knowing that healthy feeling, that truly good feeling, even for just a second, hurts. It's a reminder that you're missing out on something that the rest of the world just has. It's a reminder that you're not like everyone else, even if from the outside you look like a regular girl. It's a reminder that you live in a glass body and the slightest shake can break it all. You just don't know what is going to happen and when. You are a human full of disarray.

To not experience all the good days makes you feel that much more broken.

PART THREE

"BUT IT'S NONE OF THEIR BUSINESS"

———

This is one of those things that I hear a lot from able-bodied friends. They try and make me feel better and less obligated to tell others about my illness. For me, not sharing is more dangerous. If I don't share my health story then I'm stuck. I'm stuck because I try to pretend that I'm in a body that functions like a normal human being, which can put me in unsafe situations.

No, it is none of their business. When old men stare me down for using an accessible parking spot or give me some nod of disapproval, it is none of their business. When people ask, "What's wrong with you?" when they see me with my service dog Keller, that is none of their business.

But if I am in an environment where I will need to rely on others and function in a group, then I will let it be known. It is their business to know how my body works because my illnesses do not just affect me, but everyone around me.

For example, I make plans to see friends. I don't make them very often for fear that I will need to cancel them last minute. Canceling once is fine, twice isn't great, and three is basically unacceptable. If I don't feel well, then I can't go out with my friends.

I've been struggling with this notion of who to tell and when to tell people about my disabilities recently. As I begin my job search, I've found that my disability will often come up. The issue is I want to disclose my disability when I feel ready. Some of the job applications, however, ask if you've ever had a disability and I feel obligated to say yes. I worry that disclosing my disability before an interview will impede my ability to get a job. I've found that for companies where I don't have to disclose right away, I've been hearing back from them and have been asked when it would be a good time to have an interview.

Now, during my interviews I will often mention many of my academic feats, which I feel are all the more impressive because of my three medical leaves, and my ability to push through all the odds. In this situation, I'm getting to highlight my disability in a positive way. So, if a company can't see how valuable I'd be to them then I'm not really interested in working with them. My overall feeling about disclosing is that you should do it when you're ready. I don't know what's best, but what's best for me is taking my chronic illnesses in a positive light.

No, it's none of their business. It's none of their business if you don't want it to be. Deciding to disclose is a personal choice and whatever you decide to do is the right choice.

LOVE

——

My ability to thoroughly yet swiftly swipe through tons of profiles on dating apps could be on my resume.

I'm on them all of the time, but I often worry that love will not be attainable and you might feel this way too. For me, I worry that finding someone who is willing to support me throughout my illnesses and love me when I can't find any reasons to love my own body is going to be impossible. I want someone who is going to love me even because of my illnesses. I can't have someone in my life who is going to ignore something that is so integral to my being. I want to find someone who understands my need to take breaks on outings, or the fact that I can't always go on outings. I won't find someone who doesn't view me as a burden. I won't find someone who will be okay with a surrogate and all of the excessive money I will need to spend to have a child of my own. The money I will need to spend to live a happy life. I often worry I will be too much.

I know I have wonderful qualities. I'm not obtuse, and I'd be lying if I didn't think that what I have to bring to the table is great. My emotional intelligence is far beyond a normal person. My empathy is raging, and I have a desire to help whomever I can. I am hysterical and can make almost anyone laugh until they cry. My humor is dark and dangerous, and I can make shitty situations a little less shitty. I laugh at myself and my own situations and hopefully I can make the others around me laugh too.

Just because I know these things, does not negate the fact that it is incredibly hard to believe that someone can see past all of the bad stuff to see the good. There will be people who say, "well, everyone has baggage." I basically have a sixteen-wheeler and some u-hauls full of baggage. Baggage implies this extra stuff that people carry around. Baggage is concealed and you don't see what's inside until you truly know someone. Mine isn't baggage because it is out in the open, and it needs to be out in the open for my own safety. My issues are known because if they were not, I would be in some serious trouble.

I've been in quite a few relationships and none of them have ended particularly well. I truly don't know if any relationship ever ends "well." Only once was my mental health the reason that we broke up, but besides that there seemingly just wasn't the right connection. I use dating apps all the time, and that's where I met all but one of the men I dated. Dating apps make the dating world a lot more accessible. Most girls my age meet guys at parties and out at bars, but I do not have the stamina to go to any party or bar. Dating apps have opened up a whole new world of people who might be interested in hanging out with a disabled girl.

Dating apps make it easier, but they can also make things more complicated. When you're texting someone and asking them questions, it's hard to avoid talking about something that impacts every aspect of my life. When guys ask me, "What did you do today?" I don't want to lie. Often times I'll just say I hung out, but then they want specifics on what exactly I did. If I was being honest, I would say I spent over an hour on the toilet, bled a bit, took a few naps, dislocated my left shoulder during my nap, took some Zofran for my nausea, and napped some more. Obviously, I don't open with that, but some of my days do look for that.

If someone on an app asks me what I did during the day, I usually make something up or just reply, "relaxing and watching some Netflix," and if I don't do that, sometimes I'll end up telling white lies. I'll say that I was hanging out with friends or something small like that. I don't like to lie, but sometimes I feel like I need to say something other than I spent all day relaxing if I'm talking to someone for a while. I do this to cover up my inability to actually do things normal twenty-one-year-old people do, like partying.

In all honesty, I tend to disclose my illnesses pretty early on, mostly because I have to. I want to let people into my world and show them all my parts. What I've found is a lot of guys will say they're fine with it, then I get ghosted and it's clear that they were far from fine with it. People say that you know your own worth, but a lot of self-worth comes from society's ideas about you. You can't deny that what others think about you impacts your perception of self. Seeing time and time again that men have decided that I wasn't good enough for them hurts. One of the worst parts is that I've come to accept this fate. I try, and I try, and I try, and I know that 99 percent of the time it isn't going to end in anything great.

Christina told me all about her relationship during the time of her diagnosis. She's a much more private person and lead what she referred to as "a double life" with her partner. She was truly "unwilling to let anyone around [her] see [her] suffer or see how sick [she] was." Christina wanted to hide her illnesses, but at the same time she wanted to confide in him when she was struggling. It was difficult for her to live this double life when she had this part of her that wanted to share everything with her boyfriend.

Even though she wanted to share the emotional struggles, it was too hard for him to grasp when he didn't see the physical struggles she was going through on a daily basis. She described this as a "disconnect," as he couldn't understand how sick she was if she never let him see it. When Christina began treatments for Lyme disease at home, she didn't even want him to visit her. When he did visit her, she would use all of her energy, "put on all the make-up, do [her] hair, put on self-tanner, anything to make [her] look as healthy as possible." Christina admits that she was scared, not of being unlovable, but of her boyfriend seeing her this sick and never being able to forget that sick side of her.

I completely understand where Christina is coming from. My last boyfriend would tell me how pretty I was while I was fat and on steroids, and I couldn't even look at myself in the mirror. I would imagine my old body and how badly I wanted it back. It felt so far away from me. In my mind I looked one way, but sitting with my boyfriend, looking at my own body, it just wasn't the one I wanted to see. It was fatter and rounder, and I wanted him to see the old me. Over time, he helped me fall in love with my new body. I let someone in when I wasn't super confident, but he helped me see it in myself. I know that I have a whole team rooting for me, as I'm sure Christina does.

Meriel, one of my good friends from college, is diagnosed with psoriasis. Although confident in herself, dating and worrying about what others think and see has given her some anxiety. Psoriasis is a disorder where red, itchy, and painful patches pop up all over your skin. She's had symptoms since she was a baby and struggled to find a time when she was fully clear. For Meriel, the patches are mostly on her hands now, but she's previously had them on her legs and face.

On her first date with her previous boyfriend, she was flaring on her face. She said that her psoriasis was "so noticeable," and because of that she worried her condition was "going to make things not go well" with him. She asked him about the flare up a while after that first date and he said he didn't even notice. Sometimes our biggest insecurities aren't even noticeable to the people we're trying to impress. At some point, we'll all find the right person who loves us despite our illnesses, or even better, they love us because of our illnesses.

When chatting with Julian about his relationships, he told me all about his wife. Julian has an accepting and loving wife. He knows that he's "extremely lucky" because he knows that when a partner is diagnosed with a chronic illness, sometimes the partner will leave. When talking to me, he mentioned the harder times, the moments where they don't quite understand each other. These moments are bound to happen because "how can she fully understand? That's hard letting go of moments like that because I think when you're chronically ill you really want people to understand so bad." Julian acknowledged that expecting a partner to fully grasp what you're going through just isn't possible, no matter how badly you want that.

Another person who described her relationship as "extremely lucky" was one of my best friends, Anna. She has a lot of the same chronic illnesses as me and we relate on a deeply emotional level. Anna's boyfriend is Aaron, and they met while going to school together at Rutgers University. Aaron saw Anna's nasal feeding tube as something quite beautiful. He loved the confidence that she showed with the tube coming out of her nose. When talking about her relationship she mentioned, "Aaron showing so much interest meant that he was able to look past my chronic illnesses and love me for who I am." There was this common theme throughout all of my conversations of partners being able to look past the chronic illnesses or simply not notice enough to make them a deciding factor in the relationship.

My mom always tells me I'll find the right guy. My grandma knows I'll end up finding the right guy too, but she is aware this will be hard for me. She often tells my cousins that they should marry someone who is Jewish, a group of people that is quite small compared to Christians. She has not emphasized the same goals for me, though. She doesn't put that extra set of criteria on me because she already knows how difficult it will be to find someone who can fully accept my illnesses. She always just says she wants me to find someone who treats me well and makes me happy. Believe me, I want that too. I am also well aware that the perfect person doesn't exist, but that doesn't mean that I want to settle for someone I'm not attracted to simply because they are actually attracted to me. In this way, I want it all.

I want someone who loves me with all of my flaws. I want someone who I'm actually physically attracted to because if I'm not, our sex life probably won't exist due to my many painful conditions. I have to love this person so deeply, and they need to feel the same way about me. I want them to be healthy. I love talking with disabled guys and I do find them attractive but starting a relationship would really depend on our needs and how they match up. I often need someone who can help push my wheelchair or do physical tasks for me. So, dating an able-bodied person would be extremely beneficial.

That being said, I'm open to dating other disabled people. Disability is a spectrum and I won't count anyone out due to any disability. In terms of a lifelong partner, I physically do not have the energy to take care of another sick person and I want our kids to have at least one "fun" parent. I want them to explore, hike, go on rollercoasters, and do all the things that I won't be able to do. I want a husband who fills in these gaps I have in my ability and do so in a way that just makes our team that much stronger.

Love is already so complicated, and I truly don't understand how anyone finds each other, disabled or not. It's just hard to find that person to settle down with. I find it amazing when people so seemingly easily do so.

I worry at times. I often worry I won't be enough for a man to want to stick around. I see beautiful women who are completely able-bodied struggle to find someone. If it's that hard for them, I can only imagine that it would be that much harder for me. However, I do know that someday, at some point, I will find the right guy. I will find a man who wants to settle down with me and start a family in some way, shape, or form. For now, I'm totally okay just being a dog mom.

JUNE

———

Everyone has special people in their life. Everyone plays a different role in one's life and contributes in some way, shape, or form. Others help to mold you into the person you are today. These relationships are incredibly special, few, and far between. When you have a relationship like this, you want to cherish every moment with that person. For me, my grandma has been my person. Growing up, I only saw her a few times a year, but each time was so incredibly special. I spent many evenings and afternoons talking to her on the phone. My heart would explode into a million different pieces as we talked about our lives. I simply couldn't contain my love for her.

For the first twelve years of my life, Thanksgiving was hosted at my house and my entire family would come and stay with us. This of course included my cousins. I loved them to pieces, but I always feared when they'd arrive because that meant I had to share my grandma. She always came to my house a few days early and I savored those moments. I couldn't wait to hop off the school bus, come home, and see the world's most honest, most kind-hearted, and most lovable person waiting for me.

I can still picture the unique smell of her in my head. Grandma's signature scent during my childhood was a cashmere-mist perfume. She was a color-coordinated queen, always dressed to perfection. Looking at my grandma's impeccable outfits, it was clear to see where my mom's style gene came from. I loved watching my grandma pick her outfits out each morning and rejoining her at night to snack on Pepperidge Farm cookie assortments. I was never close enough to her, and I would cuddle up against her on our couch or hang out in "Grandma's room," which conveniently shared a wall with mine.

Grandma showed me *A League of Their Own* for the first time. A film all about women empowerment and the start of the All-American Girls Professional Baseball League. A mix of my two favorite things: baseball and feminism. She tried to teach me how to play mahjong and how to paint like a real artist, like her. Grandma Junie taught me to play spite and malice, which is the only card game I truly ever learned and loved to play. She was an elementary school teacher and had a way with kids that was different. She treated us like adults and had high expectations, yet still understood we were only children and learning the ways of the world.

My favorite of all the things she would do when I was younger was brush my hair. I've always had long brown hair with lighter brown streaks. She would brush through it ever so gently. If there was ever even the tiniest tug on a knot she would jump in her seat and ask "Did I hurt you?" in such a worried and concerned tone. She wanted to make every experience, even the small ones, feel important. She made me feel important and cared about my feelings, even if it was about a tiny knot in my hair, were noted.

As I grew up, our relationship changed. She was no longer leading me. Instead, we began to feel like peers. Once I hit high school, we had our weekly chats on the phone as she had moved from Pennsylvania to California to be closer to her other daughter. During our phone calls, we would vent, swear, and shit on whoever we wanted. The world was fair game, and we were coming at it hard. I wasn't in therapy yet, so she became my unofficial therapist. Honestly, I became her unofficial therapist as well. My whole childhood, I had been looking for this sort of relationship with people my own age, but I was finding it in an eighty-eight-year-old woman.

Once my grandma became too old and too weak to travel, basically once she moved out to California in 2011, my extended family out there stopped visiting us for Thanksgiving. Because of this, we decided to take a yearly trip out to California to see them. Every Christmas break, my mom, dad, brother, and now Keller would pack up and visit her for five wonderful days. I couldn't wait until Christmas day. It was not because Santa was coming because after all, he didn't tend to show up at Jewish girls' houses. I was excited to fly out to California.

After 2011, our Christmas visit was the one time of year I got to see her in person. We'd talk on the phone about how excited she was for me to visit and how my presence was going to keep her alive. I didn't like that joke when I was fourteen, and I don't like it now. She hasn't made that joke recently, but she continues to count down the days until my arrival. She always makes sure my service dog Keller is coming too. My grandma is the reason I have her in the first place because she said to my mom, "just get her the damn dog." This woman will truly say and do anything to help me thrive in this world.

She and I have a lot of traditions. Her biggest one is praying for me. She prays for me all of the time. She isn't even that religious of a person. Although, during one of her bouts of illness she claimed she married God and then promptly divorced him because he wasn't listening to her. Anyway, she tries so hard for me to get better, for there to be a cure, and for people to watch over me. During the times when I seem to only be getting sicker, I can feel the deep concern for me in her voice over the phone. There is a part of me that appreciated the knowledge when we hang up, she is still thinking and worrying about me. She wants me to feel as good as a young person should. While visiting her this past Christmas she said, "it's my privilege to worry about you." This is something I needed to hear. Often feeling like a burden, knowing that I wasn't one in her eyes meant the world to me.

Grandma Junie is also the person who got me into *Friday Night Lights*. She called me up one day and told me that she thought it was a show I'd love; she was correct. I would call her and tell her everything that was going on in the season I was watching. Her only complaint was that "I don't understand why they need to drink so much," but besides that we talked about how talented the actors were, and how attractive they were if we're being honest. On one of my trips to see her out in California, I requested that we watch the *Friday Night Lights* finale together. I remember sitting with her with the show on in the background and I couldn't stop smiling. I don't even think I watched very much of it; I was focused on her. I sat there trying so hard to remember every single moment because I knew it was special. This was her favorite show that she chose to share with me. It was another thing that we could have together.

One of the most special things about our relationship is that we're actually sisters. Yes, you did in fact read that correctly. She and I are both members of Phi Sigma Sigma. She started the chapter at Penn State in the 1940s and was the first archon, or president, of the sorority. Unbeknownst to me, she was in the sorority that I really wanted to get into. Growing up she had never mentioned, not even one time, that she was in a sorority, let alone started one with her best friend. It wasn't until I signed up for recruitment that my mom told me about her presidential endeavors. The day that I got my bid for Phi Sigma Sigma, I ran into this huge empty hall where a lot of guest lectures speak, huddled in the corner, and gave her a call. I said, "Grandma, guess what? I'm in Phi Sig!" and she replied, "Now we're sisters!" She hurried off the phone so she could make it to bingo on time and get her favorite card, but before she hung up, she once more told me how happy she was.

The other day I called her up. She's ninety-four now and was just taken off of hospice after a full year on it. June is a fighter who refuses to quit. She was slated to die in November of 2018. I visited her twice last year when usually I only get to see her once. I called her on the phone right before my 2018 visit in

November and she sounded weak and scared, and when we hung up, I cried. I called my mom, told her to call grandma, and said that I thought we needed to go out and see her. She wasn't even that sick yet, but I knew.

The first night of our visit, we got a phone call at my aunt's house that she tried to get up from her bed and walk. She hadn't walked without a walker in years, so she stood up and fell. Her head just missed the sharp corner of her chair. We rushed over and found her caregiver with her, sitting on the floor. She looked sad and confused and kept saying "I'm stupid" over and over again. I looked into her eyes and she looked like a small child, unknowing and scared of herself. I repeatedly told her that she was not stupid and that she just didn't know. It reminded me of the grandmother in *Friday Night Lights* who suffers from dementia. The grandma that my grandma and I always talked about. We talked about how bad we felt for her. I have never been someone who listens to their gut. I spent my whole life trying to prove to others how sick I was that I often would doubt myself. Telling my mom that we needed to hop on a plane and visit her was the smartest thing I'd ever said.

After that visit, she went into a comatose state. She ate but slept the rest of the day, couldn't talk, and struggled to breath. Then this past summer, she magically started getting better. She still has moments of confusion, but she's been stable for a while now. All year we were told that this was when she was really going to go. I mourned every time. That's an extremely draining process and it made my heart hurt over and over again. Everything I do, I do for her. I want to feel good for myself, but I want to feel good for her. I want to live a life that we're proud of. Grandma Junie wants me to have it all, to be happy and healthy.

So many times my illnesses have kept me from making choices. If I go on steroids to stop a Crohn's flare, that's great. However, the steroids give me a moon face, increase my appetite, and weight. I just never seem to get both things. I can't be happy with my health and my physical appearance. I can't go out with my friends two nights in a row if I have a school obligation the next day. I just don't have the energy or capabilities of most people my age.

My grandma has all this hope and when she prays for me, she prays for everything. She wants me to be happy. She wants me to be healthy. When I talk with my family about treatments, there are always pros and cons and sometimes I have to sacrifice my happiness for my health or vice versa. I seemingly always have to choose even when I want both. My grandma gives me this feeling that maybe not today, but one day I won't have to choose. She has this eternal hope that I'll have it all. She's the one person in my life who doesn't force me to pick because she lives outside of my direct medical world. Her prayers for me to have it all mean everything to me. She makes me feel like maybe I will be happy and healthy.

In my grandma, I always have someone rooting for me who isn't worried about me getting too excited to see a new doctor in case things don't pan out. She lets me feel what I feel when I feel it. She's happy when her prayers are working. She loves how much I push myself and only gives me love. When you're sick all of the time, it can be hard to balance complex relationships. With Grandma Junie, it's simple. At the end of our call, and sometimes at some random point in the middle, she says, "You know what?" I reply, "What?" even though I had done this a million times. Like she has a million times before, Grandma Junie says the words I always want to hear from her.

"I love you."

EMOTIONAL
INTELLIGENCE

———

When you first get diagnosed, you'll be upset. Maybe at first, you'll be happy that you finally have a word for something that you've been struggling with. However, that happiness will fade and your reality will return. You will return to the struggle of this new name and how to best treat it. If you have a chronic illness, you're most likely lost. It's okay to be sad. It's okay to have this intense and sometimes scary hatred toward your body. You might feel like the world is out of your control. You'll probably hit a moment when you feel like the world is just unfair and the cards you've been dealt are the worst.

All of that is valid. All of those feelings are true.

If chronic illness has taught me anything, it is that the smallest acts of kindness are the ones that make your day. The friend that sees you're struggling and gets you a drink so you don't have to put in that extra effort. The friend that texts you to see how the new medication is going. When you go out to eat and your friend asks, "Do you want to sit in the booth or on the chair?" because she knows that your body works differently and needs different things. Those moments were some of my happiest because I knew that someone out there was thinking about me. Everyone wants to know they're being thought about and that their needs are being considered.

With everything that comes with chronic illness, it can be easy to forget that everyone around you still has stuff going on too. Everyone is struggling in one way or another. You don't have to be on chemo to have a bad day and crave love and attention. You don't need to be in the hospital to struggle. You just have to be a person. It is important to remember that although your illness is hard and debilitating, there are others out there with their own struggles and hardships. Everything in life is relative.

Sometimes when I feel really down or upset, I'll take a minute to reach out to someone who I noticed was struggling. They are always so appreciative that I've reached out and made the effort to let them know that they are important. Just the other day I noticed that a girl at school seemed off. She was smiling and going through the motions, but I could tell that something wasn't right. Even though I had been feeling like literal crap all week, I got a meal with her. Once I gave her my attention, she unloaded everything that she was struggling with. It was personal and difficult, and she was feeling confused about so many things in life. In that moment I stopped thinking about my own pain, took on hers, and provided her with advice. More importantly, I provided her with an open heart. I showed her that I wanted to listen, and I was more than willing to be there for her in that moment.

I always say that chronic illness has made me empathetic. It is probably one of the best parts about being sick. My ability to connect with almost anyone comes from my lived experience. I know firsthand how hard it is to be in pain and suffer, to crave support and love. So, I treat everyone that I come across how I want to be treated. This is a simple concept, "treat others the way you want to be treated," but it takes on a whole new meaning when you're sick. The care and love chronically ill people want exceeds the norm, and thus we give that extreme amount of care to everyone else. We know that small acts of kindness make our days, and so we try and do the same for those around us. Chronic illness has ruined my life, while also making it a lot brighter. It's taught me about myself and others, and once you get that first chunk of grieving out of the way, you're in a state to look beyond yourself.

Your body is always in this hyperaware state because of all the diseases rummaging around in there. I mean hyperaware in a bunch of different ways. For me, one of my diseases makes me hypersensitive to touch and pain. My neurons misfire and cause an excessive amount of sensitivity. So, physically, I'm more sensitive. On top of the physical sensitivity, you're also aware of your body more than the average person. Your body makes so many changes and creates new symptoms that always leaves you trying to figure out which disease the symptom belongs to. You're hyperaware because you have to be for your health. You need to be able to verbalize what you're feeling to your doctors, family, and friends.

Because of all of these physical expressions of the hyperaware state, you are inherently emotionally aware. You naturally see what people need and when they need it because you live in such a complex world that the able-bodied world is pretty simple. Again, you know how small acts of kindness can really make someone's day. You think of thoughtful texts to send to friends who are struggling. You basically do everything that you hope people will do for you. Use that awareness to your advantage. I truly believe that your heart becomes hyperaware when you're suffering every day. Use that skill to help others.

PUBLIC HUMILIATION

When you're sick all of the time, you lack control. You lack control in every way possible. You lack control when you're changing drugs and you or your caregiver has to fight with insurance every step of the way. You need to prove that you're sick enough for it and you need to prove that those seven other drugs didn't work. This lack of control can lead to intense feelings of utter humiliation. You are begging on your knees for insurance to listen to you, for your caregiver to listen to you, for anyone to listen. You lack control over how others perceive you. People can make comments and statements that humiliate you. Your disability, even if invisible, becomes visible even when you don't want it to.

If you're like me, chronic illness has shown you that the key to it all is to follow the rules. You're conditioned to listen to your doctors because once you find one who finally believes you, you feel obligated to stay. Essentially, whatever your doctor says becomes the gospel. Someone has finally honored your words and your personal stories. They believe they have a treatment for you, something that will help. Insurance approves the drug and you're ready to learn how to administer the shots yourself.

The first visit you do four of the shots, two in each leg. They're so painful that doctors actually produced a new, less painful, version.[8] The type of pain is something that I've never experienced outside of Humira. The shot itself hurts because it's a needle, but the medicine actually burns. It feels like your leg is in a furnace and that furnace is going directly into your bloodstream. Your legs are sore, and I often would bruise from the shots. So, receiving four shots on the first visit is horrific. Even though I wanted to get the shots done as quickly as humanly possible, I actually had to take breaks in between. I couldn't even have the band aid touch my skin to cover the small hole because even the band aid grazing my skin made me scream. You have this short period of time to learn how to give the shots to yourself, they hand you the next set, and you're now on your own.

It was the winter of 2018 when I started on Humira. Humira was this biologic medication that was administered via an epi-pen looking utensil. Whenever you start a new self-administered drug, you go to the hospital and they teach you how to clean the skin, actually inject the shot, and answer any questions you may have. Before you even inject yourself, you have to take the Humira out of the fridge and let it sit out for a bit. When you give yourself the injection, you have to swab the area with alcohol wipes. Then, you take the cap off with the needle-end facing upward, making sure not to touch where the needle is located, flip the pen downward, and

---

8   HUMIRA Citrate-Free, abbvie.

smack it into your thigh. Then you actually have to hold the pen in there for around ten seconds, or until you see a "flag," or the little sign on the side of the pen, go up.

Once you're done with the pen, you put it in one of those hazardous waste bins to keep everything sanitary. A nurse is there to help you every step of the way; having a medical professional inches away is always comforting when starting a new medication. In the hospital, I gave myself the first four shots, which is called a loading dose. They amp up the medication and give you a ton at first.

After that first time at Boston Children's Hospital, I was on my own. Worse than that, the first time I administered the shots all by myself I was at school three hundred miles away without my parents. My day of shots ended up falling on a snow day, which meant that that college was shut down. I trekked from my apartment to the health center, assuming that it must be open. I was not about to miss my first dosage by myself. I had a duty to my body to get this shot done. I went through the gym entrance because, of course, that was open. I couldn't believe that the gym was open, but something as essential as the health center was closed.

I called campus safety to let me in to get my shots, but they refused. There was a secret code they needed to get into the fridge where my medicine was kept, and they said they couldn't give the code out. They could have easily had a campus safety officer open the fridge then just change the code the next day. My medicine was kept in there in case we had a power outage, since their fridge was attached to a generator.

My medicine was there because it was supposed to be a safer method.

I was quickly becoming overwhelmed. I called my Humira ambassador who recommended I find someone who can open the fridge. I started to panic. I called my parents and the school over and over again. I continued to panic. I tried my best to convince school staff to let security open the fridge because today was the day that I needed to get my shots. This was the scheduled day. I was losing all control.

I was jumping back and forth between calling my parents and calling the school, and my anxiety was becoming more prevalent by the second. I was inching closer to a panic attack. My breathing was heavier, and my mind was going in circles. I felt out of control and I was worried my problem-solving skills were waning as my brain became overloaded with stimulating input. I never cry in public. I usually hold it in until I'm going to burst, and that day I just let it go. I was crying in the gym as all of the boys' sports teams walked by, watching me break down at the end of a hallway. I had eight thousand dollars of medication and the only thing that separated me from it was a couple of doors that could easily open with a code.

I felt like I was fighting this all alone. I felt like no one was listening to me, quite literally, cry for help. How can a school have people on duty, people who are there to keep the school safe, but no one in the health center? The gym was open in case anyone needed to lift or go for a jog. Of course, the healthy people get the attention and the sick people get left behind. Even when you have everything figured out, from the doctor's approval, to the insurance's approval, to the right transportation and storing, something still goes wrong. You feel like you're fighting the entire world alone.

Finally, a woman from the health center had to drive to the school at ten in the evening, when nothing was safe or plowed, just to get me my medication. This responsibility shouldn't have been on her. Someone's safety should not have been put at risk when there were already people on campus who could have opened up the fridge. You want to know where I safely picked them up? I stood outside of the library and got my Humira from a nice lady in a minivan. I wish I was kidding, but my life, and the life of most chronically ill people, is simply weird.

The disabled community at school was persecuted in a way that no one saw coming. No one thinks of the disabled population. We are always an afterthought. However, if this could happen to me, this could really happen to anyone. The school became the controllers of my medication. They were supposed to be helping me keep it safe by keeping it in a fridge powered by a generator, but instead their involvement became a health hazard. I was humiliated on so many levels that day. I was embarrassed by how many times I called my Humira ambassador. She could not have been any sweeter, and when I stopped Humira I wanted to say goodbye to her and thank her for how kind she was to me. I was embarrassed at how loudly and uncontrollably I cried in public that day. I cried in the gym, one of the most male-dominated spaces, a place of strength, toughness.

I was humiliated that my school acted in this way. I understood the legality behind it, but they could always change the code, or have the code changed by people who are always on staff and legally allowed to help in health situations. I was embarrassed. I was publicly humiliated, and that never needed to happen. There were no practices in place for a situation like this, which is not okay.

A SPECTACLE

———

I'd like to think that I'm a pretty understanding person. I listen to people and always hear what they have to say. I give people the benefit of the doubt. I accept people for who they are. However, I become very upset and angry when people don't take the time to understand or hear me.

As a chronically ill person, I am questioned all of the time. People wonder what my service animal does and often make comments about how she probably isn't "real" because she's small and I don't "look sick." I watch people bring their pets into stores simply because they love having them around. Some of these people pass their dogs off as service animals even though they are not. Some people fake emotional support animals (ESAs) who don't have the same rights as service animals and are often confused. However, there is a huge difference because ESAs do not have to be trained at all. According to an article from *The Guardian*, "Not only can fake ESAs distract or attack working service dogs, but service providers who have been inconvenienced by bad behavior from an unruly pet often sour on accommodating all animals thereafter."[9] I know that this behavior impacts how people look at my dog. I know that part of it is her size. She is only twelve-and-a-half pounds, and people often get away with bringing small dogs into public spaces.

My friend recently told me about her experience where there was a large golden retriever wearing a service dog vest. A lot of people were going over to pet it which is almost never allowed with working dogs. The dogs are there to help. They can't help if they're distracted. My friend went over and the woman said, "oh this is my emotional support animal so he can go everywhere with me." Clearly, she knows that emotional support animals can't go everywhere because she went out and bought a service dog vest. Anyone can buy a vest and claim that their dog is a service animal. In this case, it was a large golden retriever, but often times smaller dogs are being passed off as working dogs.

Keller does work. She helps during panic attacks, with my pain from my CRPS, and with desensitization therapy. This involves many tasks including grounding me with licking when I'm panicking, as well as laying on my body when I'm in pain. She is like a portable heating pad. However, often times fake service animals are tiny and smaller dogs get away with poor behavior over bigger dogs. Because of this, and the fact that I look healthy, I get nasty looks whenever I bring her out.

Just today, I was driving back to school after my Thanksgiving break and stopped to use the bathroom at a Starbucks.

---

9   Adrienne Matei, The Number of Fake Emotional Support Dogs Is Exploding—Why? The Guardian, August 13, 2019

I walked in with Keller, and some lady had a dog in a travel backpack that was barking at Keller a lot. However, because no one saw that dog, they all looked and glared at us instead. Keller knows not to bark in public spaces. Sure, every service animal slips up now and then, they aren't robots, but other dogs in public spaces can make real service animals look bad. Humans can be a big enough distraction, but an uncontrolled and untrained animal can also cause stress for the service animal and their handler.

People make comments about me using a wheelchair because I can walk. If someone sees me stand up from my wheelchair and walk, they assume that I'm faking an injury for perks. Using a chair and having a service animal do not lead to perks. They lead to constant questioning and rude behaviors. They lead to strangers belittling you and disregarding you as a person.

I'm sick of explaining myself to the world. I can't do what I want to do. I always have to rationalize why I can't go to the party when I'm feeling ill and flaring, or why I can enter this building with my service animal. Like most things in my life relating to my health, I have to advocate. It shouldn't be my job to play doctor and lawyer but that's how I spend a lot of my time. The same comes to my service animal's rights. For example, today there was a big football game on campus. As much as I love football, it's about twenty degrees now and even colder earlier, so I had no intention of going today. However, my dog is a living, breathing animal and needs to go on walks and go to the bathroom. When I take Keller on a walk, we typically make a big loop around the school and cut through the stadium to get back to my room.

During the football game, I went to cut through the stadium and was stopped by a security guard. As I walked up, the man told me "No dogs." I explained that I go to the university. He looked at me with a blank stare, so I continued with, "I go to school here." He continued to insist that I couldn't bring my dog in. "She's my service animal and to get to my room, I have to walk through the stadium." He said, "Service animal?" and I could tell by his tone he didn't believe it. I repeated that I lived right there and was a student, and he finally let me go as if he was doing me a favor. I should be able to walk to my place of residence without getting stopped. My dog is small and "doesn't look like a service animal," so I was questioned. I don't look sick; thus, I was questioned. I am questioned no matter where I am, but especially when I bring any assistive device such as Keller or a wheelchair.

Yesterday, I went to an AJR concert in my wheelchair with one of my sorority sisters. It was amazing and one of the best shows I've ever been to. The accessibility was horrible, though. The people were horrible too. When I go out to big events like a concert, or say I'm spending the day in the city, I'll use my wheelchair. The sidewalks of Philly were far from accessible. There were bumps and cracks, and luckily, I can stand because there were some sidewalks that my chair couldn't get over. Just imagine how difficult getting around would be for someone who cannot stand up at all.

There was a direct line from where we parked to the venue, but a cop car was blocking it. We went up and I pointed to the tape to ask him to move it so we could go through. He replied, "go around the corner." So instead of getting to the venue easily, we had to ride over more uneven surfaces for a longer period of time. On top of that, I had to weave in between thousands of people waiting to get into the venue. No one moves out of the way for you. You are in the way if you're in a chair. It's on you. It's your problem.

Once I was situated, I was okay. No one really bothered me or asked me any questions. The people next to me saw me get up to go to the bathroom and I knew by the way the guy turned his head to his girlfriend and began to whisper that they were talking about me. I know they were talking about how I could walk. I always fear getting up from my chair. Annie Elainey, a chronically ill YouTube star, said it best in her aptly named episode "How to Spot a Fake Disability" when she stated, "it's a dangerous climate when people decide that they want to be witch hunters and figure out if someone is really disabled or not."[10]

It is very dangerous. I'm a young girl. I'm an easy target for a violent person, and I don't want to be put in a dangerous situation. I am always aware of my surroundings because I have to be. When I park in an accessible spot, I'm looking around to see if anyone seems disapproving or if they're going to approach me. I like to bring Keller with me when I have friends or family around because I feel as though I'm respected more. I want to avoid any kind of conflict, both verbal and physical, as best I can. I'm sure the concert goers thought I was rigging the system in some way, shape, or form. In fact, that could not be further from the truth.

---

10   Annie Elainey, "How to Spot a Fake Disability" | Annie Elainey, February 4, 2016, 4:55.

The judgmental looks were irritating but getting out of the venue at the end of the concert was the bigger issue. I told my friend it would be best to wait until a majority of people left the main event space so we could exit the venue slowly. However, I was quickly swarmed. Hundreds of people hovered over me like giraffes as I sat, small, and stuck in my chair. No one was letting us go through and I was trapped in a crowd of unaware people. A guy who around twenty years old and six feet tall stepped on me. I have no idea how he managed to do that. When he continued to be a problem, I said something and he ignored me. My friend even said something to him, and he apologized in an annoyed way as if I was the problem. This is the type of obvious ableism is accepted as disgusting amongst able-bodied people.

Able-bodied people don't get this next form. They think that people are helping when they do things like what happened in my situation, but in reality, they're not. Once that guy moved out of the way, a girl started yelling, "WHEELCHAIR. WHEELCHAIR. WHEELCHAIR" at the top of her lungs. Her other friend joined in. By yelling this, she was drawing unwanted attention in my direction. I just wanted to leave. I didn't want everyone in the venue to know that I was leaving. It was embarrassing and unnecessary. As we inched our way toward the exit, a girl standing up against the wall said, "you should really get lights for that thing." Within minutes I was yelled at and also told what I need to do to make my exit easier for able-bodied people.

Individually all of these little moments were irritating, but together they all added up to create an incredibly frustrating situation. Eventually, I became angry and mad and I didn't want to joke about this. I didn't want to make light of anything. Yes, I use humor as a coping mechanism most of the time, but sometimes it simply becomes far too much to handle. I need to accept the terrible situations I'm in and just be upset. I have to let myself feel. This was one of the first times I'd left my room for more than an hour or two in weeks. This night was supposed to be special for me in the sense that it was supposed to be normal. When I went to the concert, I just wanted to be like everyone else there and instead I was turned into a spectacle.

When I use my wheelchair, when I get out of my wheelchair, and when I have my service animal with me, I'm stared at and scrutinized. When I'm with my dog, everyone is waiting for her to mess up, as if to prove that she can't be real. When I'm in my wheelchair, people look me up and down to try and see what's wrong with me. When I stand up from my wheelchair, I often see looks of disgust. I feel like I have to exaggerate my limp or struggle more to prove that I need it. The judgmental nature of our society is extremely debilitating for people with invisible and chronic illnesses.

SO... HOW DOES THIS ALL END?

———

Chronic illnesses are unpredictable and debilitating. They change your life in every possible way. For most people, the biggest change to their life is learning to accept the fact that their illnesses aren't going to go away. Many new treatments and advancements are coming out but for most people the focus becomes all about disease management. Taking pain medications for your overactive nerves and infusions for your inflammatory bowel disease, things like that. It's all about management, not curing, which sucks to be quite frank. In order for there to be a cure, there needs to be extensive amounts of funding. You aren't living in a world where it's going to go away. You're living in a world where you just need to learn how to live with it.

Living with it comes with its perks. It teaches you skills and self-love like you've never experienced. However, I'm not denying how much it sucks knowing that very few dollars are being put toward these rarer diseases. Out of all my diseases, Crohn's most definitely gets the most funding, but there is always room for more. If there is less awareness of the diseases, the funding is subsequently lower. However, there are still advances every day. You can always advance yourself, teach others, and love the world and body that you live in.

I've been told by some of my doctors that there probably won't be a cure for Crohn's in my lifetime, but I'm sure that people with "incurable" diseases before me heard the same thing. I recently heard that maybe they'll figure something out within the next ten to fifteen years. When you google "probability of curing Crohn's," nothing really comes up. It tells you that the disease is chronic and it's all about symptom management. I'm sure if I were to google my other diseases, the same would come up. Typically, it is all about management. Not just in terms of symptoms, but you have to manage your expectations when you're sick with chronic illnesses.

I try to be as realistic as possible while not being totally pessimistic that a cure won't ever happen. Obviously, I'd love for there to be a cure now, but I know that doctors are studying and working on new drugs and revising treatments. There could be a breakthrough any minute, or it could take over a decade. If there's anything I've learned, it's that medicine cannot make promises. The best drug, a drug that saved your life, can suddenly stop working and ruin your life. When it comes right down to it, medicine is not secure or safe. Nothing really is.

All of this might sound dark and dreary, but there are so many wonderful things that come with living life with a chronic illness. You care so deeply about those you love. You savor those "good days" while also lamenting the fact that you don't have a ton of them. Most people love their families, but I love mine in a different way. Once you hit the age of twenty-two, it's rare that your family has to help put your clothes on or feed you. However, I rely on my family quite heavily. Sometimes I'm almost completely independent, but other times I feel like a burden for needing help with my clothes or food. I rely on them more than most for physical help, as well as emotional. They've spent years of their lives listening to me work through my latest diagnosis and figuring out the next steps.

I've found a group of wonderful and empowering women at school who would drop anything to come and help me. You have friends who help you when you get too drunk or are crying over a boyfriend, but I have friends who help me have a wonderful college experience by completing different acts of kindness.

When I've been on medical leave, they checked in on me constantly, and when they couldn't see me in person, they'd FaceTime me with updates. I was never out of the loop. They'll text me and ask how my new medication is going. If I'm having trouble walking, they'll ask if I need help with Keller. I tend to like walking Keller, even if I'm not feeling up to it. The walks allow me to think but can also be a time for me to get out of my own head. She has brought me such endless joy. The way she hops like a little bunny when she gets excited, or the way she rests her head on my chest when I feel overwhelmed makes me feel so incredibly loved and cared for. If I'm crying, she stops what she's doing to check in on me and see if I need to be grounded with licking, and if not, just comforts me by being by my side.

I spend a lot of time alone in my room at school, especially when I don't feel well, but I know I always have Keller. She wants to be with me all of the time, no matter how I'm feeling. She'll wait in the ER with me for hours. She'll lay on my legs during class. She'll calm me down if I'm panicking. She gives me a purpose and pushes me to keep going. I am forever grateful for my little friend.

Also, I connect with people on another level. I get direct messages on Instagram about how I inspire people and how they're grateful that I'm sharing my story. Because I'm so open about my illnesses and I've learned to talk about them in a way that isn't scary, people want to know more. They ask questions. After my summer internship, I got a card from one of my newer coworkers; the note inside described how I inspired them and made them feel good. When you're sick, at least for me, I try and overcompensate and make others feel worthy. It's going back to noticing, empathizing, and doing little things for others. Living with chronic illness has given me the amazing skill to connect. Even within the chronic illness community itself, I have met so many people who I would have never interacted with. These diseases are awful, but they allow you to bond with people in an almost indescribable way.

Lamenting and being sad and listening to your brain is okay. Being honest with yourself and where you're at in the exact moment is okay. Just know the moment will pass. Whenever I'm panicking about a symptom or I start to work myself up

I say, "Olivia, it's just a moment in time. It will pass." Sometimes, even just a few minutes later, things calm down and I'm okay. Things are complicated. Not everyone in your life will want to learn how to love you and care for you in the way that you need. To be fair, that happens with able-bodied people too so, don't worry. You will find those who want to make your world wonderful and will celebrate you for who you are.

These stories and moments in my own life have stayed so strongly in my memory because of my illnesses. My illnesses made me more aware of my body and the spaces I was in. I was always in tune with how I was feeling emotionally and physically. These experiences helped to shape my empathetic self and my ability to look at a situation and notice who needs support, love, and attention, and act on this information. I also know how little acts of kindness can really impact someone else's day for the better. When you're sick, kindness and understanding flows out of you. Knowing the value of these smaller experiences is key. These little moments might have been flashes of light for someone else, but for someone who lives for every moment like I do, they were beyond special.

Life with chronic illnesses is anything but static. The fluctuation is hard, but I think it's what keeps us all sane. Acceptance of your illness is part of the journey, but acceptance doesn't have to mean giving up on treatment options or thinking your life isn't worth living. Acceptance of your illnesses can open you up to this new world, a new way to live, a new community, and a new sense of self. We know in our hearts and from lived experience that some parts will be okay, and some parts won't. We have to live in a hopeful world because without it, life is honestly too scary.

So no, there isn't an ending that is wrapped up all nicely. The ending isn't necessarily happy, but it's also not sad. This is real life for people with chronic illnesses. The ending isn't close for most of us and the suffering will continue. But all of these nuggets of wisdom that I've shared are even more special because of their fleetingness. Every moment is more meaningful. Every outing is more rewarding because you've earned it. You are going to do great things in this world. No matter how hard things may get, and believe me they will get incredibly hard, there is a whole team of chronically ill people, friends, and family who are rooting for you. It might take an extra year to finish college, but you can do it. It might take months to relearn how to walk, but you'll do it. It might take years for you to love yourself and your body for what it is and what it does for you, but you'll do it. We are all rooting for you.

Through it all just remember to love yourself, cherish those good moments, and know that you deserve to be loved.

One last thing. You know what? I love you.

APPENDIX

Epigraph

"Our fight for disability rights — and why we're not done yet." Video. TED. October, 2016. https://www.ted.com/talks/judith_heumann_our_fight_for_disability_rights_and_why_we_re_not_done_yet#t-956453

Introduction

Minkoff, Eva. "Wellacopia interview with Nitika Chopra: Leadership, Dating, and Self-Love with Chronic Illness." Podcast. Wellacopia, August 18, 2019. https://invisiblenotbroken.com/home-chronic-illness-podcast/wellacopia-interview-with-nitika-chopra.

"National Center for Chronic Disease Prevention and Health Promotion." Center for Disease Control and Prevention, U.S. Department of Health & Human Services, October 23, 2019. https://www.cdc.gov/chronicdisease/about/index.htm. (https://www.cdc.gov/chronicdisease/about/index.htm)

Christina's First Diagnosis

"Mononucleosis (mono): Symptoms." Cleveland Clinic. Cleveland Clinic, November 24, 2015. https://my.clevelandclinic.org/health/diseases/13974-mononucleosis.

"You Know Your Body Best"

"Complex Regional Pain Syndrome Fact Sheet." National Institute of Neurological Disorders and Stroke. National Institute of Neurological Disorders and Stroke & National Institutes of Health. March 13, 2020. https://www.ninds.nih.gov/disorders/patient-caregiver-education/fact-sheets/complex-regional-pain-syndrome-fact-sheet.

Yes, This Part is Invisible Too

Chamberlin, J. Survey says: More Americans are seeking mental health treatment (American Psychological Association, 2004) https://www.apa.org/monitor/julaug04/survey

"Sarah Hyland on Her Two Kidney Transplants." Video. SELF. December 10, 2018. https://www.youtube.com/watch?v=EiR6DPzRufs

Public Humiliation

"HUMIRA Citrate-Free." abbvie. https://www.humira.com/citrate-free

A Spectacle

Elainey, Annie. "How to Spot a Fake Disability." February 4, 2016 https://www.youtube.com/watch?v=sIOcKpSVp4k

Matei, Adrienne. "The Number of Fake Emotional Support Dogs is Exploding - Why?" The Guardian. August 13, 2019 https://www.theguardian.com/lifeandstyle/2019/aug/12/ fake-emotional-support-animals-service-dogs

Made in the USA
Monee, IL
31 July 2020

37290370R00089

CHARLOTTE
LAMB
A
COLLECTION

Charlotte Lamb was born in the East End of London in December 1937 in time for World War II, where she spent most of the war moving from relative to relative to escape the bombings. Educated at St Ursula's Convent, Ilford, after school she went to work at the Bank of England in Threadneedle Street.

At the age of twenty-one she married a journalist, and later gave up her job to have a baby. It was only in 1970-71 that she began her writing career and was lucky enough to sell her first book.

She now has five children, from a son aged thirty to twins aged sixteen. The family lives on the Isle of Man in a big white Scottish baronial house set amid beautiful parklands. Charlotte Lamb has written over one hundred books to date, eighty-seven of them for leading romance publishers, Mills & Boon. With worldwide sales of more than 50 million copies, her books are translated into 26 languages and sold in over 100 international markets.

Worldwide Books are proud to bring back three of this outstanding author's earlier works with *A Collection*.

CONTENTS:

By the same author in Worldwide paperbacks:

Barbary Wharf

An exciting 6-part mini series, set amid the fast-paced world of international journalism. Each novel features an independent story, but together they form a saga as compulsive and captivating as any modern soap opera.

THE SEX WAR

BY
CHARLOTTE LAMB

WORLDWIDE BOOKS
LONDON • SYDNEY • TORONTO

*First published in Great Britain in 1983
Reprinted in Great Britain in 1993
by Worldwide Books, Eton House,
18-24 Paradise Road, Richmond, Surrey TW9 1SR*

© Charlotte Lamb 1983

ISBN 0 373 58953 0

99-9309

Made and printed in Great Britain

CHAPTER ONE

LINDSAY was in the shower when the phone rang,
and she was half inclined to ignore the ringing,
but it might be Aston to say he couldn't make
their date, so with a sigh she stepped out of the
shower cubicle, pulled on her short white
towelling robe and ran down the corridor to the
sitting-room, leaving wet footprints on the carpet
everywhere she trod. Snatching up the phone,
she said breathlessly: 'Hallo?'

'Lindsay, it's Alice.'

'Oh, hallo,' said Lindsay, feeling water trickling
down her spine from the wet tail of red hair
clinging to her nape. 'I was in the shower and I'm
very wet, Alice, is it urgent?'

'I'm sorry, I didn't . . . I just wanted . . .' Her
sister-in-law sounded incoherent, which was
unusual for Alice; a placid, quiet girl whose only
interests seemed to be her home and family.
Alice's brown eyes and hair both had a red-russet
tinge which, coupled with her demure manner,
always reminded Lindsay of a squirrel watching
everything from a safe distance but with bright-
eyed interest.

'Is anything wrong?' Lindsay asked, clutching
the lapels of her robe.

Alice seemed to hesitate, then she asked
unsteadily: 'Is . . . is Stephen with you?'

'Stephen? No, he isn't here. Is he coming to

5

see me?' Lindsay turned her head to look at the clock on the mantelpiece. Aston would be here in half an hour. They were going to the theatre and she didn't want to be held up.

Without answering her question, Alice asked another of her own, her voice even more shaky. 'Have you seen him since yesterday?'

'No.' Frowning, Lindsay wondered what this was all about, but before she could ask Alice audibly sighed.

'He hasn't rung you, you haven't heard from him?'

'No, I haven't.' The urgent note in Alice's voice seemed very disturbing, Lindsay gripped the phone tighter. 'Is something wrong, Alice?'

'If he's talked to you, tell me, Lindsay, don't lie to me, please!'

'Why on earth should I lie to you? I haven't heard from Stephen for a week or so, he rang me in the middle of last week and asked when I was coming over. I said I'd try to come and see you all soon.' Lindsay had never interfered in her brother's life, nor would she have allowed him to interfere in her own, but she was very fond of Stephen and something in Alice's voice worried her. 'Have you and Stephen had a row?' she ended uncertainly.

'He's disappeared,' said Alice on what sounded like a sob.

'Disappeared?' Lindsay felt a dart of shock. 'What do you mean, he's disappeared? Since when?'

'He didn't come home from work last night, and he hasn't been at the factory at all today, nobody seems to know where he is.' Alice stopped, swallowing audibly. 'Lindsay, I'm so worried, I don't know what to do, I'm going out of my mind!'

Lindsay stared absently at the wallpaper a few feet away from her, her eye following the curve of a green branch from which tiny pale pink rosebuds broke. She didn't quite know what to ask, how to respond. Alice's news had come as too much of a shock. Stephen had seemed quite normal when he talked to her last week. He hadn't said anything which might alert her to any change in his usual behaviour. Stephen was the last person she would have expected to disappear without warning; he was an even-tempered, cheerful man whose life seemed very much under control.

'Have you rung the police?' she asked at last, falling back on the purely practical.

'No, not yet. I wasn't sure if . . . should I? He's only been gone for twenty-four hours, there could be a perfectly rational explanation, he might have left a message that didn't get passed on. If he turns up he'll be so embarrassed, he'll be furious with me for getting into such a state, and I'll feel a fool if I've made a fuss over nothing.'

'Is he in his car?'

'Well, yes, he went off in it yesterday morning, anyway.' Alice drew a sharp breath. 'Do you think he might have had an accident?'

'Could be,' said Lindsay. Failing any other explanation that would have been the first thing that came into her head. 'Did he have anything on him to identify him? If he did have an accident, that is . . .'

'I don't know, I suppose so, he usually has his credit cards and driver's licence in his wallet.' Alice sounded as though she just wasn't thinking clearly, which was hardly surprising in the circumstances. 'And it's hours now since he left the factory yesterday. It isn't like Stephen, he always comes straight home.'

'He could have gone off on urgent business and forgotten to let you know,' Lindsay pointed out gently.

'It isn't like him.' Alice sounded as though she was on the point of tears and Lindsay had a strong suspicion that there was a great deal which her sister-in-law wasn't saying, but as she couldn't see her face she could only guess at that.

'I was in the shower, it will take me ten minutes to get dressed,' she said firmly. 'I'll be with you inside an hour, then we'll decide what to do.'

'Oh, thank you, Lindsay.' Alice's voice trembled, was husky. Lindsay had said the right thing, Alice's call had not been so much a check on whether Stephen had been in touch with her as a wordless cry for help. Alice couldn't cope with whatever was wrong between her and Stephen, and that didn't surprise Lindsay. She had always guessed that all the strength in that marriage came from Stephen, her brother had always been someone you could rely on, and Alice had leaned heavily on him from the start. Whenever you saw them together, Alice kept close to him, listened while he talked, had very little to say for herself, left all the decisions to him. If Alice was a secretive little squirrel, Stephen was a broad oak in which she sheltered.

Lindsay rang off and went back into the bathroom. She dried her hair roughly, got dressed in a formal white silk blouse and tight-waisted, pleated black skirt, then blow-dried her hair into the style she liked best, the red-gold strands gleaming loosely around her face, in a casual light wave. She had just finished doing her make-up when the door bell rang. She knew it was Aston, he always gave three short rings. He was early, which was just as well, she wouldn't have to leave a note pinned to the front door for him.

'Hallo, gorgeous,' he said as she opened the door, and held out an enormous bunch of flowers; roses, carnations, freesias, their scent masked by the polythene envelope holding them.

'They're beautiful—thank you,' said Lindsay, smiling, as she accepted the flowers. 'Come in, I'll put them in water before they wither.' She walked back into the kitchen and Aston followed her, closing the front door behind him. Her flat was on the second floor of a large block of service flats in central London. The rooms were tiny, just big enough to swing a cat, but they were modern and comfortable and she was within easy walking distance of the West End.

She filled a large, green-glazed pottery jar with water and unwrapped the flowers, while Aston leaned against the wall watching her. Over her shoulder, Lindsay said apologetically: 'I'm sorry, Aston, I'm going to have to break our date tonight. Something's come up—family troubles.

I've got to go over to see my sister-in-law, she just rang me and asked me to come at once. I'd have tried to get in touch with you, but . . .'

'What's wrong?' Aston asked, frowning. He wasn't exactly a good-looking man; but his rugged face had strength and humour and a very distinct personality. His hair was a goldy brown, the colour of a new penny, coppery bronze, and his eyes were hazel and smiled a great deal. For a very big man, over six foot and built on muscular lines, he walked lightly and moved with grace, but there had been nothing subtle about his interest in her. He had begun to pursue her from the minute they met, bombarding her with phone calls and dropping in at her flat without warning all the time. Lindsay had begun by giving him the cold shoulder; she had been in no mood to encourage any man when she met Aston and when her icily polite refusals did not have any effect she had been forced to tell him bluntly that she wasn't interested, so goodbye. It hadn't made any difference that she had noticed. Aston had kept on turning up, amusement in his face, as though Lindsay's snappy rejections merely made him laugh. His water-dropping-on-a-stone technique was irresistible. Lindsay started to laugh, too, in the end, and found herself saying: yes, instead of: no way!

'My brother seems to have done a bunk.' Lindsay was briskly pushing the flowers into the vase, her eyes on their colour, her nostrils assailed by their muted scent. 'There, how do they look?' she asked, turning back to Aston.

'Nice,' he said. 'What do you mean, he's done a bunk? Left his wife?'

'I'm not sure what he's done, Alice wasn't very coherent on the phone. I'm sorry about the theatre tickets, Aston, maybe you could find someone to go with you? A pity to waste them.'

'That doesn't matter,' he said, shrugging the suggestion aside. He was a man who talked with his body, his broad shoulders and hands in movement when he spoke, like an Italian. 'Where does your brother live? I'll drive you over there.'

'That's very kind—are you sure?'

'Get your jacket and we'll be on our way,' he said, grinning at her. Lindsay smiled back wryly; it was typical of Aston to take charge of whatever was happening. He was an organiser to his fingertips, he ran his life the way he ran his firm; with humour and determination and unstoppable energy which did not make him disliked by his employees. He had several shops in London, selling electrical goods. Lindsay had met him through her brother, who manufactured electrical components. Stephen had made friends with Aston at an international trade fair in Germany two years ago. They did not deal directly with each other on a business level, they were merely drinking companions on occasion.

His car was parked outside the flats, a sleek Ferrari with an engine that purred like a cat and could eat up the miles without really trying. Aston liked fast cars and good clothes and, not being married, could afford them. He slid Lindsay into the passenger seat, closed the door on her and walked round to get behind the wheel.

As he drove off with a roar, he asked quietly:

'Stephen in some sort of trouble? Or is it a private matter?'

'I told you, I have no idea at the moment what's wrong. I suspect he and Alice have had a row, but she wasn't saying on the phone. I can't think of any other reason why he should go walk-about.' She looked sharply at Aston, her dark brows lifting. 'Unless you know different? Have you heard something? His factory isn't in trouble, is it?'

'We're all in deep waters these days.' Aston wasn't looking at her and his face was not giving anything away, he watched the road as though afraid to take his eyes off it. 'There's a recession, in case you hadn't heard.'

'Stephen's been hit by the recession? He hasn't said anything. At least, not to me he hasn't.'

'Would he?' Aston put the question very gently and she sighed.

'I suppose not, he does tend to hug his problems to himself. Stephen never forgets that he's my big brother.'

'He's about five years older than you, isn't he?' Aston asked, tongue in cheek.

'Seven, do you mind?' She laughed and Aston turned his head to smile at her, eyes teasing.

'Which makes you . . .?'

'Twenty-five.' Her glance mocked him. 'I've packed a lot into my life, if you're wondering how I got so wise at my age.'

'I wasn't actually. I was thinking that Stephen looked much older than thirty-two. I'd got him down as nearer forty.' He put on speed, frowning again. 'His face is quite lined. How long has he been running the factory?'

'Since my father died. Stephen was nineteen, then, and the factory only employed three or four men. Stephen began to expand about five years ago. Now he employs around forty.' Lindsay was very proud of her brother's business achievements. She had only been twelve when her father died, and within three years her mother had been dead, too; of pneumonia caught because she neglected a bad cold. Mrs Grainger had stopped caring about her health after her husband's early death. His heart attack had been a bitter shock to her from which she never recovered. Left alone to carry the family, Stephen had taken over at home as well as in the business. Stephen hadn't married until after Lindsay left home, and brother and sister had been very close. Their relationship might appear outwardly offhand and casual, but although they were neither of them openly affectionate they cared very much what happened to each other.

'Five years?' Aston repeated. 'I suppose that was around the time . . .'

'I got married,' she agreed flatly.

'Did Randall take an interest in your brother's firm?' Aston sounded very casual, but she felt him watching her out of the corner of his eye.

'Financially, you mean? I don't think so. It has always been a family firm, Stephen wouldn't have wanted to part with any shares, even to Daniel.' Lindsay laughed shortly, her face derisive. 'Not that Daniel Randall would have been interested in a firm as small as Graingers—quite out of his league, they have to be pretty big fish for him to start angling for them.'

'I'd have thought that as Stephen is your brother——' Aston began, and she cut him short, shaking her head.

'I can tell you don't know Daniel. He'd be the first to tell you that sentiment has no place in business.' She paused. 'And how!' she added with emphasis.

'I've heard that he's ruthless.'

'Who told you that? It must have been a friend of his—it's far too generous. Daniel Randall is red in tooth and claw. He doesn't merge with other firms, he devours them and spits out the pieces, and he doesn't care who gets hurt in the process. I'm grateful for the fact that Graingers didn't arouse his attention, it was just as well for Stephen. God knows what would have happened after I divorced Daniel Randall if he had had any hold over the firm.'

'You don't like your ex-husband much, do you?' Aston asked wryly, half smiling as he drew into the kerb outside the modern white house where Stephen and Alice lived.

'Like him? Boy, is that an understatement!' muttered Lindsay, swinging her long legs out of the car. 'I loathe the man!' She walked round to join Aston, the light from a street lamp gleaming on her red-gold hair, and he looked down at her with appreciation, his hazel eyes very bright.

'I'm glad I don't have to worry about competition from that quarter, any way,' he admitted. 'When you kept turning me down, I did wonder if you still hankered for him. He's a good-looking guy, it wouldn't have been surprising if you had still carried a torch.'

'For Daniel Randall? Do me a favour, I have too much sense. I was too young to know what I was doing when I married him, but once I'd found out what a bastard he really was I lost no time in making my escape.'

Aston laughed. 'How green your eyes look at night, like an angry cat's. I wouldn't like to feel your claws!'

'As long as you realise I've got them,' said Lindsay, sliding him a wicked look from beneath her lashes.

'Oh, I'd noticed them. You made sure I did right from the start, didn't you? I was paying Randall's bill, was I?'

'I was off men then,' she agreed, shrugging, as she started to walk up the drive to the front door of the house.

'And now?' Aston asked, catching up with her after a second's pause. 'How do you feel about men now?'

Before she could answer, the front door flew open and Alice stood in the doorway with the light behind her, staring at them eagerly for a moment before the light in her eyes went out and her mouth trembled in disappointment.

'Oh, it's you, Lindsay.' It was obvious that she had thought it was Stephen returning, no doubt she had heard the car and jumped to conclusions. She was pale, her usual colour absent from her small face and her hair was ruffled and untidy. It looked as though she had flung on her clothes without thinking; her jeans were creased and shabby, her red shirt had come out of the waistband of the jeans and the top button of it

was missing, her neckline giving a clear vision of
her small breasts. She looked amazingly young,
almost childish, and Lindsay could see she had
been crying; her brown eyes were red-rimmed,
her eyelids puffy.

'No word from Stephen yet?' Lindsay asked,
giving her a quick kiss on the cheek, and noting
the cold dampness of her skin.

Alice shook her head, then looked at Aston.
'Have you seen him?' Again that eagerness, that
nervous pleading in her voice.

Aston said gently: 'No, but don't worry too
much, there could be a hundred explanations
of why he hasn't been in touch with you.'

Alice went back into the house and Lindsay
and Aston followed her into the sitting-room. It
was very untidy; toys were scattered on the floor,
children's books open on the couch, a large red
setter dog padded to meet them, his tongue
lolling out, and barked in token threat before
allowing Aston to rub his head behind those long,
silky ears.

Alice watched him, her expression uncertain.
She did not know Aston very well and was
always very quiet in the company of someone
unfamiliar to her. Shy and wary, she was more or
less the same age as Lindsay but gave the
impression of being much younger, perhaps
because she had married Stephen only a year
after leaving school and had seen very little of the
world outside her home. Her first baby, Matthew,
had been born only eighteen months after she and
Stephen got married, and little Vicky had
followed her brother just a year later. Alice hated

leaving her children in the care of babysitters, even Lindsay was barely acceptable to her as a mother-substitute, it was on very rare occasions that Alice allowed Lindsay to take over from her. Most nights, Alice and Stephen stayed at home together, listening to music, watching TV or reading. Alice was very far from being an outgoing girl, and Lindsay could see that Aston's arrival had disconcerted her.

'Why don't we make some coffee?' Lindsay suggested, and her sister-in-law looked at her gratefully. 'Like some, Aston?' Lindsay asked, and Aston looked round, smiling, still playing with the dog.

'I'd love a cup of coffee.'

'We won't be a minute, clear a space on the couch and sit down.'

Alice looked embarrassed. 'I'm afraid the place is very untidy, I haven't had time to . . .'

'Doesn't matter, it looks cosy and lived-in,' said Aston, giving her a comforting smile. As Alice hurried out of the room, Lindsay gave him a wry grimace.

'I'm not famous for my tact, I should have realised she'd be touchy about the way the room looks, but with small kids around nobody can keep a house tidy for long.'

'Go and talk to her,' Aston said. 'She looks as though she's in the middle of a bad trauma.'

'Yes,' Lindsay agreed, sighing. 'I wonder what on earth has been happening?'

'Marriage,' said Aston drily, and she made another face.

'Oh, yes—why do we do it?'

She found Alice in the kitchen laying out cups with a dull expression, her movements slow. Lindsay watched her with compassion and uneasiness. What had gone wrong between her and Stephen?

'What was he like yesterday morning?' she asked, and Alice jumped, looking over her shoulder with open distress.

'What? Oh, Stephen, you mean?'

'Who else? Weren't you thinking about him?'

'I was wishing I knew what to do—I feel so helpless, not knowing where he is or what's happening to him. How can he do this to me?' The cry broke out of her suddenly, her voice rising, and her body trembled, she caught hold of the back of a chair and leaned on it, her head hanging down.

Lindsay put an arm round her and felt the tremor running through her. 'Now, calm down and try to think. Have you two quarrelled? Come on, Alice, you can tell me, these things do happen in the best marriages, you know. Was there a row?'

'No,' Alice said vehemently, lifting her head so that Lindsay could see her face. 'What would we quarrel about? We never quarrel, Stephen isn't the quarrelsome sort, neither am I.'

That was true enough, Lindsay thought, watching her. She never remembered hearing the two of them come anywhere near having a row.

'Is Stephen worried about the firm?'

Alice hesitated, biting her lip. 'I don't know, he never talks about work, he never has . . .'

Lindsay caught the faint hint of something

unspoken in her voice and frowned. 'But?' she pressed.

'But what?' Alice broke away from her and went over to make the coffee as the kettle boiled. Her hands were shaking, the spoon rattled against the sides of the cups as she spooned instant coffee. Lindsay looked at the ruffled red-brown hair, the curls tangled and lifeless as they clustered on Alice's thin nape, and she felt an impatient sympathy for her sister-in-law. Alice was waiting for someone else to tell her what to do, as Stephen had always told her what to do until now. Any self-confidence Alice had ever felt had apparently atrophied during her marriage— what you never use you may well lose entirely. Lindsay understood how Alice felt, she might well have gone the same way if she hadn't divorced Daniel Randall, she thought. Daniel had wanted to rule her life the way Stephen had always run Alice's life for her, but Stephen's motives had been generous and tender. Lindsay wouldn't say the same for Daniel.

'Come on, I picked up something from you just now—do you suspect that Stephen's worried about the firm?'

'I'm not sure.' Alice put the cups on to a formica tray. 'I don't know, he didn't talk about it, but there was something wrong with him lately. He was always sitting about staring into space, always in a daydream—he had something on his mind, but he wouldn't talk about it.' A little flush had crept up into her face, it burned along her high cheekbones. Lindsay stared at her, frowning.

'Didn't you have any idea what was wrong?'

Alice's voice was harsh when she spoke. 'I thought there might be someone else.'

Lindsay's eyes opened wide. 'Another woman?'

Alice turned on her suddenly, speaking quickly and angrily. 'Well, it happens, doesn't it? And look at me.' She flicked a dismissive hand down herself, her mouth bitter. 'I'm always a mess, I haven't got much energy. Matt and Vicky beat me into the ground most days, by the time Stephen gets home I'm worn out, I hardly have enough life to do more than say hello and put his dinner in front of him. I flop out on the couch all evening and crawl upstairs to bed like a zombie. I can tell you, there isn't much fire in what goes on in our bed these days. If Stephen has fallen for someone else I wouldn't be amazed.' She stopped talking and bit her lower lip to steady it, then said: 'But he might have rung me before going off with her.'

'Who . . .' Lindsay began, and got a brief look. Alice's eyes were far too bright, there were unshed tears behind them.

'No idea. His secretary is a married woman of fifty with a daughter older than me—it certainly isn't her. I talked to her several times today, and she's as worried as I am, she wanted to ring the police this morning.'

'I think she's right,' Lindsay said. 'That's what we ought to do.'

'Stephen would never forgive me if . . .'

'Stephen isn't here to forgive you or otherwise, and we're wasting time. The sooner we tell the police the better, they can check up and find out if anyone of his description has been involved in an accident. Stephen could be lying in some hospital ward, unconscious—anything could have happened to him. He could have been mugged and all his belongings stolen, or . . .'

'Don't!' Alice protested shrilly.

Lindsay sighed. 'It's the only sensible thing to do, Alice. You must see that.'

After a long silence, Alice nodded slowly.

'Would you like me to ring the police?' Lindsay asked, and Alice nodded again. 'Right, then you take Aston his coffee while I get on the phone, and don't look so worried, it may turn out to be . . .' She stopped speaking as Alice walked out, carrying the tray, the cups clattering together.

The police were polite but made no pretence of being seriously concerned. 'We'll check the hospitals, miss,' the duty sergeant at the local station said. 'But unless he's been involved in an accident there isn't much we can do. He could be anywhere. It happens all the time, you know, men walk out on their families without saying a word and just disappear into thin air. But we'll do our best. Give me a few details about him. How tall is he?'

'Five foot nine or ten, I think.'

'Colour of hair?'

'Dark red.'

'That's unusual, might be a help,' the sergeant said. 'Long or short, is it?'

'Short, Stephen keeps it very neat and well-trimmed.'

'Colour of eyes?'

'Hazel—more green than brown.'

'And distinctive marks? Moles? Birthmarks?'

'He has a mole on his neck just under his ear.' Lindsay felt sick suddenly, she had a feeling she was describing a man she would never see again. Until that moment she hadn't been taking Stephen's disappearance seriously, but now her stomach plunged with anxiety.

'What was he wearing?' the sergeant asked.

'I don't know, I'll have to ask his wife.' Lindsay put down the phone and went into the sitting-room. Alice was sitting on the edge of a chair, her hands clasped tightly in her lap. Aston was trying to make conversation, but Lindsay got the feeling it was uphill work.

Alice had to think for a minute before she could answer. 'His dark grey suit, a blue-striped shirt and a blue tie,' she said, and Lindsay went back to repeat that to the policeman.

'What sort of car was he driving?' she was asked. 'Could I have the number?'

Lindsay could answer that without checking with Alice, Stephen had often driven her home to her flat after visiting them. Her voice wasn't quite steady as she answered and the policeman said soothingly: 'Now, don't worry too much, miss, it's a hundred to one he's perfectly safe somewhere. Sometimes a man feels he has to get away to think things out.' He paused. 'Is there anyone at the factory we could contact? Anyone in his confidence who might have an idea why he's gone?'

'His secretary? I could ask my sister-in-law for her name and address.'

'Would you do that, miss? It would help.'

'Hang on,' said Lindsay, and went back to Alice, who frowned in a distracted way.

'I've spoken to her, I told you, she doesn't have any more idea than I do . . .'

'It won't hurt for the police to talk to her,' Lindsay said. 'What's her name?'

Alice shrugged wearily. 'Mrs Temple, she lives in the new close behind the factory—I don't know the number of the house; I remember her telling me how pleased she was when she moved in because the house was so compact. I thought she was crazy, it was a rabbit hutch.'

'Watford Close, miss? Right, we'll see if we can talk to Mrs Temple tonight. Will someone be with Mrs Grainger? We might call round to have a chat, it depends if I can spare a man. We're light-handed tonight.'

'I'll be here,' said Lindsay, and rang off a moment later, her spirits very low. Talking to the policeman had made Stephen's disappearance real. Where could he be and why had he gone?

She went slowly back to join Alice and Aston, who looked round at her in question. 'No news?' Aston asked. Alice said nothing, but her eyes were like holes poked in a white sheet, her lips were colourless and trembled. Lindsay sank down on to her knees beside her sister-in-law's chair and held her shaking hands tightly.

'It's going to be okay, don't look like that.'

'What will I do if he never comes back?'

'Of course he'll come back, you mustn't think like that!'

From upstairs came a thump and a wail. Alice

jumped to her feet. 'Matt's fallen out of bed again.' She was out of the room and running up the stairs a second later. Lindsay heard her voice in the small bedroom which the children shared; soothing, calming, in a murmur. Getting up, Lindsay joined Aston on the couch, her hands linked behind her head and her body relaxing with a sigh.

'I could kill Stephen! If he was worried, couldn't he have talked to us about it? Did he have to clear off like this? He must know what it's doing to Alice.' She turned her head and Aston touched her cheek with one hand gently.

'Don't get so upset, it's early days yet, he could walk in through the front door any minute.'

Tears welled up in Lindsay's eyes, she buried her face against Aston's shoulder. 'I'm scared,' she whispered. 'It isn't like him. Stephen's always been so strong. What if . . . if something has happened to him?' She couldn't bear to put her fears into words, but she was afraid that Stephen might not ever come back. She might have brushed aside Alice's worry, but secretly she was beginning to feel the same—how could you help being afraid when you didn't know what had happened? The fear of the unknown prompted all sorts of dark ideas, suspicions, dreads.

'Ssh . . . Alice is coming,' Aston murmured. 'Don't let her see you like this, you've got to put a brave face on it for her sake, Lindsay.'

Sitting up, Lindsay brushed a rough hand across her wet eyes and Aston slid his arm round her, squeezed her comfortingly. They heard Alice coming slowly down the stairs, then another sound caught their attention, a car engine which shut off as they sat up. Lindsay stiffened and began to get up.

'Stephen!'

'It could be the police,' warned Aston.

They heard Alice running. Lindsay went to the door just in time to hear Alice fumbling with the lock on the front door, then it was open and a cold wind blew into the little hallway. Lindsay stared in rigid disappointment at the stranger facing Alice, whose thin shoulders had slumped as she realised it was not her husband.

'Mrs Grainger? Has Mr Grainger come back yet?'

'No,' Alice said in a husky voice.

'How long has he been missing, Mrs Grainger? Can I come in and talk to you?' The man was young, thin and sallow-skinned, wearing an old sheepskin coat. He smiled at Alice and flicked a quick look at Lindsay over her shoulder as he began to insert himself into the house, talking fast. 'Have you any idea why he's disappeared? Is there any trouble at his factory or . . .'

'Who are you?' Lindsay cut across his sentence. 'Are you from the police?'

She saw his hesitation, then he smiled charmingly at her. 'I won't take up much of your time,' he began, and Lindsay interrupted again.

'Are you a reporter?'

'Oh!' Alice gasped, falling back from him.

'Isn't Mr Grainger related to Daniel Randall?' the young man asked, ignoring Lindsay's question and keeping his eyes on Alice, obviously deciding she was the softest target.

'Out!' snapped Lindsay, advancing on him and pushing him back through the front door. 'Go on, get out, we have nothing to say to you.' Mention of Daniel was a red rag to a bull, she was flushed and very angry.

'All I want to do is help you find your husband,' the reporter protested.

Lindsay shut the front door in his face. Turning to look quickly at her sister-in-law, she found Aston in the hall, watching her with a wry smile.

'You're a tough little lady, aren't you?' he mocked. 'I thought for a minute you were going to hit him.'

'So did I,' Lindsay muttered through her teeth. 'What a nerve, trying to talk his way in here!'

'You haven't got red hair for nothing, I suppose,' Aston commented.

Lindsay put her arm round Alice. 'Come and sit down. Have you eaten tonight? Are you hungry?'

'No,' Alice whispered. 'How did that man know Stephen was missing? Who could have told him?'

'He probably picked it up at the police station, reporters always have a contact in the police,' Aston said. 'And I'm hungry, Lindsay.' He gave her a plaintive little smile and she laughed.

'Okay, you talk to Alice, I'll get us a meal.'

'I'm not hungry,' said Alice.

'Nobody's going to force you to eat if you don't want to,' Lindsay said, giving Aston a secret look. He steered Alice back into the sitting-room and

Lindsay went into the kitchen to see what she could find.

She was no more hungry than Alice was, but she felt it would do them all good to have something to occupy their minds while they waited for news. No doubt Alice hadn't touched food all day, she looked hollow. While Lindsay scrambled eggs and grilled tomatoes, made toast and more coffee, she was trying to think of some place Stephen might head for if he was in trouble. As small children they had always had holidays in Cornwall, might he go there? She mentally made a list of their relatives, but their family had never been very close and Stephen had often told her how much he resented the total indifference of their aunt in Yorkshire, their uncle in Scotland, when their parents died. Nobody had come to help Stephen then, they had appeared at the funeral, drunk some sherry and made soothing noises then departed without making any offer to help. Stephen would be very unlikely to look for help from any of them now.

She carried a loaded tray into the sitting-room and practically force-fed Alice, who was still reluctant to eat but managed to get down some of the scrambled egg and a half slice of toast. While Aston and Lindsay drank the last of the coffee, Alice wandered over to the window and stood, the curtain drawn back, her nose pressed against the glass like a hopeful child, waiting.

Lindsay collected together the plates and cups. Aston took the tray from her and carried it out into the kitchen. 'Are you staying here tonight?' he asked, and she nodded.

'Of course. You'd better go now, Aston. I'm very grateful for your help, you've been very kind.'

'Sure you wouldn't like me to stay tonight?'

'We'll be okay. I'll to get her to go to bed soon, she looks worn out. I've got some sleeping pills in my handbag, I'll give her one of those.'

'Do you need to take sleeping pills?' Aston asked, frowning and eyeing her in surprise.

'Not often, but I had insomnia after my marriage broke up and now and then it comes back.' She flushed as she met his eyes. All that was behind her now, she preferred not to remember the anguish Daniel had put her through, the black nights when she lay awake and ached for him, the long-delayed dawns which brought no hope of any end to her pain. When you are trapped in bitter, hopeless feeling you always think there can be no escape from it, but Lindsay had freed herself at last. She had begun to sleep regularly, without dreaming of Daniel; she had woken up without that dead sense of depression.

Aston's face gave no hint of his reaction, he merely nodded. 'I see.' He looked at his watch. 'I'd better be on my way, then. If you need me, give me a ring, don't hesitate to ask. You know I'll do anything I can.'

She smiled at him and stood on tiptoe to kiss him. 'I know—thanks.'

He put his head round the door of the sitting-room to say goodnight to Alice, who looked at him in startled surprise. 'Oh, yes, goodnight, thank you for . . .' Her voice trailed off and Aston smiled at her.

'Try to get some sleep, remember your children will need you tomorrow.'

Tears came into her eyes again and Lindsay pushed Aston down the hall. 'Sorry, said the wrong thing,' he whispered, and she shook her head, then opened the front door.

'Of course not, don't be an idiot. She's just off balance.'

He caught her head between his hands, looked down into her face, his hazel eyes smiling. 'Did I tell you I think you're gorgeous and I'm crazy about you?'

'Goodnight, Aston,' Lindsay said.

He kissed her mouth lightly, then released her and walked out of the house into the dark night. She stood in the doorway, a yellow stream of light falling down the drive in his wake, and watched him climb into his car. The engine flared and he drove off. Lindsay closed the front door and went back to Alice who was sitting on the couch staring at nothing, her legs curled up under her, her hand propping up her head.

As Lindsay sat down next to her, Alice said; 'If I only knew what had happened to him, where he was . . . not knowing is the worst, I think I could even stand it if I knew for certain he had gone off with another woman or just left me because he was tired of me. I could bear anything but this, I keep trying to think, going round and round in circles getting nowhere.'

'You ought to try to get some sleep—you're exhausted. I'll stay up in case there's any news and I'll come and wake you if . . .'

'No,' Alice said. 'I couldn't sleep, I'd never be

able to close my eyes. I can't shut off my head. Lindsay, what if he's d . . .'

'Don't say it!' Lindsay said sharply, wincing. 'Don't even think it, of course he isn't.'

The door bell rang briskly. Alice stumbled to her feet, white as a sheet, her eyes widening until her skin stretched tightly over her cheekbones. She looked old, suddenly. Lindsay wanted to cry, but she forced herself to stay calm.

'I'll go, it's probably the police to ask you a few questions,' she said.

She took a deep breath before she opened the front door. What if the police had bad news for them? There was no point in thinking about it. She pulled the door open and made herself look at the man on the doorstep, only to feel a deep thrust of shock as she recognised him. Even in that shadowy light Daniel Randall was unmistakable, then he stepped forward into the yellow light from the hallway and his hard-boned, arrogant face came into full view. Lindsay was stricken, she couldn't speak or move, she half believed she was imagining things. He was the very last man she had expected to see.

CHAPTER TWO

'CAT got your tongue?' Daniel looked at her stunned face with a derisive smile, and the question broke the spell of disbelief holding her rigid. She felt a wave of hot colour rushing up to her hairline. What was he doing here? She hadn't set eyes on him for over a year, why had he turned up like this tonight?

'What do you want?' She stepped sideways to block his way; she didn't want him walking into the house and saw no reason why she should pretend he was welcome.

'As quick-witted as ever, I see,' he drawled, and the way he spoke was all too familiar. Daniel Randall always used that slow, iced voice when he wanted to make someone feel stupid; he was a past master at destroying people and using the simplest means to do it—a lifted eyebrow, a smile, a drily succinct comment.

Lindsay wanted to hit him, and that feeling was familiar, too; hostility was the safest emotion to feel towards Daniel Randall.

'What the hell do you *think* I'm doing here?' he asked before she could say anything. 'And are we going to stand here much longer? I'm not a door-to-door salesman, I don't enjoy talking on people's doorsteps.'

Over his shoulder Lindsay saw his car parked under a street-lamp, a sleek, powerful white sports car with elegant lines which had been carefully designed for effortless speed. For some reason, the sight of it annoyed her.

'Get back in your car and hit the road, I've got nothing to say to you,' she snapped, closing the door. Daniel's foot met it and the door jarred. Lindsay glared at him through the opening. 'Go away!'

'Don't be a fool, Lindsay,' he said, and at that moment a car roared up behind his and parked with a screech. Someone leapt out of it and Daniel looked round, frowning.

'Get inside,' he said to Lindsay, thrusting her back into the hall with a violence which stopped her arguing. Daniel followed her and slammed the front door behind him.

'What . . .' Lindsay began furiously, and he gave her a sarcastic smile.

'Want to talk to the press, do you?'

Her mouth opened and nothing came out. The front door bell rang, but Daniel ignored it. He walked towards the sitting-room, catching Lindsay's arm en route and pulling her in his wake, struggling to free herself without success. The door bell went on ringing and Alice stared at them, pale-faced, wide-eyed, nervous apprehension in the way she stood there.

'What's wrong? What's happening? Aren't you going to answer the door? Lindsay . . .' Her voice died away as she recognised Daniel.

'Hallo, Alice,' he said in a gentle voice, and smiled at her. When he chose, Daniel could give out charm and warmth; his grey eyes held both now, and Lindsay resented the way Alice relaxed and smiled back.

'Daniel! I didn't realise it was you, how are you?'

'I'm fine, how are you? Any news of Stephen yet?'

Her lower lip trembled and she caught it between her teeth, her eyes too bright. 'No. . . .'

'How do you know Stephen's missing?' Lindsay asked suspiciously, staring at him.

He turned that wry glance on her, his eyebrows raised. 'A reporter told me.'

'I thought you never talked to reporters.'

'I wouldn't have talked to this one if he hadn't convinced Henshaw that I'd want to speak to him.'

'Really?' Lindsay asked with sarcasm in her voice. 'That was clever of him, how did he do that?' Daniel's London home was run by a married couple who were far too well trained to talk to the press. What could a reporter have said to one of them to make them think Daniel would want to speak to him?

'He told Henshaw you were in serious trouble and the police were involved,' Daniel said drily, and Lindsay was stunned.

'He did what?' She was so angry she could scarcely speak, and Daniel laughed briefly at her expression.

'Once he was actually put through to me, of course, he came across with the truth about Stephen vanishing; by then he'd achieved his object.'

'What a rotten trick!' Lindsay exclaimed and Daniel shrugged.

'You should know by now that reporters can be unscrupulous in pursuit of a good story.'

'You're a fine one to talk about scruples,' Lindsay muttered, turning her anger in his direction. 'You wouldn't know a scruple if one came up and bit you!'

'Watch yourself!' There was the hiss of rage in Daniel's soft voice, and Alice took a step backwards in alarm, but Lindsay refused to budge, meeting his cold stare without blinking. She wasn't afraid of him, she meant him to know it, and her chin lifted defiantly. Other people might back off when he gave them that narrow-eyed look; in the past she had often done so too, but not any more, he needn't imagine he could frighten her with that air of controlled menace which he was so expert at giving out.

How did he do it? It wasn't just his height and build, other men of his physical type didn't have that effect—it was the mind behind that tautly structured face that was so disturbing.

Just over six foot, Daniel Randall was lean and tightly muscled; a man with a deep chest and wide shoulders which breathed power, but whose height added elegance to the impression he left, those long slim legs and supple hips moving with grace. Lindsay had often watched people watching him, seen the way women's eyes followed him. At first it had made her glow with pride, but in the end she had resented it; it underlined for her the fact that Daniel Randall was not a domesticated man, he was not cut out to be anybody's husband, he was a ruthless predator at home in the jungle of his own choosing.

Alice had backed until she sat down on the couch. Daniel detached his eyes from Lindsay and went over to sit down next to Alice, taking one of her hands between both of his.

'Now, Alice,' he said, one long sinewy thumb stroking the back of her hand in a soothing rhythm, 'what's this all about? Why has Stephen gone off?'

'I don't know,' said Alice, her voice high. She was grey, tired, her eyes great pools in that colourless face. 'He didn't come home last night, that's all I know.'

The door bell rang again, someone had his thumb on the bell and wasn't lifting it. Daniel turned his head, a flash of rage in his eyes.

'I'll knock that guy's teeth down his throat if he keeps that up much longer!'

'Maybe it's the police,' said Alice, stiffening.

'It's the reporter who was here before,' Lindsay told her in a flat tone. 'I recognised him.' She glanced at Daniel and then away. 'He must have been the one who rang you. He tried to talk his way in here earlier and I shut the door on him.'

Daniel detached himself from Alice, getting up. 'What are you going to do?' Lindsay asked, frowning. 'Don't lose your temper, if you hit him it will be all over Fleet Street tomorrow morning.'

'I'm going to ring the police,' Daniel said curtly. 'Alice has a right to be left alone in her own home, they can send someone over here to keep the press away.'

'They're shorthanded,' Lindsay told him.

'They told me so when I rang to tell them Stephen was missing. They won't be able to spare anybody to stand outside here all night.'

Daniel stared at her, then turned and went out. Lindsay followed and watched him pick up the phone. 'What are you going to do?' she asked again, and he gave her a dry smile.

'I'm getting a couple of men to mount guard over the house until this blows over.'

He dialled and Lindsay went back into the sitting-room, hearing his deep cool voice talking in the hall as she sat down next to Alice.

'Stephen won't like it if this gets into the newspapers,' Alice warned.

'He should have thought of that before he went off without telling you where he was going.' Lindsay found herself see-sawing between worry about her brother and impatience with him, her fear kept turning into anger and she could understand why Alice wouldn't go to bed. How could anyone rest when their husband was missing? She heard Daniel replace the phone and walk back towards them. Her reactions to his appearance on the scene were confused too; she was relieved to have him take charge and start organising events, but she was irritated that he should feel he had the right to do so. It was all part of that calm arrogance which she found insupportable—who did he think he was?

'I've got some sleeping tablets in my bag, why don't you take one and try to get some sleep, Alice?' she asked her sister-in-law, who frowned petulantly, her forehead lined.

'I couldn't—no, how can I go to sleep not knowing . . .'

Daniel halted in the middle of the room, listening. 'That's a very good idea,' he said, cutting into her stammered sentence. 'Give Alice the pill, Lindsay. Alice, go upstairs, have a warm bath and get into bed, then Lindsay will bring you some hot milk and you can take her pill and get off to sleep.'

Alice would have argued, but he bent and took her arm in a firm grip, hoisted her to her feet and smiled at her.

'If Stephen was here, that's what he would tell you to do. We'll wake you up the minute there's any news.' He led her to the door and Lindsay followed, watching them wryly. His cool assumption that Alice would obey him was maddening, especially as it was working. Alice reluctantly began to climb the stairs. She paused as the door bell rang again and Daniel said: 'Off you go, Alice,' his voice insistent. Alice went, dragging herself upwards like a weary child. Looking round, Daniel said to Lindsay: 'Get her that milk and stay until she's taken her pill, make sure she swallows it.'

'Yes, sir,' Lindsay muttered through her teeth, bristling, but her antagonism merely made his brows lift.

'Don't you want her to get a few hours' sleep?'

'Of course I do, I just object to being ordered around as if I was a halfwit.'

He smiled. 'Well, you said it. Anyone with any sense would have got her off to bed hours ago, she's on the verge of breaking up into a hundred little pieces.'

'Do you think I couldn't see that? I tried to talk her into going to bed, but she wouldn't hear of it, and I could hardly make her go.'

'I managed it,' shrugged Daniel, and Lindsay felt like screaming, his self-satisfaction put her teeth on edge. She turned on her heel and went into the kitchen to heat some milk. Daniel came into the room a moment later, he had shed his smoothly tailored camelhair overcoat and was running a hand over the ruffled black hair as she turned to look at him.

'Now that we've got Alice out of earshot, tell me what you know—why has your brother gone off like this?' He got a kitchen chair and sat down on it, astraddle, his arms folded across the back of it and his chin resting on the dark sleeves of his formal suit. She wondered what he had been doing this evening—had he been dining out? A business evening, or a private one? Had he been with a woman? The elegance of the suit, the crisp white shirt and wine silk tie suggested that he had been with a woman, but Lindsay refused to think about that, it was none of her business any more.

'I don't know any more than Alice. Stephen didn't come home from work last night and there hasn't been a word from him to explain why he's gone away. Alice says they haven't quarrelled, she doesn't know about any business worries he might have, she hasn't a clue why he's gone.' Lindsay watched the milk beginning to bubble in the small saucepan. 'She did say she wouldn't be surprised if it was another woman, but I don't believe it. Stephen isn't the unfaithful sort.'

'What sort is that?' Daniel asked drily. 'He's a

man, isn't he? He isn't a saint, it could happen to anyone.'

'Don't judge my brother by your standards!' snapped Lindsay with a bite in her voice. The milk was beginning to boil now, she took the saucepan off the hob and poured the milk into a tall glass, stirred it with the spoon. 'Stephen loves Alice, I don't believe this has anything to do with another woman. I think it's something to do with the business.'

Daniel nodded, his chin still on his arms. 'You're probably right. What was the name of that accountant who worked at the factory? The old guy with the grey hair and rimless spectacles?'

'Mr Datchet?' Lindsay was surprised by his memory. She hadn't even thought of asking Henry Datchet, although now she realised that if there was any trouble at the factory he would know all about it.

'Datchet,' agreed Daniel, nodding as he stood up. 'That's the guy. Take that milk to Alice, I'll get in touch with Datchet and see if he can provide any answers.'

She followed him into the hall, balancing the milk on a saucer. 'I don't know his address.'

He picked up the telephone directory, giving her a sarcastic smile. 'I'll find him,' he said, and Lindsay went upstairs without a word. She was sure he would—Daniel Randall always managed to do what he wanted to do.

She found Alice just climbing into bed in a short pink nylon nightie printed with little white flowers. She looked small and helpless and childlike as she settled against the pillows, her russet hair damp from her bath, the edges of it curling around her pale face.

'Drink this and take the pill, then try to sleep,' Lindsay said gently. It was hard to believe that the girl in the bed was the mother of two children, her usual quiet confidence had all been erased by worry.

Alice took the pill reluctantly, sipped the milk, her throat moving as she swallowed it, then she lay down and Lindsay switched off the light. 'Goodnight, we'll be downstairs if you need us and we'll wake you up the minute there's any news.'

She heard Alice sigh as she closed the door, then Alice turned over and the bed rustled. Lindsay quietly went downstairs.

Daniel was still talking on the phone, propping himself up against the wall with one brown hand. His skin was slightly sallow and took the sun easily, retained that tan longer than most people seem to do, which threw his light grey eyes into more prominence, their silvery gleam sliding sideways to watch Lindsay as she walked past. She felt a shiver run down her spine and looked away. She did not want to be aware of Daniel Randall in that way; there was too much sensual assessment in his glance. She felt it even with her back towards him, those cynical eyes seemed to burn a hole into her head.

'I see,' he was saying. 'That would explain it, of course. How much leeway does he have?' There was a little silence, then he whistled softly. 'Mr Datchet, could you come over here first thing tomorrow morning with the books? I think we should have a quiet discussion with the figures in front of us.'

Lindsay stood just inside the sitting-room, listening, her brows drawn.

'I understand and I admire your integrity,' Daniel said a moment later, 'but I assure you it will be in Mr Grainger's best interests, Mrs Grainger will be here, you could talk to her before you talk to me.' He paused again, then said: 'Yes, of course. I perfectly understand your position, but this is a matter of urgency. Don't you agree? If it will help you to make up your mind, ring the bank, ask their advice—after all, it's their money which is at stake.' Another silence, then he said: 'Good, I'll expect you at ten o'clock, then. Goodnight. Mr Datchet.'

A moment later, Daniel sauntered into the sitting-room, his hands in his pockets, whistling softly, the lazy air of satisfaction he wore making Lindsay's nerves jump. She didn't trust him, particularly when he smiled to himself like that. What was he up to?

'Well?' she demanded, and he eyed her with distinct mockery.

'Well, what? Oh, Datchet? He was being pretty cagey, but he did admit that Stephen had a hefty bank loan outstanding which falls due in a week or so. Datchet wraps everything up in sub-clauses like a lawyer, but I gathered that Stephen didn't have a hope in hell of repaying it and he's been trying to raise the money for weeks without any success. Until I see the books I won't have any idea whether the firm's on the rocks or not, but it's clear enough that Stephen is in serious trouble. Datchet seemed very worried.'

Lindsay sat down. She felt cold, she thought of her brother desperately struggling to raise the money to repay that loan and she wanted to cry. What do you ever know about other people? Stephen hadn't given her any idea that all this was on his mind, he had been wearing a bright smile whenever she was with him, yet all the time he must have been out of his mind with worry.

'Why didn't he say something?' she asked, mostly talking to herself. 'Why keep it to himself? Not even to tell Alice—how stupid can you get?'

Daniel shrugged, cynicism in his smile. 'Alice is the sort of woman men try to protect, she can't take pressure, as we see.'

'What would you know about Alice?' Lindsay flung back at him with barbed hostility. 'About any woman, come to that?'

His smile died away, and the grey eyes hardened. 'Don't snarl at me, Lindsay. I'm only trying to help your brother.'

'Accepting help from you is like taking it from a tiger,' Lindsay said bitterly. 'When you offer to help someone, you usually end by swallowing them whole. Stephen won't have a company at all by the time you've finished with him.'

'Thank you,' he said harshly. 'Your gratitude is overwhelming.'

'You want gratitude too?' Lindsay mocked angrily. 'As I remember you, the price tag on your help is high enough without any value added tax of that sort.'

He didn't like that remark; the hard-boned face tightened and a dark red stain washed through the brown skin.

'Don't push me, Lindsay, I might hit back, and you wouldn't like that, believe me.'

'I'm not afraid of you!' Lindsay threw at him, shaking with temper. She was lying, she was afraid of him, she was terrified of what would happen to Stephen and his firm if Daniel Randall decided to take an interest in it. Daniel enjoyed acquiring other firms, streamlining them into profitability through ruthless asset-stripping and what he called rationalisation, which meant in practice that he cut man-power and a lot of people lost their jobs. It was undeniable that the firms usually seemed to make more money afterwards, but Lindsay had been appalled by what she saw of her husband's cold-blooded, hard-headed business techniques. It had all fitted the other things she had learnt about him! Daniel was merciless in the pursuit of his own way.

Daniel took a step towards her and she shrank back against the couch cushions; her skin prickling with nerves as she suddenly became aware that they were quite alone down here and that all around them the house was silent.

'I thought you weren't afraid of me?' Daniel asked in dry menace, watching her restless eyes as she looked towards the door. 'What's the matter, Lindsay? Not quite as brave as you thought you were?'

'I just don't like being loomed over, that's all,' she said sulkily, looking back at him, and he smiled in a fashion which sent waves of heat up her body.

'I'd better sit down, then, hadn't I?'

She realised her mistake at once, but it was too late; he had sat down next to her, that long, lean thigh touching her, his body turned towards her, his eyes travelling in lazy speculation from her flushed face downwards over her white silk blouse and pleated skirt to her long, shapely legs. His gaze came back to her face at last, after he had reduced her to a seething cauldron of fury and resentment over the way he was inspecting her, but her open rage merely made him laugh.

'Aren't I allowed to look? You're still stunning, but I'm sure your boy-friend tells you that.'

'Boy-friend?' she repeated, startled, staring into his watchful eyes.

'The guy who left just as I arrived—I saw him getting into his car after a long kiss. Is it serious? Planning to marry him?'

'Mind your own business, what's it got to do with you?'

'Just curious,' Daniel said with a casual shrug. 'What's his name? Do I know him?'

'Not as far as I know. His name is Aston Hill.'

'It's what?' he asked laughing, and her flush deepened resentfully.

'What's funny about that? I like his name, and I like him, too; Aston's a wonderful man.'

'I'm sure he is,' agreed Daniel and she heard the bland, mocking note in his voice and glared at him.

'He is!'

'Did I deny it?'

'You were making fun of him, don't think I

didn't hear you. I'll tell you this—he's worth ten of you.'

'In what way?' he asked in all apparent soberness, but the glint in the grey eyes betrayed that he was still having fun at her expense and Lindsay looked at him with bitter dislike. 'Financially or . . .'

'All you think about is money,' she muttered.

'No, he isn't as rich as you are, but . . .

'In bed?' Daniel prompted, and alarm bells went off inside her.

'I don't want to talk about Aston,' she said hurriedly. 'I'm worried about Stephen, isn't there any way we can trace him?'

'I doubt very much if Stephen is in any danger,' Daniel dismissed coolly. 'He's far too intelligent to do anything really stupid. At a guess, I'd say he's gone away to think things out and he'll be back in a day or two. If he's been under some heavy pressure lately he could have felt that life was just too much to cope with, he had to get away by himself. He might even have felt resentful because nobody seemed to realise the sort of load he was carrying. That may be why he didn't have any message for Alice. Someone who's used up all their energy gets into a burnt-out state where they want to hit back at the people around them for not noticing what was happening to them.' He gave her a hard glance, his eyes hostile. 'Men are human beings, you know.'

'Some may be,' Lindsay muttered, then her pulses leapt with alarm as Daniel's body swung sideways, his arm going across her to fence her

into the corner of the couch and his face suddenly
only inches away from hers.

'Don't touch me!' The panic-stricken words
escaped before she could stop them and she saw
his smile harden on his mouth.

'If you wave a red rag at a bull you must expect
him to charge,' he told her, his grey eyes sliding
down over her, insolence in them, as though he
could see through the formal clothes to the warm
flesh beneath. 'That remark was deliberate
provocation and you know it—I'm a human being
and I can prove it.' Before she could stop him his
hand was touching her breast, shaping the silken
roundedness in the curved cup of palm and
fingers, while he watched her intently, his other
hand taking hold of her wrist in an iron grip and
pulling her hand towards his shirt. He held her
hand against his chest, still staring into her
nervously flickering eyes.

'Feel my heart,' he said softly. 'Hear it beating?
I'm flesh and blood, Lindsay, and when I touch
you, every nerve cell in my body knows it.'

'Get your hands off me,' she began unsteadily,
and the words were smothered as his mouth came
down on hers, parting her lips with crushing
force; a fierce demand which almost amounted to
cruelty because it did not care if it hurt her or
not, his mouth hard and insistent.

The hand touching her body moved sideways,
she felt the long fingers opening her blouse, and
tried to struggle free, her hands pushing at his
shoulders, hitting him, thrusting at him while she
writhed and fought to get away. His hand slid
inside, the fingers cool on her skin, and she

caught her breath shuddering, as she felt him touch her naked breast. Wild tremors ran through her, she was trembling with shock, her body arching in bitter tension. A great part of her anger was with herself because she couldn't disguise from her own mind that her body was alight with excitement at what he was doing to it; fire flashed along her nerves, her flesh was melting, and she knew that Daniel was unlikely to miss the telltale signs that betrayed her.

Desperately dragging herself back from the edge of surrender, she deliberately ran her nails into his neck and felt him jerk back in pain.

'You little bitch,' he muttered, sitting up. His face was flushed and hard. He put a hand to his neck and looked at his fingertips as he took it away again. A faint smear of blood showed on his skin.

'You've made me bleed!' he exclaimed, sounding shocked. 'Look at your claw-marks, you vicious little cat!'

'I told you to leave me alone.' Lindsay got to her feet, slightly unsteady as she moved; her head spinning, the blood beating in her ears. 'I think you'd better go,' she said in a voice made raw by the wave of misery which had swept up inside her. Her body was aching with unsatisfied desire, and she hated him for having made her feel like this, she wanted him to go now before she broke down in tears. It was so long since she had felt his hands touching her, her flesh had seemed to dissolve in the furnace-like heat of her emotions.

'I'm staying here tonight,' he muttered, and she stiffened.

'Oh, no, you're not!' Did he really think she would let him stay the night? She moved backwards, watching him with nervous, frightened eyes that spat green fire in defiance, and Daniel looked back at her, his mouth crooked in sardonic mockery.

CHAPTER THREE

'DON'T be stupid, Lindsay,' he said with an
impatient smile that she found infuriating. 'You
need sleep as much as Alice does, but there ought
to be someone awake in case something happens—
I'll stay down here on the couch. I can go without
sleep for days if I have to, you should remember
that.' She did, of course; Daniel could work
through the night and still get up at the crack of
dawn looking as bright as a daisy, she had often
marvelled at that ability to go without sleep. If he
felt tired he could catnap in a chair for half an
hour; she had seen him switch himself off like a
machine, close his eyes and be asleep within
seconds, to wake up bright-eyed and bushy-
tailed, ready to cope with whatever emergency
was needing his attention.

'It's very kind of you,' she said hesitantly, and
he gave her one of his sardonic glances.

'So gracious!'

'I meant it!'

'But it hurt to say it,' he drawled.

'If I sound surprised it's because kindness isn't
something I expect from you.' She ran a shaky
hand through her tumbled red-gold hair, sighing.

Daniel watched her, his face calm now. 'You
look like death—I suggest we discuss your
distorted view of my character in the morning

when you've had some sleep and can talk rationally.'

'I'm perfectly rational now.' Lindsay said, smothering a yawn, and his mouth twisted.

'That,' he said slowly, 'is a matter of opinion.'

She opened her mouth to argue, then closed it. 'I'll get you some blankets and a pillow.' He was quite right, she was too tired to talk clearly, the emotional onslaught of the last few hours had shredded her nerves and left her feeling like someone who has just been in an accident. Anxiety and tension were killing, you couldn't switch them off for long enough to restore your equilibrium, and this evening she had had a series of mental shocks which she certainly couldn't have anticipated. It seemed an eternity since she had stepped into the shower with nothing on her mind but the prospect of a lively date with Aston at the theatre, she hadn't had any premonition of what was about to hit her.

She quietly went upstairs to the bathroom airing cupboard, found some blankets and a pillow on the top shelf and took them down to Daniel, who was looking along the bookshelves that filled the alcoves on each side of the fireplace. Lindsay was moving so softly that he hadn't heard her come back; she stood there, her arms full, staring at him. In the lamplight his black hair shone like polished jet, the ends of it tapering in to his brown nape, brushing his collar as he bent forward to pull out a book. He straightened again, his movement supple, the muscled elegance of a tiger rippling beneath his tailored suit. Her breath caught and Daniel turned his head quickly.

Lindsay pulled herself together and came into the room. She dropped her burden on the couch. 'Will two blankets be enough?'

'More than adequate.' He moved towards her and she felt her nerves prickling, and hurriedly walked back to the door before he glimpsed anything of what she was feeling. 'Goodnight, then, you'll wake me if anything happens.'

She heard his soft laughter as she closed the door and was furious with herself for fleeing like a routed army. She might have known that it would be a dead give-away—Daniel Randall didn't miss a thing; she should have stood her ground and tried to look as cool as a cucumber. The very last thing she wanted was for him to guess how she felt about having him around. Their marriage was over, thank heavens, and it had cost her enough to cut herself free from him the first time around, she didn't want to get involved with him again. She had that much sense, now. She hadn't had any when she first met him, she had been too young.

It had been one of the malicious jokes of fate that she had met him in the first place—she had been nineteen, working in London as a junior secretary in a merchant bank, sharing a flat with two other girls from the bank and living as cheaply as possible on her tiny salary. Each Saturday morning, one of the secretarial staff had to come in to work to open the mail and deal with routine enquiries which couldn't wait until Monday. The girls worked a rota for this duty, so that it was only around six times a year that each one to give up her Saturday morning.

The second time Lindsay had to do it, one of the directors came into her little office and asked her to take some urgent dictation. Daniel had been with him and had wandered around the room with his hands in his pockets while the other man dictated. Lindsay had held her head down, nervously concentrating on her shorthand, but she had been very much aware of Daniel. She had never seen anyone like him, the men who worked at the bank were usually pretty boring, either stuffed shirts without two words to say for themselves or shy young men who stared at her and stammered over their dictation. Daniel had seemed like someone from another planet; she had been stunned by his electric sexuality, the masculinity of that strong face and powerful body. He wore the same dark suit and striped business shirt as the other men, but he wore his clothes with a casual panache which made them seem very different, and the way he moved somehow made it impossible not to be aware of the male body underneath the clothes. Lindsay had found herself trembling every time he came near her, she kept stealing looks at him from under her lowered lashes. He hadn't seemed to be looking at her most of the time, but once their eyes had met and Daniel had given her a quick, amused, aware smile, sending a wave of bright pink flowing up her face. She had felt so obvious, he must have realised she couldn't keep her eyes off him, and he was laughing at her. After that she had kept her eyes firmly riveted on the shorthand pad.

When she left the bank at noon to walk to her

nearest tube station she had found Daniel waiting outside in a red sports car. Lindsay hadn't noticed him at first, she had been about to walk past without a glance when he leaned over, opening the passenger door, and smiled at her. Halting in surprise, she had come over to the car, imagining that he was going to ask her some question about the work she had done that morning. Questions had flashed through her mind: had she made a mistake when she typed those letters?

'Can I give you a lift?' Daniel had asked instead, and she had hesitated, wary caution in her eyes. Daniel had watched her face, reading her expression without difficulty.

'My intentions are strictly honourable,' he had teased. 'I was only going to suggest lunch, seduction isn't on the agenda.'

She had blushed, then hated herself. He must think her so gauche and unsophisticated, she had thought, and with as casual a smile as she could manage she had got into his car, saying: 'Lunch would be fun.' Daniel had given her a smile that glinted with humour at the airy tone, and she had blushed again.

'You look like a poppy,' he had said, touching her cheek with one finger, and she had jumped about six foot in the air.

It all seemed a hundred years ago now, she had been so young and she hadn't had a clue how to talk to him. He had had a walk-over with her, one smile and she had been on her knees at his feet, amazed that anyone so godlike should want to take her out.

It was only after they were married, when Daniel was so rarely at home, always too busy to make dinner engagements or meet her at the theatre as they had arranged, that she began to view their first encounter in a different light. How many other wide-eyed little secretaries had he picked up so easily? He had accomplished it so smoothly, with the ease of someone who made it a habit. A smile, a come-hither look and she had been in his car, her heart beating like a drum and her senses wildly aware of every movement he made.

Daniel had kissed her on their first date; on their second he had taken her out to dinner and afterwards they had sat in his car for what had seemed eternity, the expert caresses he was giving her turning her blood to fire. Now she had no doubt that if she had been a different sort of girl, she would have been in bed with him that night, but Daniel had come up against a barrier he, perhaps, hadn't expected. Lindsay had never been to bed with a man in her life, she had pulled back in panic when she realised where they were heading.

'No, don't—I'm sorry, I can't, I've never . . .' Her incoherent stammering had seemed to amuse him. He had looked into her flushed face, brows lifted, then he had smiled and run a long, gentle finger over the trembling curve of her mouth.

'Don't get into a state, honey, I'm not going to turn nasty, you can stop shaking in your shoes.'

'I'm sorry,' she had said, feeling a failure, afraid that he would lose interest in her if she refused, yet unable to relax and let it happen. She had never thought of herself as inhibited, but her mind obstinately refused to lift that invisible barrier; she went stiff from head to foot every time she thought about it.

'Don't apologise,' he had said, and there had been a faint snap in his voice then, he had frowned angrily, sitting up.

For a minute they had sat in silence in the car, not looking at each other, and Lindsay had heard the roughened drag of his breathing, betraying his frustration, tearing at her nerves and the nagging frustration she felt herself. She had hated herself, she had desperately wanted to turn to him and say: 'Yes, please, I want to . . .' But she couldn't, her tongue seemed to have turned to wood in her mouth, she could barely swallow. The dry heat behind her eyes had become tears which stole down her face, she put up a hand to brush them away and Daniel turned his head, catching the gesture.

'Oh, hell,' he had muttered, seeing the wetness on her cheeks, 'Lindsay, you baby . . .'

There had been impatience, tenderness, exasperation in his voice, but he had put out an arm to gather her against him and his hand had pushed her head down on to his chest, his long fingers stroking her hair, ruffling it, rubbing her scalp as though she was a nervous animal he was trying to calm. Lindsay had burrowed into him, muffling a little sob, and he had put his face down on her hair.

'If I'm not careful I'm going to fall in love with you,' he had whispered, and she had closed her eyes, her body melting with happiness, hearing his heart beating beneath her cheek.

During one of their bitter rows later, she had turned on him and asked angrily: 'If you feel like that about me, why did you marry me?' and Daniel had said in barbed mockery: 'I couldn't see any other way of getting you into bed, you frigid little bitch.'

It had been an admission she never forgot—if she hadn't refused to sleep with him from the start, he would never have married her, and it had taken him six months to make up his mind then, he had kept up the pressure mercilessly until he finally conceded defeat, and asked her to marry him. If Lindsay had planned the whole thing as a cool campaign she couldn't have been more successful, but she hadn't had any plan, she had merely been unable to break through that inhibition which her unconscious had had buried within it. When she first met him she hadn't even been aware of her own sexual inhibitions, she had never wanted to make love with anyone before, and if she did ever daydream about it, she had somehow pictured love as something which would happen naturally. Her imagination had not wandered beyond kisses and caresses, ending mistily, in delight, but a delight Lindsay had never looked at too closely.

She wasn't so innocent that she didn't know how men and women make love, but it was one thing to have a vague idea of the physical realities of the sexual act and quite another, she found, to bring yourself to the point of surrender that first time, and once she had said no to Daniel she found herself unable to say yes, the original inhibition had been joined by another, equally baffling to her. She had become too selfconscious about it, she was too nervous and she wanted him too much.

Looking back at herself across the years of her marriage and divorce, the painful growing years when she discovered her own identity as a woman and shed the shy uncertainties of adolescence, she felt angry and resentful now, she was very sorry for that blushing girl who could neither bring herself to say yes nor find the courage to walk away from Daniel, until he had inflicted on her wounds that still hadn't fully healed.

She went softly into the spare bedroom next to the one used by the two children, hearing their regular breathing faintly as she paused to listen for it. There wasn't a sound from Alice's room, presumably she was fast asleep too. Lindsay sighed, closing her bedroom door. Where was Stephen? Why hadn't he rung, or at least sent a telegram to ease Alice's mind? Was Daniel right when he said that Stephen was a bad case of burn-out and wanted to make Alice suffer because she hadn't even been aware of his anxieties? Undressing and slipping into bed in her white nylon slip, she switched off the light and lay on her back, her arms crossed behind her head, staring at the dark ceiling, thinking about her brother for a long time until she finally fell asleep.

She slept so deeply that she didn't hear a sound when someone opened the door and came over to the bed. It wasn't until a finger stroked her cheek

that her lids flickered upwards and her eyes
blinked in the morning sunlight, staring straight
into Daniel's grey eyes and coming awake with
speed.

'I brought you some tea and toast,' he said,
those dark brows raised in wry comment on her
immediately wary expression.

She must have slept restlessly, she had flung
off the bedclothes during the night, and she felt
him look at her bare shoulders, the half-revealed
breasts under the transparent nylon slip, the soft
pink flesh only too visible to him. Hurriedly she
dragged the sheet around her and sat up,
wrapped in a sort of toga, to drink the tea and
nibble the toast while Daniel lounged on the edge
of the bed and watched her.

'No news yet?' she asked, and he shook his
head.

'Your reporter friend sat outside all night in his
car, I think. At any rate, he's there this morning,
but he hasn't tried to get near the house with my
men outside.'

'Have they been there all night?'

'All night,' he agreed. 'Two more will relieve
them any minute, I gather.'

'I should think they could do with some tea
and toast, too, after standing around all night.'

'They sat in their car on the drive, taking turns
to stay awake and on watch,' Daniel told her.
'And they've had some tea. They had sandwiches
with them—they're used to this sort of work,
they came prepared.'

'Like the Boy Scouts,' Lindsay remarked,
finishing her toast. 'Is Alice up?'

He shook his head. 'I gave the children their breakfast at seven o'clock—they wake up early. I heard them squeaking and went in there, they seemed surprised to see a strange man, but luckily they didn't make much noise.'

Lindsay was taken aback. 'You fed them and got them up? All by yourself?'

He gave her a derisive look. 'It wasn't that difficult—women make too much fuss about looking after kids. The boy told me where to find their clothes, he dressed himself more or less while I dressed his sister, then I carried her downstairs and he told me they both wanted rusks in warm milk. They seemed quite happy with them.'

'Where are they now?' Lindsay had visions of Matt electrocuting himself by sticking his finger into the wall points, or Vicky eating one of her shoes, something Alice was always worrying about. Vicky had a habit of putting everything into her mouth, and Alice permanently fretted in case her baby died a sudden death by accident. Children, she often said to Lindsay, seem to be fascinated by fatal objects, you have to watch them twenty-four hours a day.

'I belted them both into high-chairs in the sitting-room and left them staring at the test card on the TV.' Daniel seemed pleased with his achievements as a baby-sitter, he grinned at her in self-congratulation.

'That must be exciting for them,' commented Lindsay, on the point of getting out of the bed to go and rescue the poor children when she realised she was practically naked under her sheet.

Flushing, she said: 'I want to get dressed—would you mind?'

'Not at all.' Daniel said smoothly, settling himself more comfortably on the bed. 'Carry on, don't worry about me.'

Eyeing him with distaste, she said: 'Oh, but I do worry about you—I'm not getting dressed in front of you, so go away.'

'You know your problem?' Daniel asked slowly uncoiling himself with reluctance.

'Yes, it's standing in front of me and it's six foot tall.'

'Apart from me,' he said, moving to the door. 'Your trouble is, you're no fun any more. You've lost your sense of humour.'

'I didn't lose it, I still laugh at you,' she assured him from behind her veil of sheeting. 'All the time, believe me.'

He gave her a look which was not amused and went out. Lindsay waited until she heard him going down the stairs, then she slid out of the bed and picked up her clothes. Opening the door, she risked a quick dash to the bathroom, showered rapidly and got dressed. When she had brushed her hair and applied a little make-up she went downstairs to say hallo to Matt and Vicky, who were, as Daniel had told her, deeply engrossed in the test card, but were also playing with some toys arranged on the trays of their high-chairs. At the sight of her, Vicky threw a yellow wooden brick at her, beaming, and Matt gravely offered her one of his miniature cars.

Lindsay gave them both a kiss. 'Having a good time?'

'Mumma get up,' said Vicky, hurling some more bricks at her while she displayed all her pearly teeth in a wide grin. 'Up, up, Mumma get up, bad Mumma.'

'We had rusks,' Matt announced. 'And blackcurrant juice and banana, and Vicky ate mine, she ate my banana.' He looked at Lindsay with his father's eyes and she kissed his nose.

'Too bad, darling, I'll get you another banana.'

'I don't like bananas,' he said. 'Vicky ate mine.'

'Oh, I see, it was a friendly arrangement, was it?'

He looked vague. 'Vicky ate my banana.'

'Don't let it weigh on your mind,' Lindsay advised. 'If you don't like bananas, that's okay by me.'

Daniel came in and grinned at her. 'I'm relieved to discover other people have the same inconsequential conversations with them that I had—I thought it was me, I just wasn't on their wavelength.'

'Vicky ate my banana,' Matt told him.

'He's obsessed with that damned banana,' Daniel said to her. 'I offered him another one and he refused.'

'He doesn't like them, but he feels guilty about it,' Lindsay explained, deciphering Matt's worried expression.

'Why on earth should he?'

'I expect Alice feels he ought to like them, she does tend to do things by the book, and babies are supposed to like bananas.'

Daniel studied Matt, who was pushing one of his toys cars backwards and forwards. 'If she isn't careful, he'll grow up with a banana phobia.'

'He worries,' said Lindsay, and frowned, reminded of Stephen—yes, Matt was just like his father; why had she never seen it so clearly before? There was that little nervous frown, the sober anxious look of the eyes, the smile which was too eager to please, the awareness of what was expected of him and the desire to be approved of by everyone. 'Poor Stephen,' she said, mostly to herself, and Daniel looked at her sharply.

'I thought his name was Matt.'

'It is,' said Lindsay, stiffening as she heard movements on the stairs. The door was pushed open and Alice came in, smiling as the two children leapt about and shouted to her. She looked much better, Lindsay thought, watching as she kissed them both. This morning she had more colour, some of the drawn tension had left her small face and she was wearing a very pretty coral linen dress which flattered her slender figure. The curly red-brown hair had been brushed until it gleamed and she was wearing make-up, Lindsay noted. A woman who is very depressed forgets to look at herself in mirrors, she doesn't bother to do her hair or make-up, she no longer cares what she looks like. Alice was obviously feeling less miserable after her long sleep.

'Any news?' she asked Lindsay a second later, and in her brown eyes Lindsay saw anxiety. Shaking her head, Lindsay admitted there was none.

'Daniel talked to Mr Datchet last night, though,' she said before Alice's spirits could sink too low. 'Stephen owes the bank a lot of money, it seems, and Mr Datchet said he was very worried about it. Daniel thinks maybe Stephen has gone off to try to raise a loan from somewhere.'

Alice sat down with Vicky on her lap. 'Oh,' was all she could say.

'So you see it was money, after all.' At least it wasn't another woman, Lindsay thought, but carefully did not put into words. Alice could do her own thinking, and, from the look of her, that was just what she was doing, both arms clasped around the little girl's wriggling body in the vivid green dungarees and striped T-shirt, which made her look like an elf. Alice was holding Vicky far too tightly as though she needed the comfort of that small, plump, warm body, and Vicky was squawking in protest.

Daniel had leaned there, listening and watching but saying nothing. He wasn't wearing a jacket or tie, his white shirt was open at the collar; he looked casually and maddeningly good-looking, and as Lindsay irritably glanced his way he winked at her, which made her prickle with resentment.

'Mr Datchet is coming over here at ten,' he intervened a second later. 'He's bringing the firm's account books. I thought they might give us a clearer picture of what's wrong. I may be able to help Stephen, he should have contacted me long ago.'

Alice looked round, sighing. 'He's much too proud, you're the last person he would ask for help.' She flushed at Daniel's expression and hurriedly added: 'Don't be offended, I didn't mean . . . it's just that Stephen would feel that—the divorce, I mean, Lindsay isn't your wife any more and it would be embarrassing for both of you. Stephen wouldn't have wanted to put you in an awkward position by asking for a favour.'

'I could always have said no,' Daniel said drily.

'He was perfectly well aware of that,' snapped Lindsay, glaring at him. 'That's obvious, but it would still have been embarrassing to have to ask—Stephen isn't the type to trade on family loyalty, he would much rather ask a bank. If they said no, neither side need feel embarrassed, it would just be business, but if he had asked you and you had said no, Stephen would have felt two feet high.'

Alice nodded. 'Lindsay's right.'

'Well, that's a first,' Daniel drawled, and got a dagger-bright smile from Lindsay.

Before she could say what was hovering on the tip of her tongue, the doorbell went, and Daniel straightened.

'I'll go, it may be Mr Datchet,' he said, going out.

'Perhaps Stephen will ring today,' said Alice, putting Vicky back into her high-chair. 'If he's only worried about money . . .'

'I told you it wasn't another woman—Stephen loves you,' Lindsay said in a low voice. 'He's probably worried sick about telling you about the bank loan.'

'How could he be so stupid?' Alice broke off as the door opened again and Daniel walked into the room, bringing with him a distinctly dangerous air of menace and Aston Hill wearing a grey suit, a pale blue shirt and a wryly amused expression.

'Your boy-friend,' Daniel said acidly, hurling the words at Lindsay as if he hoped they would knock her head off with the force of their arrival.

'Hallo, darling,' said Aston, just as deliberately, with the smile of one determined to enjoy a difficult situation just for the hell of it.

Vicky decided she liked the look of Aston, and held out her arms to him lovingly. 'Uncle,' she said, and Lindsay could have killed her. She had such a small vocabulary, why couldn't she have chosen one of her other words?

Playing up to her, Aston advanced and gave her a kiss on her cheek. 'Hallo, sweetheart, you look gorgeous as usual.' He had only set eyes on Vicky once or twice before, he was being difficult, but Daniel deserved it, acting as though Aston was an interloper.

'I came round right away,' Aston said. 'I gather Stephen hasn't got in touch with you yet?'

Alice tried to smile, it was not a success, her lips trembled too much. 'No.'

'Then I've got news for you,' Aston told her. 'He rang me an hour ago, he's quite safe, so you can stop worrying.'

CHAPTER FOUR

'HE rang *you*?' Alice's voice went up several octaves and she flushed angrily. 'Stephen rang you, not me? Why? What did he say to you?'

'He wasn't very coherent,' Aston explained. 'He was upset . . .'

'Upset? *He's* upset? What does he think I am? He vanishes without a word of explanation, stays away for hours and then rings a perfect stranger?' She looked at Aston, shrugging. 'Oh, I'm sorry, I didn't mean to sound rude, but he hardly knows you. I'm his wife, how can he do this to me? Where is he?'

'He's staying at a country pub, he didn't say where. It seems he couldn't face coming home, so he drove and drove until he was tired, then he stopped at this pub for a drink and ended up staying the night.'

'Why didn't he come home next day?' Alice was walking about the room restlessly, her hands clenched, spots of burning colour in her cheeks.

'He woke up with a hangover, a blinding headache. He felt sick, so he stayed in bed all morning. By the time he had got over that, he didn't know what to say to you. He tried to ring Lindsay last night, but she wasn't answering her phone, of course, she was here. So he rang me this morning.'

Alice faced him belligerently, chin up. 'And

why hasn't he rung me? He could talk to you but not to me—how am I supposed to feel about that?'

Lindsay glanced at the children, who were very quiet, studiously playing with their toys and hoping not to be noticed. 'What we need is some coffee,' she said brightly. 'I'll make some. Matt can help me—come on, Matt.' She scooped up Vicky under one arm and headed for the door; this conversation was not one which the two children should hear. They might not entirely understand what was being said, but they would be picking up far too much from their mother's angry excitement and the way she talked about their father.

Alice didn't even seem to notice, she was too distressed. 'If he's in trouble I'm the one he should be talking to, not a stranger,' she protested to Aston, who made conciliating noises. 'I'm sure he'll ring you any minute . . .'

Lindsay closed the door on the rest of that sentence and went into the kitchen with the children. Before she made the coffee she got them dressed in their identical little knitted jackets and put them both into the garden to play in their sandpit. It was a warm morning, the sky was blue and cloudless, there was a slight breeze blowing through the trees. Lindsay stood for a moment, watching Matt digging with a plastic spade while Vicky sat on the sand and picked up handfuls that trickled through her plump pink fingers in a silvery shower. Stephen had built the sandpit for them. Lindsay sighed and went back into the house.

She found Daniel in the kitchen, spooning ground coffee into the percolater. He looked up. 'Will they be okay out there on their own?'

'Of course.' She took the percolater from him and plugged it into the wall point, pretending not to be aware of his narrow-eyed stare.

'Odd that Stephen should ring Hill and nobody else,' Daniel observed. 'Are they close friends?'

'They get on well.' Lindsay got out the cups. The sun was streaming through the window, giving the small room a much happier look this morning, or was that merely because she saw it with different eyes now that she knew her brother was safe?

'Is Hill in the same business?' Daniel asked, leaning back against a formica-topped cabinet, his arms folded across his chest.

'He has some shops; he sells electrical equipment, so I suppose in a sense he is in the same business as Stephen.'

'So he might be in a position to help Stephen out of trouble?'

She looked round at him. 'How should I know? You'd have to ask them, I'm not involved in Stephen's business.'

'Your sister-in-law said something about Stephen being reluctant to ask for help from me because we were divorced,' Daniel drawled.

'I'm sure she's right, Stephen's very proud.'

'So why would he ask Hill for help? Unless he thinks that any day now Hill's going to be his brother-in-law?'

Lindsay heard the terse note in the voice and felt herself flushing. She didn't answer, and luckily the coffee started bubbling right then and she could make a big show of being too busy to say anything, switching off the percolater and unplugging it from the wall. Daniel moved softly, she didn't hear him until he was right behind her, and his voice made her jump when it came so close he was almost whispering into her ear.

'No comment?'

'None of your business,' Lindsay retorted, checking the tray to make sure she had everything: cups, sugar, coffee pot, milk. She kept her eyes down, her back towards him, trying not to be aware of his close proximity.

'You're not in love with Hill!' Daniel sounded self-satisfied, his voice purring, and her temper began to rise like mercury in an exploding thermometer.

'Who says?'

'I do,' he told her in maddening amusement.

'What you know about love could be written on a postage stamp,' Lindsay muttered in an impeded voice, trying not to lose control. She was too old to slap his face, she wasn't going to descend to that level, although no doubt he'd like that, it would give him an excuse to use his own hands in a very different way. She was going to keep calm, whatever his provocation.

'You can't hide love, I don't have to be an expert on the subject to know that,' Daniel drawled, smiling. She heard the smile in his voice and grew angrier. What was so funny? 'And I saw how you looked at Hill,' he added, giving the remark an intonation which she disliked intensely.

'Maybe I'm not as obvious as you think I am,' she returned with a bite, wishing she dared turn and hit him, because there was an element of truth in what he had said and to herself she couldn't deny it. She liked Aston very much, she admired and respected him, but she couldn't pretend she was head over heels in love with him, he didn't make her pulse beat faster, he didn't set her body on fire, but then she had outgrown that sort of love, it didn't last, and she wanted something more real, more permanent, which Aston *could* give her. Going up in flames is all very well, but what happens when the fire goes out and all that's left is charcoal? She never again wanted to end up in charred, blackened little pieces.

'Did I say you were obvious?' Daniel took hold of her elbows and spun her round to face him, so fast she didn't have time to break away. Angrily, she glared up at him, which was a mistake, because there was a wicked mockery in those silvery eyes, and more than that, an intention which she glimpsed too late, his gaze drifting downwards to her mouth just a second before his head swooped down. 'Only to me,' he whispered as his lips parted her own.

Had he used brutal force she would have struggled violently, hit him, fought free somehow, but Daniel was not making the mistake of using force this time, and he took her off guard by his devious, unscrupulous tactics, enlisting her own body as an ally against her. His mouth coaxed and incited, moving with slow, warm sensuality, the tip of his tongue flicking between her trembling lips, and Lindsay felt perspiration spring out on her forehead, she couldn't keep her eyes open. The way he was kissing her made her dizzy, she had to cling to him to stay upright as her head spun. She didn't want to feel like that again; the intensity of her passion for him had almost destroyed her once before, she had told herself she was free of him now, he couldn't get to her again, but where Daniel Randall was concerned she seemed to be schizophrenic, split into two. Torn between love and hate, between bitter contempt and a fierce compulsion, her body was dissolving in heated excitement as his hands touched her with that lingering seduction, one of them moving up and down her back while the other softly stroked her throat, her shoulders, her breasts. Her hands went up jerkily to catch his head, hold it, her fingers in his black hair, she swayed closer, wanting to melt into him, and remembered that that was how it had been, that was what love meant, this nagging desire to merge with him, hold him inside her and never let him go.

Daniel moved, breathing harshly, and she was separate from him again, their bodies parted, their mouths disentangled. She felt cold and desolate, she shuddered as she pushed him even farther away, almost too dazed to realise that they were in Alice's kitchen in the sunshine with the fragrance of fresh coffee filling the air. Time had seemed to stop, she had moved outside herself into Daniel, existing in a black velvet world of hands and lips and smothering, sweet sensations. It hurt to come back to reality.

She couldn't bring herself to speak. Trembling and darkly flushed, she picked up the tray of coffee and walked unsteadily towards the door.

'That's it, run away from it,' Daniel said behind her, but she pretended not to have heard, she kept on going with her eyes fixed on nothing, the cups on the tray rattling as her hands shook. What had just happened had not come as any real surprise to her; she had stayed away from him just because he could do that to her. The physical chemistry between them was explosive, Lindsay couldn't deny that, she had always known that he could reach her on that level. Daniel was a male animal with powerful sexual magnetism, Lindsay couldn't deny that, either, but neither could she forget that other women felt his attraction. Daniel wasn't a man who belonged to anyone, Lindsay had wasted too much of her life burning with jealousy because he was turning those mocking grey eyes on another woman.

How many evenings had she spent alone during their marriage, wondering who he was with? How many parties had she gone to with him only to see him dancing with someone else and ache with misery over the way he was smiling down at his partner? He was ruthless in business, she hadn't expected him to be so ruthless in his private life; she had thought he was hers, but she had discovered just how wrong she was—Daniel Randall belonged to himself. Lindsay's dazed incredulity when he first told her he loved her and asked her to marry him had become gradually a bitter disenchantment. Her first uneasy suspicions had hardened into certainties, she had become sure that Daniel had only married her because he couldn't seduce her, but once he had got what he wanted he had gone back to his old way of life. Her jealousy began to corrode her every waking moment, she couldn't bear the unremitting pain, she had had to get away from him.

She shouldn't have let him get so close to her just now, she would be crazy if she walked back into that trap. However temptingly baited, it would end the way it had ended before, with her getting badly hurt.

In the sitting-room, she found Alice walking round and round, her arms clasping her shoulders, a hard flush on her cheeks. 'I'll kill him,' she was saying. 'I'll kill him.'

Aston glanced towards the door as Lindsay came in and winked at her surreptitiously. To Alice he said: 'He was worried about you.'

'Funny way of showing it!' Alice would not be placated.

Lindsay put down the tray. 'Coffee,' she said. 'Come on, Alice, sit down and relax.'

'Relax? I'm on wires, I couldn't sit down.' She kept on walking, scowling.

'We ought to tell the police that Stephen's okay,' Lindsay said to Aston as she poured him coffee.

Alice stopped dead. 'I'd forgotten them— whatever will they think? I feel such a fool—there was I ringing the police, crying my eyes out, and all the time he was sleeping off a hangover!'

'Drink your coffee,' said Lindsay, handing her

a cup. 'I'll ring the police and explain, I'm sure they'll understand.'

They did; Lindsay heard the amusement in the duty sergeant's voice. 'Thought it might be something like that,' he said. 'Happens all the time.' I told you so, his voice silently breathed. Far from being angry at the waste of police time he was pleased with himself for having been right.

'I'm sorry to have troubled you over nothing,' Lindsay said, all the same.

'No trouble, miss, that's what we're here for. Very glad the gentleman turned up safe and sound.' He could hardly wait to ring off and tell his friends he had guessed right. Lindsay put down the phone, grimacing.

As she turned round, Aston joined her. 'I've got a vital appointment this morning. I must be off,' he said, smiling at her, and she linked her arms around his neck, leaning towards him.

'Did I say how grateful I am? It was good of you to come over to give Alice the news, you're a darling.' She kissed him lightly and Aston's hands closed on her waist, drawing her nearer. His mouth came down with warm insistence on her own and Lindsay swayed against him, kissing him back.

A moment later, Aston murmured: 'What's Randall doing here? Didn't he go out of your life a long time ago?' The question made Lindsay stiffen.

She leaned back to look up at him. 'A reporter rang him and told him Stephen was missing, so he came round to find out what was going on.'

'This morning?' Aston asked, and her eyes flicked down, she felt herself flush. Before she could think of a way of answering that awkward question, he said drily: 'He looks very much at home here, and who are the two gorillas out on the drive? They made me prove my identity before they would let me near the front door, and even then they hung around until Randall had spoken to me. I picked up that they came from his zoo and took their orders from him.'

'The press kept ringing the door bell. Daniel felt we needed protection.'

'How long have they been out there?'

'All night,' said Lindsay, and then her eyes met Aston's and she sighed.

'Which means so has he,' Aston thought aloud.

'Yes, he arrived just after you left last night.' Lindsay felt she ought to be apologising, Aston made her feel guilty, as though she had invited Daniel here.

'And stayed all night.' Aston's air of good humour was not so much in evidence at this moment, his jaw had hardened, he was frowning and she read accusation in his eyes.

'On the couch downstairs!' Lindsay knew she was very flushed, she hoped she did not look guilty.

'And where were you?'

'Upstairs,' she said crossly. 'In the spare bedroom.'

'All night?'

'All night!' she agreed, her chin up defiantly, meeting his probing stare without flinching. 'And before you ask—no, he did not make love to me last night. If he'd tried, I'd have knocked him into the middle of next week!'

Aston relaxed slightly, half-smiling. 'He seems very concerned for an ex-husband,' he said, though. 'I didn't expect to find him here.'

'He's interested in Stephen's business, if Stephen isn't careful Daniel Randall will be running his firm.' Lindsay heard the sting of bitterness in her own voice and saw Aston's eyes widen.

'Like that, is it? He isn't interested in you, then? He seemed very hostile when I told him I'd come to see you, I thought for a minute he was going to punch my face in . . .'

'Daniel's an aggressive man.'

'You mean he always talks like that?' Aston whistled softly, his face wry. 'That must be wearing to live with.'

'It is—I told you, I can't stand the sight of him.'

Aston laughed. 'I'm not too smitten myself, but then I have good reason not to be—even if he'd been charming to me, there was no way I'd have liked the guy.'

Lindsay didn't pretend not to know what he meant, she smiled up at him, shaking her head. 'You don't need to be jealous of Daniel Randall, nothing would tempt me back to him.'

Aston wound a hand into her gleaming red-gold hair, kissed her gently on the mouth. 'I hope you mean that—in case you hadn't noticed, I'm your fan for life and you're much too beautiful to be wasted on a hard case like Daniel Randall.' He opened the front door, waved a hand at her. 'Stay in touch, and don't let Randall within a foot of you.'

'I won't,' she promised, and stood at the door waving as he got into his car and drove away under the watchful gaze of Daniel's security men. Lindsay resisted the temptation to put out her tongue at them, closing the door with a slam.

Slow clapping made her spin in shock. Daniel stood at the door of the kitchen, lounging casually against the frame, derisively applauding her.

'Were you eavesdropping?' Lindsay asked angrily.

'I was a fascinated audience,' he drawled. 'Your performance was touching—such wide-eyed sincerity, you almost convinced me.'

'I meant every word!'

'And I just imagined the way you kissed me half an hour ago!' he mocked, bringing a hot wave of colour flowing up to her hairline.

'*You* kissed *me*!'

'I don't remember you struggling.'

'Your memory has never been very reliable.'

'On the contrary, my memory is infallible,' Daniel corrected with a smile which she found detestable, the crooked amusement in it brought back too many memories of her own.

'Oh, of course, it would be,' she flung back, seething. 'Infallible and omniscient, aren't you?'

'I know you rather better than you seem to know yourself,' he told her, and she turned away, shaking with temper, to go into the sitting-room. Daniel did not follow her and a moment later she heard him talking to someone in the hall. Alice went to the door, looked out and came back a second later.

'Mr Datchet,' she said dully as Lindsay eyed her enquiringly.

'You ought to see him,' Lindsay said. 'Stephen might not be too happy to come back and find that Daniel Randall has been inspecting his account books.'

'I suppose you're right.' Reluctantly, Alice left the room. Lindsay heard her voice from the hall. 'Hallo, Mr Datchet . . .'

Lindsay went to the window and looked out. The sky was clouding over, the sun had vanished behind a bank of stormy slate-blue cloud hanging low over the surrounding roof-tops, and a sudden wind was whipping the tops of trees into frothy green tangles of leaves. She decided she should bring the two children back into the house, it looked as if it might rain at any minute.

The hall was empty, and she heard Daniel's voice from a little room leading off it which Stephen used as a study and office. Lindsay walked through the kitchen and into the garden. Matt was running aimlessly around the lawn while Vicky shovelled sand into a small bucket. They both started towards her eagerly.

'It's cold,' Matt said. 'Can we come in?'

'In,' said Vicky, lifting her arms.

Lindsay hoisted her up and Matt darted past her into the house, shouting: 'Mummy, Mummy!'

When Lindsay went into the kitchen a moment later, Vicky clinging to her like a little monkey, she found Alice kneeling on the floor unbuttoning Matt's jacket.

'Your hands are frozen,' she was saying, and Matt was looking reproachfully at Lindsay.

'Auntie made us stay in the garden for hours!'

'He's almost blue!' complained Alice turning a glare on Lindsay.

'It was sunny when I put them out there, I thought they would have fun playing in their sandpit.'

'Poor baby!' crooned Alice snatching Vicky from her. 'Is she cold, then?'

'Sorry,' said Lindsay under the barrage of three pairs of accusing eyes, and slipped out of the room, feeling very guilty.

A few moments later Alice took the two children upstairs, talking cheerfully to them. Lindsay heard the sound of a vacuum cleaner in the bedrooms—Alice had decided to vent her fury with Stephen on the housework and the children were helping, Lindsay heard Vicky chattering to herself as she fetched and carried for her mother. Daniel and Mr Datchet were still in the study, their voices low. Conspiratorial? wondered Lindsay, listening at the door unashamedly. What exactly was Daniel up to in there?

It was a Saturday morning; Lindsay should have been doing her own housework in the flat, or her shopping, which she always did at weekends. After she had divorced Daniel she had had to go back to work, of course. She hadn't been able to face the idea of working in another bank, secretarial work didn't exactly enthrall her and she had had no training for any other career. For a few months she had worked for an agency, doing temp work in a variety of firms, but always keeping an eye open for a job which might be exciting. When she was sent to work for a few weeks in the publicity department of a national cosmetics firm she had enjoyed herself so much that she had jumped at the chance of working there full-time. Her first job at Vivons had been badly paid, tiring and repetitive; she had been put in charge of answering letters from the public for which a standard letter had been printed. All Lindsay did all day was to type in the name of the person to whom the letter was going, then type their name and address on the envelope. After a week of this, she was almost climbing the wall, it was even more boring than working in a bank. But she had gritted her teeth and stuck it out, and after three months, which had seemed like an eternity at the time, she had been promoted to a job with more responsibility and a lot more job-satisfaction.

Now she was second in command in the public relations department, she earned more than she had ever earned before and she loved her work. She had discovered she had a flair for thinking up ideas, she had learnt how to work with the press and how to block stories which could harm the firm. She worked in a busy, lively office full of people with quick, alert minds, she was successful and self-reliant. She was no longer the un-sophisticated innocent who had been bowled over by Daniel Randall's first smile, it had cost her a good deal, but she had made herself into a woman she could respect. When you despise yourself, life isn't worth living.

From learning to respect herself, she had learnt more about other people, too. She saw Daniel Randall far more clearly, for a start, and she did not trust him. She met a lot of men like him in the course of her job; opportunistic, devious men with corkscrew minds and no scruples. Lindsay was worried about his intentions towards her brother's firm. Stephen was going to be horrified when he found out that Daniel had been prying into his affairs. Why had Alice allowed Mr Datchet to show Daniel the books?

The sound of rain on the window made her look up. The weather had broken, the clouds sagged low over the roofs opposite and the pavements were dancing with great spots of rain. The two security men sat in their car staring out glumly. There was no sign of the reporter—he must have given up and gone.

Stephen still hadn't got in touch with Alice—what was the matter with him? Now that Lindsay knew he was safe, she saw his behaviour as even more out of character. Stephen had always taken his responsibilities so seriously, it wasn't like him to let Alice worry. Was he having a nervous breakdown? Something must be very wrong with him or he wouldn't be doing this. He must have been carrying an intolerable load for months without any of them noticing. They took him for granted, Stephen had always been able to cope, whatever life had thrown at him. Lindsay loved and respected her brother, she had always felt she could depend on him whenever she had problems, but now she realised that she had never wondered if he needed any help or support; he had seemed so much in control of his life. This silence of his was a cry for help which he hadn't been able to put into words, she saw that now, and she was angry with herself for not having realised anything was wrong with him until now.

A car drew up outside the house. Lindsay glanced at it and did a double-take, her body stiffening. Stephen's car! She started towards the sitting-room door. From upstairs she heard the vacuum cleaner—Alice must have missed the engine note. Lindsay flung open the front door and looked out. Stephen was talking to the two security men, a few feet away. He was wearing a cream raincoat, his head bare, and the rain was pelting down around him.

'Stephen!' Lindsay called, and he turned towards her. The men stood back, watching. Stephen slowly came up the drive, his body heavy and slumped, his hair plastered to his skull, rain running down his face like tears. He couldn't meet her eyes, he looked haggard and beaten. Lindsay ran to meet him and hugged him, trying not to cry.

Pulling him into the house, she shut the front door on the watching security men, resenting their curiosity.

Stephen looked up the stairs. Alice stood at the top of them, staring down at him, her face working. Lindsay walked into the kitchen and shut the door; when she was alone she let her tears escape, they stung her eyes and made her throat ache. Poor Stephen! she thought, remembering his expression as he stood looking at Alice. She had never thought she would ever see her brother look like that.

CHAPTER FIVE

'WHAT did Stephen have to say when he realised you'd seen his firm's books?' Lindsay asked Daniel later.

He was driving her back to her flat in the slashing rain which had apparently settled in for the day, and Lindsay had to raise her voice to be heard above the clatter of the windscreen wipers and the hiss of tyres on wet roads. She would have turned down Daniel's offer of a lift if it hadn't been for the weather, but it was a long walk to the nearest tube station and she hadn't wanted to ask Stephen to take her.

Daniel glanced at her sideways, shrugging. 'He didn't have much to say about anything, did he?'

Stephen had come downstairs and gone into the study, talked to Mr Datchet for a few minutes and then walked with his accountant to the front door. Both men had been very quiet; Lindsay had got the impression Stephen was too depressed to care what happened to his firm. If Daniel's interest in his financial position bothered him, he hadn't shown it, and Lindsay had decided not to say any more to her brother than she could help. As soon as Mr Datchet had left, she had told Alice she was going, too, and Alice had been openly relieved. Obviously, she had wanted to be alone with Stephen. They had a lot to say to each

other, and they didn't want a third party around,
even if she was a member of the family.

'Stay out of his life,' snapped Lindsay, glaring
at Daniel now. 'He can do without your brand of
help.'

'Can he?' Daniel smiled without looking at her,
she caught the dry movement of his mouth and
fumed.

'Yes, he can!'

'Of course, you're an expert on how to salvage
wrecks.'

Lindsay wasn't sure what he meant by that,
but she didn't like the sound of it. 'I'm serious,
Daniel!' she warned. 'Leave Stephen alone
or . . .'

'Threatening me?' he mocked. 'I'm shivering
in my shoes. What happens if I don't do as I'm
told?' He pulled up outside her block of flats and
glanced out of the window without waiting to
hear her answer. 'We'll have to run for it,' he
said, and Lindsay sat upright.

'We? I don't remember inviting you into my
flat?'

Daniel produced an umbrella from the back of
the car. He got out and opened it and Lindsay
ran round to dive under its shelter. They ran up
the steps, the rain beating down on the thin silk,
but once she was inside the building, Lindsay
stopped and gave him a frosty look.

'Thanks for the lift.'

'What are you afraid of?' Daniel asked,
watching her with cool grey eyes which saw too
much and had too much intelligence behind
them.

'I'm not afraid of anything, I'm just tired, and I'm not in the mood for one of your barbed chats.'

'We're going to have to talk soon,' said Daniel, shaking drops of rain off the umbrella.

'We've got nothing to talk about.'

'Oh, yes, we have,' he contradicted, and there was a distant triumph in his voice, he was smiling tightly, his mouth curling up at the ends yet not parted.

Lindsay felt her stomach cave in suddenly, she grew alarmed. Why was he looking at her like that?

'About what?' she faltered, and Daniel lifted his brows, glancing around.

'I don't think this is the place for that sort of discussion.'

Lindsay turned and went up the flight of stairs, her footsteps echoing on the stone floors, and behind her she heard the sound of Daniel's following footsteps and shivered, listening to them; he somehow contrived to give the very way he walked an air of menace. She felt as if she was being hunted down, she involuntarily quickened her own pace and Daniel followed suit, his breathing calm and level while Lindsay's was far too quick and uneven.

At first she couldn't find her key and even after she'd traced it down in her handbag she couldn't get it into the lock, her fingers were too unsteady. She felt Daniel watching her and flushed, angry with herself for letting him get to her. She was playing into his hands by making a fool of herself in front of him. She pulled herself together as the front door opened, mentally scolding herself. She was not going to let Daniel undermine her.

'I'm going to make some tea—would you like some?' she asked as casually as she could manage.

'Fine,' said Daniel, walking into the sitting-room as though he owned the flat. She glared at his back but decided not to lose her temper. Shedding her jacket, she went into the kitchen to put on the kettle. She was just making the tea when she heard Daniel's voice, talking on the phone to someone. Lindsay carried the tea tray into the room as he put the phone down, turning towards her.

'Make yourself at home,' Lindsay said sarcastically, and he grinned at her.

'Thanks.' He watched her put the tray down, but as he started towards her, the phone rang again and he whirled and picked it up before Lindsay could get over there. 'Hallo?' he said, listened, then frowned, holding the phone out to her. 'Get rid of him sharpish,' he said, walking away as she lifted the receiver to her ear.

'Hallo?' she said, and Aston demanded: 'What the hell is he doing in your flat?'

'I just got back from Stephen's, Daniel drove me home,' Lindsay told him, keeping her back towards Daniel's intent figure and angrily aware that he was listening to every word she said.

'I know, I rang them—I spoke to your brother. Lindsay, I hope Randall isn't going to be around too much in future. What is he up to?'

'I don't know, I'm going to find out,' said Lindsay in a casual voice.

'Watch yourself, darling,' Aston urged, sounding anxious. 'Have dinner with me tonight? We can talk then.'

'I'd love to,' said Lindsay.

'Pick you up at seven?'

'Seven? Fine, see you then.'

'I think you're fantastic,' said Aston, and she smiled.

'Same here.' Her voice had lifted, become confident and intimate; there was something exciting about talking to Aston while Daniel listened and could only hear half the conversation. Aston blew her a kiss and she laughed.

' 'Bye, see you soon.' She would have liked to send him back a kiss, but she didn't quite dare with Daniel listening, which was ridiculous, because why should she be inhibited by his presence? She put down the phone and turned to feel a shock of alarm as she met the fixed stare of his dangerous grey eyes. Her smile withered and she flinched, then rallied. How dared he look at her like that? He had no right to resent another man's interest in her, they weren't married any more, she was a free agent.

Managing to smile brightly, she said: 'Aston just wanted to ask me out to dinner.' He needn't think she was going to hide her relationship with Aston from him, because she certainly was not going to, she had a right to a love life, as much as he did. She could be quite sure Daniel had dated other women since they broke up, why shouldn't she do the same?

'Tonight?' Daniel asked, and she nodded. 'Sleeping with him?' he asked, and her nerves jarred, she flushed.

'Mind your own business!' Then she spoilt her offended attitude by demanding crossly: 'Who are you sleeping with?'

Daniel's smile mocked her. 'Tonight? Who knows? Are you offering?'

Crimson, she snapped: 'You've got to be kidding! I'm not into masochism.' She sat down in a chair and began to pour the tea. Daniel sat down on the couch and took the cup she handed him, sipping the tea thoughtfully.

'What did you want to talk to me about?' Lindsay demanded.

'Stephen's bankrupt.' The statement was flat and cool, and Lindsay heard it with shocked incredulity.

'Bankrupt? But surely if he raises a loan to pay off the bank . . .'

'Nobody with any commercial acumen would lend that firm a brass farthing,' Daniel said brutally, and she winced. 'Stephen owes more than he owns, for the past two years he has been running at a heavy loss and he's used up all his spare capital. He'll have to sell up, even the house will have to go.'

'Oh, no!' Lindsay breathed, paling. 'Poor Alice . . .'

'The firm does have some potential,' Daniel told her. 'It will need a large influx of capital to make it viable, but with the right management it could become profitable in a few years.'

Lindsay looked at him with bitter anger. 'You, you mean?'

'I could make something of it,' he agreed coolly, watching her stormy face, then added with a shrug: 'It would hardly be worth my while, though—I wouldn't get much of a return on my time, trouble and money.'

She trembled with contempt, her green eyes shooting sparks at him. 'That's all you think about—making money!'

'Not all,' he said in a silky voice, smiling. 'I might be persuaded to make an investment in your brother's firm on the right terms.'

'What do you want? Blood?' Lindsay muttered scathingly, and he laughed.

'No. You.'

She almost dropped her cup and saucer. Slowly she put them back on to the tray, her eyes fixed on his bland face, her body rigid and chilled.

'What's that suppose to mean?'

'Don't pretend to be dumb, Lindsay, you know exactly what it means. You're even sexier than you were when I met you.' His assessing gaze moved down over her without haste and she felt her skin burn as though he was actually touching her. Her mouth went dry and a quiver of nervous reaction went through her. Daniel's eyes were undressing her, and she hated it and was excited by it all at the same time.

'You bastard!' she burst out, her voice shaky. 'No way. You can forget that idea—I'd rather die!'

'Would you? I wonder,' he said drily, and laughed, which made her feel about two inches high.

Scrambling to her feet, she stammered: 'Get out of here before I lose my temper!'

Daniel rose and she backed, very much aware
that they were alone, her hasty movement making
him smile in sardonic enjoyment. He strolled
towards her and she looked around for something
to hit him with if he touched her, but he pushed
his hands into his pockets as he halted and tilted
his black head to one side, amusement in his lean
face.

'I'll give you twenty-four hours to think my
proposition over,' he told her as lazily as though
it had been a formal business offer.

'You've had my answer. I meant it.' She had to
take a deep breath before she could answer him,
she was so angry.

His mouth twisted crookedly. 'It's a woman's
privilege to change her mind.'

'Not this woman. My mind's made up, it has
been for two years, as far as you're concerned. I
don't want to know about you.'

There was a hint of cruelty about his tight
smile, a brooding anger in the grey eyes. Daniel
had not liked that. 'We'll see,' was all he said,
though, and he walked past her without looking
at her again.

She stood there, frozen on the spot, and heard
him open the front door and close it with a
controlled quietness which was even more
menacing than that look he had just given her.
Daniel Randall was a man who enjoyed getting
his own way, he was ruthless and determined,
and when Lindsay walked out on their marriage
she had offended him bitterly. He might still find
her very attractive, but she couldn't avoid
suspecting that revenge was an even more

powerful motive for the proposition he had just offered her. He knew it would humiliate her to accept his terms, it had humiliated her merely to have them suggested to her, and Daniel wanted to make her pay for the humiliation she had once inflicted on him.

She had often wondered if it hadn't been his ego which had pushed him into asking her to marry him in the first place. A man with Daniel's fierce desire for success would find it hard to take rejection in any shape or form, but particularly where a woman was concerned. The more she got to know him, the more she had realised how that drive to succeed dominated him. Opposition always flicked his ego raw. He was too clever to show it on the surface, he had learnt how to use his charm to get what he wanted, but during their marriage Lindsay had spent a lot of time watching him and she recognised the flicker of anger, the glimmer of hard impatience in his eyes, and she had soon noticed that he would go to any lengths to achieve his ends, use any means; force, charm, money, and especially his own sex appeal. Daniel knew he was attractive to women, damn him, she thought, running an angry hand through her hair.

But if he thought for a minute that he could browbeat her by using her brother's situation to blackmail her, he was going to find out how wrong he was!

I must talk to Stephen, she thought, going to the phone, then stopped, her hand on the receiver. Not yet, Stephen was in no state for that sort of conversation today. She would have to

leave a frank discussion until he was more
himself.

She forced herself, instead, to do housework
and shopping. It helped to turn her mind to more
mundane things, the boredom of cleaning the flat
and galloping around the supermarket with her
trolley was an antidote to the hectic emotional
impact of her clash with Daniel. She refused to
think about him, she stared at baked beans and
washing powder instead with a pretence of
interest. The rain had stopped, the sky was a
clear, washed blue from which the clouds slowly
drifted during the late afternoon. By the time
Aston rang her doorbell that evening, the weather
was back to high summer.

He looked at her cool, summery dress with a
smile. 'You look delicious, what colour do you
call that? Asparagus?'

'Lime green, thank you,' Lindsay told him, but
laughed. 'Will I need a jacket? What's it like out
in the streets?'

'Warm—you're fine as you are,' he assured her.
'I've booked a table at that brasserie where all the
film stars go when they're in London, I thought
you might enjoy spotting celebrities.'

'How extravagant of you.' Lindsay said,
closing the front door. 'It sounds marvellous,
thank you.' They walked down, talking about the
change in the weather.

His hand touched her bare arm lightly. 'Did
you have to use Judo on Daniel Randall, or did
he go quietly?'

'Don't let's talk about him.' Lindsay was trying
to forget Daniel existed, she did not want to give

Aston a blow-by-blow account of what Daniel had said to her.

'That's fine by me,' said Aston with a wry glance. He was wearing a tailored linen suit, cream and very elegant, under which she saw a dark brown shirt. He looked pretty good himself. 'Don't we make a handsome pair?' Lindsay asked, her green eyes teasing, and he grinned at her. Aston had a strong sense of humour.

As they drove to the restaurant, she asked him: 'What exactly did Stephen tell you on the phone? How serious is his financial problem?'

Aston sobered, staring at the road, his brows meeting. The gold-brown hair gleamed in the last rays of the sun, she saw the tips of his eyelashes glowing gilt too, as he lowered his eyes. His face was not striking, it had too much rugged strength for that, but it pleased her to look at him, his personality came though every time he smiled.

'Bad, I'm afraid,' he said tersely.

'Daniel said something about Stephen being bankrupt. Is it that bad?' Lindsay was nervous as she asked that, she hoped Aston would deny it, but he sighed and shot her a quick look.

'You'll have to ask Stephen that yourself.'

'Does that mean he is, but you'd rather not admit it?'

'It means that Stephen spoke to me in confidence and I can't repeat the details of what he told me.' Aston spoke gently but in a firm tone. 'I know you're very concerned, but the firm is Stephen's business, you really must talk to him, Lindsay.'

She was quiet for a moment, then she said

uncertainly, 'Did he ask you for help, Aston?'
She saw his frown and added hurriedly: 'Please
don't think I'm pressuring you—I have a reason
for asking, believe me.' If Stephen had been
desperate enough to ask Aston for help, Daniel
might be telling the truth.

Aston sighed. 'Purely as a hypothetical case,
Lindsay, even if Stephen had asked me for help I
wouldn't be in any position to give him the sort
of help he would need if he was in danger of
going bankrupt.' He spoke very slowly and
carefully, choosing his words. 'My capital is all
tied up in my shops, I don't have any spare
money floating around.'

'I understand,' Lindsay said flatly.

'Randall would be a much better prospect,'
said Aston, pulling up near the Mayfair brasserie
at which they had booked a table. He turned to
look at her, an arm draped over the wheel. 'He
has the money, but Stephen would have to watch
out for the strings attached to it.'

'Yes,' Lindsay agreed with bitterness.

Aston stared at her. 'And so would you,
Lindsay. He struck me as a very possessive guy,
he didn't like me at all, did he? For an ex-
husband he shows far too much interest in you.'

He had said something like that to her already,
she could see her protests hadn't convinced him
that she was indifferent to Daniel. Pushing a
curling lock of her vivid hair from her flushed
face, she said defiantly: 'Daniel Randall sees
women as objects, and if they've belonged to him,
they're his property even if he rarely sees them.
His vanity wouldn't let him see them any other

way. If he came on like a possessive husband in front of you, that was to make sure you know I'd been his . . .'

'And still were?' Aston murmured, watching her.

'No way.' Lindsay met his eyes levelly. 'He's part of my past, nothing more. I've locked him away with the old photos and theatre programmes.'

'He seems to have escaped,' Aston commented drily, and she laughed, relaxing.

'Houdini is his middle name.'

'So long as you can laugh at him,' he shrugged. 'If you took him seriously, he'd be quite alarming, I should think.'

'Understatement is your forte,' Lindsay agreed. 'Oh, don't talk about him, let's enjoy ourselves and forget Daniel exists.'

'I'll drink to that,' said Aston, getting out of the car, his rugged face alight with dry amusement.

They walked into the restaurant together, talking, and the head waiter came over to greet them politely but without warmth. The place was crowded, every table seemed to be taken, but when Aston mentioned his name the man inclined his head. 'Your table is ready, Mr Hill. Would you like to have a drink at the bar first or . . .'

Aston glanced at her. 'Want a drink, or shall we go to the table right away?'

'We'll go straight in,' said Lindsay, and they followed the head waiter through the closely set tables a moment later. A group was playing on a

tiny dais at one end of the room, their blend of
traditional jazz kept low so that it didn't interfere
with the conversations of clients. As she walked
past tables, Lindsay saw any number of familiar
faces, the restaurant was a popular night spot
with film and stage people.

The head waiter seated her and Aston at a
small table in a corner of the room. A blue glass
vase holding a white carnation and a spray of
feathery fern occupied the centre of the table, and
Lindsay glanced up to smile at Aston. 'Pretty,
isn't it?' she said, and as her eyes moved away
from his amused face she found herself looking at
Daniel. He was sitting at a table on the far side of
the room and he was watching her with an
impassive face. Lindsay felt her face freeze, she
looked away quickly, but not before she had
noticed the girl sitting opposite him. She was tiny
and blonde and very pretty, she was also a
familiar face from television since she was one of
the stars in a current soap opera. Lindsay both
recognised her and was surprised, she looked
much smaller and more human in that atmosphere. In that one quick glance, Lindsay took in
the stunning red silk dress she wore, the carefully
casual chic of her hair-style and the fascinated
glow with which she was talking to Daniel. She
felt her heart constrict as she looked away.

'Aperitif, madame?' the head waiter was
asking.

She forced herself to concentrate. 'Oh, yes,
thank you, I'll have a glass of white wine—
Sauternes, I think.' She accepted the large menu
he handed her and he bent forward to recommend

several of the dishes which were the speciality of the house. Lindsay tried to listen, smiling too tightly. She couldn't keep her mind on food while Daniel sat there, one brown hand lying casually on the white tablecloth only an inch away from the blonde girl's fingers. She could see the two hands out of the corner of her eye, she didn't want to watch them but she couldn't help herself.

What was Daniel doing there with that girl? Lindsay couldn't even remember her name, she only knew her face, like everybody else she had watched the soap opera now and then. The girl was too pretty for their relationship to be anything to do with business.

Of course, a girl like that would be a feather in his cap; everyone would recognise her and envy him. Lindsay had never liked the soap opera much, herself, the character the girl played was bitchy, and silly into the bargain, and from the way she was turning on charm for Daniel she didn't need to do much acting, either. Risking another quick look, Lindsay was rewarded by seeing Daniel's hand touching the other girl's now. Her teeth set and she looked back at the menu fixedly.

'Seen something you like?' Aston asked, and she looked up at him, her eyes wide and startled.

'What?' He had his back to Daniel, she didn't think he had noticed him.

'On the menu,' said Aston, laughing. 'What did you think I meant? I hope you haven't been smitten by some famous star at another table, I wouldn't want to be forced into drastic action to get rid of him.' He put out a hand and took hers, raised it to his lips and kissed it softly. 'I can be possessive, too.'

She smiled at him and felt Daniel's eyes on them, but refused to look in his direction again, angry with herself for the brief, agonising stab of jealousy she had felt as she saw him touch the other girl's hand. She wouldn't let herself care, hadn't she learnt even now that Daniel Randall refused to belong to anybody? Tonight he was here with a blonde, tomorrow he would be with someone else. It was none of her business, thank heavens, he could date a whole harem and she wouldn't care!

'I'm having difficulty choosing, it all reads like a poem.'

'The chef is a very good,' Aston agreed. 'That's why it's so popular.'

'Crowded, isn't it?' Lindsay let her eyes move around the room, being careful not to look towards Daniel's table. 'I can see why it takes all evening to be served.'

She let her gaze drift casually over Daniel and felt her throat close up in agitation at the expression in those hard, grey eyes. He looked grim, his jaw taut, his mouth straight, and Lindsay was angrily pleased, she felt a fierce rush of satisfaction at knowing that Daniel was not pleased to see her with Aston. It might only be a dog-in-the-manger sense of possession because she had been his wife, but at least he wasn't indifferent, and despite the melting smiles of his blonde companion his attention was on what was happening at Lindsay's table rather than his own. Lindsay liked that, she smiled at Aston over her menu.

'I think I'll start with the Waldorf salad,' she said. 'I like this place, it's fun.'

'Good,' said Aston, his eyes wrinkling in amusement. 'I told you we would enjoy ourselves, didn't I?'

'So you did,' Lindsay agreed. 'And that's just what I mean to do . . .' And then she had a twinge of conscience about him, because she knew she was far more interested in scoring off Daniel than she was in Aston. Keeping her eyes firmly on Aston's face, she asked: 'How are your sister's twins? They must be nearly two by now, or is it three?'

'Three,' he said, smiling, and settled down to talk about his family while she listened intently, and did not allow herself to look away. Why couldn't she fall in love with Aston? He was a fantastic man, the nicest she knew, he was funny and kind and attractive, and she ought to be mad about him, anyone with any sense would adore him. An intelligent girl wouldn't even be aware there was any other man in the room; certainly not one who was selfish, egotistic, totally ruthless and hadn't a scruple to his name.

CHAPTER SIX

DANIEL rang her the following evening. She had spent the day with Aston, in the country, and had barely got back into her flat when the phone rang. The weather had been gorgeous all day, Lindsay had sunbathed in a tiny white bikini, and her skin had that tight, warm glow the sun leaves, she felt lazy and relaxed, she was still smiling after Aston's parting remark. Aston always made her smile, and today he had helped her to banish Daniel from her mind, but as she picked up the phone Daniel sprang back again like the Demon King in a pantomime, scattering her thoughts.

'Where the hell have you been all day?' he demanded without telling her who it was—not that he needed to, Lindsay knew at once from the first syllable. 'I've been ringing since early this morning—did you spend the night with him?'

'Hallo, Daniel,' she said while she tried to gather herself together, then could have kicked herself. It would have been much better to say: 'Who *is* that?'

'Did you?' Daniel repeated, his voice harsh.

'Did I what?' she fenced.

'You haven't been at home all day, where have you been? I told you I was going to ring you.'

'I spent the day visiting Aston's sister, she lives in the country. It's a long drive, Aston picked me up at eight o'clock this morning.'

'Visiting his sister? How cosy—his intentions must be serious.' Daniel's voice held a sneer.

'You sound like a Victorian father.' Two could play at that game, if Daniel wanted to turn nasty Lindsay was more than happy to do the same.

'Can he lend Stephen enough to keep the factory going?' Daniel put a bite into that question and Lindsay winced. She didn't answer and after a brief silence, Daniel asked: 'Well, have you thought over my offer?'

'I've tried not to think about it at all,' she muttered, and he laughed shortly.

'I'm sure you have.'

'It's too disgusting!' Lindsay spat that at him, her hand gripping the phone so tightly that her knuckles turned white.

'Take it or leave it,' Daniel shrugged. 'Stephen's your brother, he isn't mine, nobody does anything without getting something back.' He sounded brisk and businesslike and she hated him, then his voice deepened and darkened. 'And Aston Hill's out of the picture, for a start,' he added. 'I don't want him around in future.'

Lindsay thought of the blonde actress he had been with last night and her skin burned with fury. 'You're not dictating my life to me—I had enough of that when we were married!'

'Up to you,' Daniel said tersely. 'If Stephen hasn't paid back that bank loan by next Friday he'll have to liquidate. You have until Thursday to decide.' He slammed the phone down and she jerked as her eardrum rang with the noise. She put back her own receiver, her hand fumbling, trembling, then looked at her watch. It was gone

nine, too late to ring Stephen. She would have to
talk to him tomorrow, he should have recovered a
little by then.

When she got to her office next day she found her
boss lying back in his chair with his feet on the
table and his eyes closed, his face turned towards
the sunshine streaming in at the window. Chris
was a calm, lazy man who moved very rarely and
when he did performed each action with the
considered grace of a two-toed sloth. Small,
slightly built, with smooth blond hair and bright
blue eyes, he would have been exceptionally
good-looking if it had not been for that lack of
vitality. His face was happy but distinctly
unimpressive.

'Busy as usual, I see,' Lindsay remarked,
standing in the doorway of his office and
watching him with resigned amusement.

Chris opened one eye to observe her. He
flapped a welcoming hand, 'Hi.' The effort of
speech apparently exhausted him, his eye closed
and he sank back into golden slumber.

'Have those stills come yet?' Lindsay asked,
cruelly insisting that he should make some
pretence of working.

The hand flapped at his desk. She saw a large
brown envelope lying on it and went over to pick
it up, shooting a small pile of glossy photographs
on to the desk. She leaned over, a hand propping
her up, and spread them out, recognising some
faces, looking at others with curiosity. Most of
the girls in the photographs were models, some
were actresses, and over the month Lindsay and

Chris had seen hundreds of different girls without feeling that any one of them was the girl they were looking for, the girl whose face would fit an image they wanted.

Vivons were about to launch a new range of cosmetics and they wanted someone very special to appear in their advertising campaign. The managing director of the firm had begun to be impatient, because so far they hadn't come up with what he called 'The Face.'

'It's hopeless, Charles won't go for any of these,' Lindsay said gloomily. 'They don't say a thing to *me*—what about you?'

Chris turned a thumb downwards without opening his eyes. He didn't waste time or energy in pointless discussion, yet he always managed to get what he wanted, although Lindsay often wondered how he did it. Whatever magic he performed, he did it when nobody was looking. Every time you saw him he seemed to be asleep, but Vivons would have fought tooth and nail to keep him if another firm tried to steal him away.

'Perhaps we're going about this the wrong way,' said Lindsay, sitting down on the edge of the desk and swinging her legs. 'We're waiting for The Face to come and find us, maybe we should go out and find her.'

Chris opened both eyes, they looked at her, so blue they sparkled like clear sapphires, and she stared into them, raising her brows.

'What do you think?'

'Keep talking,' Chris encouraged, shifting very slightly in his chair and crossing his feet. He almost always wore jeans and a thin, tightly fitting shirt open at the neck and worn without a tie. Shoes were his one extravagance, he had them hand-made for him because his feet were incredibly small and thin for a man and he could never get mass-produced shoes that fitted. Today he was wearing soft, supple blue leather, so velvety it made you want to stroke it.

'Why don't we draw up a list of what we're looking for? Should she be brunette or . . .'

'Blonde,' Chris decided. 'With the sexy, sweet look of a Marilyn Monroe, we don't want to put women off buying the range, they've got to like her, want to look like her.' For him that was an enormously long statement. He had obviously been thinking about it, he knew precisely what he was looking for, Lindsay should have known he wasn't just haphazard in his search.

'Why do you let me talk myself into looking silly?' she asked wryly. 'You had it all worked out already, didn't you? Why didn't you tell all the agencies you were looking for a sexy blonde? Then they wouldn't keep showering us with girls we can't use?'

'One of them might be perfect,' he said, his wide mouth amused. 'A brunette we can always dye into a blonde, it's the face that matters, not the hair colour,' he yawned, running a hand through his hair. 'I'll know her when I see her.'

The phone rang and Lindsay picked it up, listened, then handed it to Chris. 'Charles,' she mouthed.

He cradled the phone on his thin shoulder. 'Hi, Charles,' he murmured. Lindsay shuffled through the photographs again, her eyes almost blurring with boredom. The girls were all so beautiful, so perfectly packaged, so plastic—when you had seen one you had seen them all, she found it hard to distinguish one from another. Vivons did not a want a girl people couldn't remember, they wanted someone whose face made people rush out to buy their cosmetics.

'Not yet,' said Chris. 'But we'll find her, don't worry.'

Lindsay slid off the desk and went over to the window to stare down at the street below. London hummed and roared all around them, the roads thick with traffic, the buildings throbbing with noise and people. Somewhere out there was the girl they were looking for, but how could they find her when the agencies kept coming up with the same girls everybody used? They wanted someone new, someone with immediate impact, someone so special she focused the eye and held it.

'Don't flap,' Chris said lazily. 'Charles, just leave it with me—I'll come up with the right girl in time.'

A moment later he put the phone down and Lindsay turned to look at him wryly. He smiled and closed his eyes.

London was sweltering in heat all day, Lindsay found it hard to concentrate, her thin yellow cotton dress was sticking to her and every time she moved she felt perspiration trickle down her spine. Chris was in apparent hibernation, whenever she went into his office she found him in the same position, eyes shut, body limp. For once she felt like following suit, it was much too hot to work, but somebody had to keep the routine jobs going and from the start Chris had made it plain that that was what she was there for; he needed a girl who could carry his workload as well as her own. At times she had resented doing two people's work, but now she realised that in his way Chris was a genius; his methods were his own, but they succeeded, which, in that business, was all that counted, so Lindsay worked on without complaining.

By the time she left the office that evening she was exhausted, her spirits as flat as a pancake. She took the tube to Stephen's nearest station, feeling sticky and grubby and dying for a long, cold shower. First, though, she must talk to Stephen.

Alice opened the door to her. She was wearing jeans, a T-shirt and a printed plastic apron, and her face was flushed.

'Oh, it's you,' she said, moving back to let Lindsay walk past.

'Hot, isn't it?' Lindsay could hear the children playing in the garden, their voices cheerful. She walked into the kitchen. Alice had been chopping cucumber, the smell of it filled the air. 'How's Stephen?' Lindsay asked, lowering her voice as Alice joined her and closed the door.

'He's in the garage working on his car,' said Alice.

'Is he okay?' Lindsay wasn't sure how to talk to Alice, her sister-in-law seemed rather aggressive today, it wasn't like her.

'I wouldn't know,' said Alice, picking up her small kitchen knife and chopping with noisy conviction.

'Oh,' Lindsay said, watching her in dismay. People were acting out of character all round her, she didn't know this Alice whose face had set like concrete and who was slicing the cucumber as though she was guillotining an enemy.

'I'm not talking to him,' Alice told her, chop, chop. 'If you want to know how he is, better ask him.' Chop, chop. 'He doesn't confide in me, I'm only his wife.' Having despatched the cucumber she looked around for something else to use her knife on; so Lindsay decided to leave and talk to Stephen. It seemed wiser.

He was inside his car bonnet, only his legs visible. 'Hallo,' Lindsay said to them, and Stephen turned his head to peer.

'Oh, hello, Lindsay, when did you get here? Have you been into the house?'

'Alice is getting the supper,' Lindsay told him. 'I think.' Either that or the cucumber-chopping was therapy, she thought. Stephen extricated himself from the bonnet, wiping his hands on a filthy piece of rag. She watched him, trying to read his expression, which wasn't difficult, he looked drained and pale and quite hopeless.

'I wanted to talk to you,' she told him, and he nodded.

'I'm sorry Alice dragged you into all this . . .'

'Don't be silly, you're my brother, of course I'm concerned. I'm glad she did ring me.'

'I should have rung her earlier, don't think I don't know that, I just couldn't think of anything to say to her.' Stephen kept on wiping his hands as though trying to erase more than the stain of black oil, and Lindsay felt like crying. He looked so defeated.

'How bad is it?' she asked tentatively, and he grimaced, his eyes down.

'I'm wiped out.' He flung the rag into the back seat of the car and closed the bonnet, still without looking at her.

'Have you tried ...' she began, and Stephen turned those weary eyes on her, their rims pink as though he had been crying. Her stomach turned over and she bit the inside of her lip.

'I've tried everything I can think of,' he said. 'Short of a miracle, I've had it—know any good miracle-workers?'

'Daniel,' she began, and Stephen laughed curtly.

'Has too much hard-headed business sense to be bothered with me. Do you think that didn't occur to me? No, I'll have to declare myself bankrupt, sell up everything and get a job.' He paused, his body wrenched by a deep sigh. 'If I can, if anyone will employ me—I know I wouldn't.' He walked round the car and Lindsay followed slowly. She had never expected to feel so deeply worried about Stephen, he had always been the one who worried about her; now their positions had been reversed and it made her feel uncertain of herself, she wasn't sure how to handle the situation, how to talk to him.

'Don't do anything in a hurry,' she said to his back. 'Wait for a few days ...'

'Don't tell me something may turn up,' Stephen muttered. 'I can do without the bromides.' He opened the front door. From the kitchen they heard Alice talking to the children in a brisk, no-nonsense voice. Stephen sighed again. 'She's furious with me, and I can't blame her. I should have told her, but I just couldn't face it. I didn't have the guts.'

'She'll forgive you,' Lindsay assured him, hoping she was right.

'We'll have to leave this house, it will have to go,' he said. 'Alice will hate that, she loves this place.'

The kitchen door opened and he stopped talking. Alice ignored him, looking at Lindsay. 'Are you staying for supper?' It was very far from being an invitation and Lindsay hurriedly pretended to smile.

'I'd have loved to,' she lied. 'But I've got a date, I just called in to see how Stephen was.' Alice's face was stony; that remark didn't go down at all well. 'I must rush,' Lindsay added quickly, gave her brother a quick kiss on the cheek and fled. She felt resentful as she made her way back to her own flat. Alice was being very unsympathetic, why was she punishing Stephen when it must be so obvious that he was miserable? Lindsay had been angry with her brother herself, while he was missing, she had understood then why Alice was so angry, but face to face with Stephen's helpless defeat, how could Alice go on being unkind to him?

When she got home, she stripped and had a cool shower, washing away the city dust and stale perspiration of the day, her thirsty skin drinking in the water through every pore. She towelled her hair lightly, slipped into a short white towelling

robe and padded into the kitchen. It was far too
hot to eat, she decided, looking into the fridge.
She got herself a long, cool drink and went into
the sitting-room, flinging herself down on the
couch with a sigh.

What was she going to do? If she had ever
had any hope that Daniel was lying it had
evaporated in the face of Stephen's despair. She
couldn't let her brother's firm and home be
taken away from him if she could stop it, she
owed Stephen too much; he had carried the
burden of managing their home for years, he
hadn't married until Lindsay herself had married, all his life he had been strong, responsible,
hard-working. Now he needed her help—how
could she refuse it?

As she sipped her drink the phone rang and she
started nervously, almost swallowing a piece of
ice. Putting down the glass, she went over to pick
up the phone.

'Hallo?' Her voice sounded low and wary, she
was afraid it would be Daniel, and she was only
too right.

'Thought about it yet?'

A flare of rage went through her. 'I thought
you gave me until Thursday to make up my
mind?'

'Just making sure you don't forget about it,' he
said mockingly.

'As if I was likely to!'

'You have a genius for forgetting things,' he
said, and the words carried a heavy load of
sarcasm. There was a pause, then he asked drily:
'No date tonight? Or is Hill there?'

'No, he isn't,' Lindsay snapped, then wished she had lied—Aston made a good cover, but she hated herself for using him as one. Quickly she said: 'But he may come round later.' It was true enough, Aston had said he might call in at the flat some time that evening. He was having dinner with one of his suppliers, if the evening ended early Aston would try to get to see her, but if the other man felt like talking for hours over drinks, Aston wouldn't make it.

'You looked very pretty last night,' Daniel said softly, and she felt a shudder run down her spine. 'That dress suits you, green is your colour, it makes your eyes look brighter.' His voice seemed to stroke her skin, she despised herself for trembling.

'I'm surprised you noticed—you seemed too busy looking into your girl-friend's eyes. How did you pick her up? Don't tell me you've started manufacturing soap?'

'Miaow,' he mocked, laughing, and she was furious with herself for coming on like a jealous woman.

'I met her to talk business,' Daniel said, and Lindsay laughed angrily.

'You don't expect me to believe that? Nobody talks business with a blonde sex kitten over a lengthy dinner.'

'Carolyn used to model for us before she went into acting,' he told her. 'We're trying to persuade her to do some more work.'

'What sort?' Lindsay asked sarcastically. 'And where? The bedroom, by any chance? Auditioning her last night, were you?'

'Careful,' he drawled. 'Your claws are showing, pussycat.'

Lindsay flung the phone down and walked away. The angry exchange had been bitterly familiar, how many times had she heard herself sniping at him like that over some other girl? She had never seemed able to stop herself, the jealousy had sprung up inside her and she had been shaking with it, she had wanted to scream, hit him, slap the other girl. When they were alone the black emotion had come pouring out of her, and only afterwards when she had calmed down had she been able to think clearly. Then she had felt sick, ashamed, shabby, and she had hated herself.

She wrapped her arms around her body, bent over, fighting the stabbing knives of misery that were tearing at her. Her jealousy had ruined her marriage, she had been so uncertain of herself, of Daniel, she hadn't been able to believe he could really love her and she had despised herself. The intensity of her feelings for him left her scared, she was terrified that someone else would take him away from her. She was so ordinary, so young and unsophisticated, how could she hope to hold a man like him? Every time he looked at anyone else, every time another woman looked at him, fear had tormented her. She had told herself that Daniel had only married her because she wouldn't sleep with him, and she had waited for him to wander away to fresh woods and pastures new. She knew the sort of life he had led before they married, he was far too attractive to be content with one woman, she knew he must be bored with her.

It had been so easy to convince herself, their marriage hadn't a hope of success from the start. When she left him, she hated him for the pain she had suffered for months, the pain which refused to die down even after their divorce, but over the past year she had managed to evict him from her mind. It hadn't been easy, some nights she had wallowed in grief only to get up next day and despise herself for giving way to an outworn emotion. Aston had helped, dating him had given her other things to think about. Why had fate brought Daniel Randall back into her life?

She finished her drink and watched a programme on TV to take her mind off Daniel. Aston didn't show up, presumably his supplier had had other plans. At ten o'clock, Lindsay went to bed and lay in the darkness giving herself a stern lecture. She was not going to get involved with Daniel Randall again. He was bad for her, it made her ill to feel jealous, and if she let herself think about him she would start being jealous of every girl he saw. She couldn't reach the source of her jealousy with her reason, it didn't respond to logic; it was bitter, obsessive, destructive, and she refused to let it take her over again.

Chris didn't arrive at the office next morning until after eleven. He wandered in, sleek and lithe in his usual jeans and shirt, moving at his normal pace and Lindsay glanced up from a desk covered with paper. 'Good heavens, don't say you've decided to do some work?'

He sleepily propped himself against her door. 'Anything happen?'

'The sky fell in, that's all.'

He surveyed her through lowered lids, un-excited. 'Any casualties?'

'Charles rang. He sounded like a man in a state of panic. He wanted to know when you meant to get off your chair and do something to find The Face.'

'Did he ask where I was?'

'What do you think?' Lindsay leaned back in her chair and smiled at him. 'I told him you were out hunting for the girl of his dreams.'

Chris put two fingers to his lips and blew her a kiss, and she laughed, shaking her head at him.

'He also asked if you'd have lunch with him,' she pointed out. 'So that he could harangue you on the subject for a few hours.'

'What did you tell him?'

'That I thought you had an appointment.'

'So I do,' said Chris, ruffling his blond hair thoughtfully as he stared at her. 'And so do you, my angel.'

'Do I?' She leaned over to flick open her desk diary. 'I haven't written it down—who with?'

'Me,' he said. 'We're going to have a long, quiet lunch and put our thinking caps on . . .'

'I thought you had yours on already,' she said, glancing down at the pile of work she had in front of her. 'Chris, I've got to get all this stuff done.' She had been working flat out since nine o'clock that morning, but she didn't seem to have made any dent in the work which had been piling up in her in-tray for days. None of it was urgent, which was why she had left it untouched for so long, but it had to be done sooner or later, and she was in the right mood to be efficient.

'It can wait,' Chris said as he strolled away. Lindsay glared after him—that was the motto he lived by, everything could wait and usually did. What was amazing was that he got away with it. Problems he left unsolved seemed to solve themselves, letters that didn't get written ceased to be necessary, people he ignored went away without complaining. He was just born lucky, she decided.

'Lady on the phone, came out in a rash after using Moonglow Seventy-Nine,' her secretary said on the intercom, and, sighing, Lindsay picked up the phone, her voice automatically becoming soothing, horrified, sympathetic.

She had no sooner put down the phone again than her door opened and one of Vivons sales team came in to complain about the way complaints were handled by the office. 'I'm sick of promising we'd look into it,' he said, perching on her desk and picking up her pen. She watched him doodling with it on a spare piece of paper as he talked.

'I'll give the complaints section a talking-to,' she promised.

'Don't forget,' he said, sliding off the desk. He looked at her with appreciation and gave a coaxing grin. 'Have lunch with me and we'll discuss it further.'

'Sorry, I have a date.' Lindsay put out her hand. 'Thank you.'

He was putting her pen into his jacket pocket. Blankly, he said:'What?'

'Pen,' she said.

'Oh, sorry, just habit,' he said, handing the pen

back with his eyes on the smooth curve of her figure from her high, rounded breasts to her slim hips. He backed out, talking and staring. Lindsay made a face at the door after it had shut behind him. He had a fantastic sales record, buyers ate out of his hand, and she could see why: he responded to women like a man in a desert spotting an oasis, and most buyers working with cosmetics were women, it was not a male territory. Lindsay found it irritating to try to work with a man who couldn't stop looking at her figure. Given half a chance, he would use his hands as well as his eyes, he was a bottom pincher and an arm fondler. Her secretary came in, flushed, and wailed: 'I'm black and blue! I should get danger money!'

'Sorry, Ann,' said Lindsay, laughing. 'Next time he comes in, keep the desk between you,' and Ann said she would remember that.

Lindsay dictated several letters, read a few of the snarling memos which their managing director was fond of despatching around the building, then tried to get back to her paperwork, only to have Chris saunter in and ask: 'Coming?'

'It isn't lunchtime already!' she protested, looking at her watch. It was almost one o'clock. 'Where's the morning gone?' Lindsay moaned, pushing back her chair and getting up. 'I haven't done anything!'

'You should be organised,' Chris told her. 'Like me.' He yawned, his thumbs in his jeans back pockets, and she eyed him with suppressed fury. A lot of the paperwork she was wading through should have gone to him, but if it had, he would have dealt with it by the simple method of screwing it up and chucking it into the nearest wastepaper basket.

'I'm going to the cloakroom,' she announced with dignity, and walked out. The office was almost empty, everyone else had gone to lunch, only the office junior remained at her desk, eating an apple and drinking a low-calorie orange juice.

As Chris and Lindsay left five minutes later, the girl smiled at them, gazing at Chris with wide-eyed eagerness. Everyone in the office liked him, he had a smile for everyone, but then they didn't have to do his work for him, they didn't have to run around in his wake dealing with all the problems Chris decided to ignore.

He took her to lunch at a small back-street restaurant that took its time over serving you and didn't seem to mind how long you took to eat your meal. The menu was limited and Italian, groaning with calories. Lindsay skipped past the tempting pasta and ordered melon, then chose a main course of chicken with a side salad. Chris ate his way through a banquet, rich in sauces and highly spiced, but then he always did eat without caring about calories and got away with it. He was as thin as a rake, it wasn't fair.

Sighing, Lindsay slowly ate her melon while Chris twirled spaghetti on his fork. 'This is delicious, you should have had some,' he told her.

She averted her eyes. 'Are we really going to discuss The Face? Have you had any new ideas?'

'I'm hoping some will come,' he said, his eye roving over the other tables. 'What we want is a new face . . .'

'Someone who isn't a professional model, you mean?' Lindsay asked, and he looked back her, blue eyes blazing.

'Why not?' he stopped talking, stared at her fixedly. 'Like you,' he said. 'You're the sort of girl I'm looking for—a girl with a vital, alive face, someone special but not artificial.'

Lindsay laughed, her green eyes vivid with amusement. 'You'll never sell that idea to Charles, he'll send you to the funny farm.'

Chris put down his fork, his face alight. 'I'm serious, I just looked at you properly and you're terrific. Bone structure sensational, eyes beautifully spaced, good nose . . .'

'Hey, do you mind?' She was beginning to get alarmed, she did not like being analysed feature by feature, even though Chris was being heavily flattering. She knew he was using only the best butter, he didn't mean those things, and it made her feel uncomfortable.

'Sexy mouth,' he said, taking no notice. 'Nice rounded chin, slim neck.'

'Stop it!' she protested, very flushed, then, as his eyes moved lower and he opened his mouth, 'I mean it—you can stop right there.' She did not want to hear his description of her breasts, the way he was looking at her made her feel like a slave on the auction block, she objected to his stare and his personal comments.

'What's the matter?' he asked, all innocence. The blue eyes were open and frank, smiling at her. 'I'm perfectly serious.'

'Don't be so ridiculous,' Lindsay muttered.

'It came to me in a flash,' said Chris, looking

quite excited for him. 'I looked at you and I knew
. . . you're The Face.'

CHAPTER SEVEN

'I DON'T think that's funny,' Lindsay said.

Chris leaned towards her, his fingertips drumming on the table. 'But don't you see—it could be you? It could be her.' he flung out a hand at the small, dark waitress who was serving the next table. 'It could be that tall blonde over there. It could be anyone.'

She relaxed. 'Well, obviously . . .'

'Hang on,' he said impatiently. 'I haven't finished my point. We're not looking for a professional model, we're looking for an ordinary girl. So where do we look?'

Lindsay thought, frowning. 'Well, I suppose . . .' She hadn't got a clue.

'We run a competition,' Chris said triumphantly.

Her mouth parted on a gasp, and he laughed at her expression, nodding.

'That's right, a competition,' he repeated. 'For our girl, The Face, the girl who could be anyone in the country.' He was talking faster than she had ever heard him talk before, his words tumbling over each other to get out. 'Anyone who wants to enter will have to buy one of our products to get an entry form. They have to send in their photograph and . . .'

'My God!' Lindsay had caught fire from him, she was so staggered she couldn't think of anything else to say, so she said: 'My God!' again, and he laughed, highly delighted.

'Think Charles will like it?'

'He'll eat it,' she said without a shred of doubt. 'It will be terrific publicity, it will sell products like hot cakes and we'll get an entirely new face out of it, someone special is bound to be thrown up by a campaign like that.' She looked at him with admiration. 'You're a genius!'

Chris relapsed into his normal torpor, smiling lazily. 'You've noticed at last! I wondered how long it would take for the light to dawn.'

'Did it just come to you in a flash?' Lindsay asked curiously. 'I mean . . . just now? Did you really just think it up or . . .'

'I've had it hovering around my mind,' he admitted. 'Ideas are like that sometimes, you just catch a glimpse of them out of the corner of your mind's eye, then they're gone, but if you sit round without worrying and wait—they come back.'

'So that's what you're doing for most of the day,' she said drily. 'Just waiting for ideas. I've often wondered.'

'Nasty,' he said, grinning.

'Finish your spaghetti,' she advised. 'You've deserved it. You ought to eat fish, really, for brain power.'

'Spaghetti works even better,' Chris assured her, turning his attention to his plate.

They walked back to the office in brilliant sunshine, waves of heat coming up from the pavements, the cars driving past giving off metallic flashes of reflected light. Charles was going to be over the moon, thought Lindsay. Chris had come up with his best idea ever.

All that afternoon she was caught up in the maelstrom which Chris's brainwave had caused. She didn't have a chance to do any of the routine work, she was too busy discussing the details of the campaign with Charles and the other top executives of the company. Chris always left such minor matters to other people. Having done his part, he collapsed in a chair like a rag doll and smiled beatifically on them, saying almost nothing. Nobody minded, he could do no wrong today.

While she talked and listened, Lindsay's mind kept wandering away to the subject that was engrossing her secret attention, but she refused to let herself dwell on Daniel's proposition. He had given her until Thursday to make a decision, and it was already Tuesday, which left her only two days. Every time she faced that fact, she felt an icy dart of anxiety. He had left her without options, she couldn't think of any way of saving Stephen from bankruptcy. Glancing at Chris, she wished she had his inspiration—she could do with a brainwave herself.

If Daniel had walked out on her, he wouldn't want to hurt and humiliate her now, but she had committed the unforgivable sin by walking out on him. He might have lost interest in her, he might have regretted getting married at all, but his ego couldn't take the shock of having her end their marriage. That had been Daniel's privilege, his choice—he had decided to marry her in the first place and he felt aggrieved because she had had the temerity to leave him.

Lindsay had no doubts about his motives. He was using her brother as a weapon against her. He must hate her, she thought, staring at the ceiling. It hurt, she felt cold and on the point of tears, but however she felt she still had to make up her mind what to do, and there was no one she could confide in, it would be too painful to tell anyone. This was one decision she had to make alone, without advice.

Aston rang just before she left the office. 'I'm working late tonight, but tomorrow should be an easier day. Could we have dinner?'

'Love to,' Lindsay said warmly. She wished she dared tell him about Daniel's blackmail, but what could he do?

'Miss you,' he said softly and she smiled.

'Same here. Don't work too hard. I'll see you tomorrow.'

'I'll pick you up at the flat at seven,' he said before ringing off. Lindsay put down the phone, sighing. She made her way home in the rush-hour traffic, her clothes sticking to her again, the heatwave showed no sign of diminishing. People were irritable, impatient, flushed, many of them showing signs of sun-worship, their faces and arms reddened. Men were in shirt-sleeves, tie-less. Women were in thin summer dresses, their legs bare. Lindsay wondered if she looked the way they did; her skin beaded with perspiration, her eyes tired, her movements lethargic. That was how she felt, she had no energy at all, she just wanted to flop out and keep still. This was no weather to be in a city, she longed to be on a beach.

When she got back to the flat she showered and put on a brief white cotton tunic cut on simple lines; the neck low and rounded, the hem just above her knees and the sides split for easy movement. It had a Grecian look, she had bought it in Athens on a holiday a year ago but had rarely worn it because the cotton was so thin it was more like gauze and totally transparent. It was not a dress she could wear to the office or in the streets, but it was perfect for relaxing in weather like this; the filmy material floated around her as she walked, she felt free and at ease.

She had a glass of lime-juice and a tiny salad, then lay on the couch listening to Spanish guitar music.

The doorbell went, and her heart skipped a beat, then hammered inside her ribcage, making her feel sick. She stumbled to the floor, dropping her book. She knew who it was before she got to the front door of the flat and opened it—every instinct shrieked a warning.

He leaned against the door; very tall and powerful, a lean-hipped, unsmiling man with narrowed grey eyes that openly took in every detail of her appearance, travelling from her curling, still damp hair to the quivering curve of her pink lips, down over the curve of her body in the far too revealing, gauzy dress. Lindsay bore that look with nervous defiance, her chin up.

'I'm busy!'

Daniel smiled with dry sarcasm and walked past her with such cool confidence that she made no attempt to stop him. Closing the door slowly, she followed and found him standing in the sitting-room, looking at the book on the floor, the empty glass. Without a word he went over to the record player and lifted the arm. The guitar music stopped mid-beat.

'Do you mind? You've got a nerve!' Lindsay burst out, and he turned to survey her with a crooked little smile.

'I like the dress.' But it wasn't at the dress that he was looking, it was at what was under it, and Lindsay felt her skin burn. Helplessly, she wished she had put on something else, she might as well be naked.

'What's the matter?' Daniel mocked, watching her with eyes which pinned her to the spot.

'What do you want?' she asked shakily, and he laughed.

'Care to re-phrase the question?'

'Aren't you witty?' she muttered, hating him. 'You know what I mean—why are you here?'

'I can't keep away from you,' said Daniel with the same mockery, and her temper flared.

'You've managed it for two years!'

His smile hardened and the grey eyes were fierce with an emotion she couldn't decipher. 'I wasn't coming crawling after you on my knees.'

Her throat tightened. 'What's different now?' she flung back at him, refusing to believe the force she heard in his voice.

'Now it's going to be you on your knees,' he said through his teeth, his eyes harsh, and she went cold from head to foot. 'I only deal on my own terms,' Daniel added. 'You didn't think I'd accept yours? You left me, I wasn't chasing after you, but now you'll come back knowing I own you.'

What he was saying came as no real surprise to her, she knew she had wounded his ego and she knew Daniel's pride was monolithic, his sense of himself impenetrable, unshakable, but hearing him state his hostility so openly made her tremble in shock.

'You can't own human beings,' she stammered, nevertheless, holding her head up and refusing to betray the fear which had swallowed her.

His eyes flashed with bitter humour. 'Can't you? That depends on your definition of ownership. If you want to save your brother's neck, you'll come back to me, and on my terms.'

She was so angry her teeth were chattering. 'You're crazy,' she said. 'You won't get much enjoyment out of forcing me to . . .'

'Won't I?' he asked, moving with a speed that made her jump in alarm.

She didn't have time to escape, the next second he had one arm around her while the other forced up her chin. Rigid and shaking, Lindsay looked into the hard grey eyes, her mouth dry.

'Don't,' she whispered, and Daniel's eyes glittered as he smiled in threat.

'That's one word you'll never use to me again.' His mouth came down on her lips, burning with a fever she felt leaping up inside herself, and it did not matter that his hunger was born out of hatred and a wish to humiliate her, the demand of the kiss was met by an answering demand in her, desire fountained inside her body and she weakened in his arms, swaying towards him. Bending her backwards, Daniel slid his mouth down her throat and with closed eyes she trembled, a husky little moan breathed through her crushed lips. Behind her lids, light flashed and gleamed, she was dizzy and hot.

'You want me,' Daniel muttered, his mouth at the base of her throat, and she sighed, shuddering with pleasure, feeling his hand moving under the gauze, stroking the smooth flesh of her thigh.

Her arms went round his neck, she touched his hair, his nape, the muscled shoulders, her lips parted, aching for the touch of his mouth. Her mind had given up trying to think, she was in a state of weak confusion, the throb of desire in her body dominating her. Daniel's hands explored the naked flesh beneath her dress, caressing her warm breasts while she trembled, feeling the urgency inside him and knowing she felt it, too, a mounting need which grew with every movement of his hands. He was breathing quickly, thickly, she could hear his heart thudding in the same wild rhythm as her own.

She began to be frightened by the intensity of her feelings, a part of her standing aside like a voyeur, whispering mental warnings. She was letting Daniel have things all his own way, she was out of control, her mind had no part in what was happening. He was pulling the thin material down from her shoulders, bending his head to kiss the hardened nipples on her breasts, and that separated part of her protested, despised her for the husky little moans he was wringing out of her.

What had he just said? That she would never say no to him again? That would make her a puppet, without a mind of its own, and wasn't that how she was behaving now, moaning in abandoned excitement while he touched her?

This was not lovemaking, it was a deliberate, cynical manipulation of her body by a man who wanted to humiliate her, and she was playing the accomplice to her own destruction when if she had an ounce of self-respect she would stop him and throw him out of her life again.

She wrenched herself away, her breathing husky and impeded. Daniel stared at her and she stood facing him, trembling, her gauzy dress half off, her bare shoulders and breasts exposed.

'No,' she said, her hands clenched.

His eyes darkened, his jaw taut. 'That wasn't the message I was getting a moment ago. You wanted it . . .'

'No!' she said again, much louder, to drown what he was saying, to drown the feverish admission of her own body.

'What's the matter? Afraid Hill will walk in? Has a key, does he?' Daniel was angry enough now to grind the words out through teeth that barely parted, rage showed in the grey eyes.

'Aston has nothing to do with this!'

'Hasn't he?'

'It's you,' Lindsay said incoherently. 'I won't let you do this to me.'

'You're lying to yourself if you think I'm doing anything you don't want me to do,' he broke out angrily. 'You wanted me to make love to you. Oh, you'd have died rather than admit it to me, you prefer to get me to force you, don't you? Then you can tell yourself you weren't responsible, I made you do it, but that's a lie. I can have you any time I want you.'

'Get out!' she shouted, tension making her body shake.

'You've always had a frigid fear of sex,' he went on, ignoring her.

'I'm not frigid and I'm not afraid of sex, I don't have to be either to refuse to go to bed with you, you know!' Lindsay was insulted by his accusation.

'When we first met, you were practically walled in ice,' Daniel sneered. 'I had to chip my way through. I got frostbite just touching your hand.'

She was white. 'You bastard! I was only just out of school . . .'

'What was it? A convent?'

'Just because I wouldn't let you rush me into bed on our first date!'

'I had to make it respectable by putting a ring on your hand first, didn't I?' he snarled, and Lindsay slapped his face so hard his head jerked back in surprise. He looked at her with dangerous eyes for a split second and before she had moved again his own hand came up and to her disbelief she felt it sting her cheek. Shock brought tears to her eyes, Daniel was darkly flushed, his brows black above brooding, angry eyes.

'Don't ever hit me again or next time I'll do more than give you a token slap!' he grated.

She touched the hot mark on her cheek with her fingertips and he watched her, frowning.

'Did that make you feel better?' she asked

contemptuously. 'You get your kicks in a funny way.'

'You hit me first, but then that's typical—you provoke a reaction, then turn round and complain about it. Right from the first, you've done the same thing. When we met you kept giving me inviting smiles, but promise was one thing, delivery something else, wasn't it?'

'You just had a one-track mind. In my book accepting a dinner date doesn't mean you automatically go to bed with a man.'

His smile was hard. 'How long did Hill have to wait?'

'I haven't . . .' She stopped, biting her lip, and Daniel's eyes widened and gleamed.

'Well, well, well,' he said softly, and smiled. 'Haven't you, now? He must be one hell of a patient guy—and very frustrated.'

Lindsay did not like his smile, it held too much satisfaction and far too much self-congratulation. If she hadn't been afraid of his response, she'd have hit him again, but the glowing mark on her cheek urged caution.

'And so must you be,' he added slowly, watching her as a hot tide of colour ran up her face. 'Two years is a long time to go hungry, isn't it, Lindsay?'

'Will you leave my flat or do I have to call the police?' She descended to bluff because she couldn't think of any other way of ending his taunts, she could have kicked herself for giving away the fact that she wasn't sleeping with Aston, it would only make Daniel more sure of himself.

'I'm still waiting for my answer,' he said

without showing any sign of leaving. 'The sooner you agree, the sooner Stephen will be put out of his misery. He must be out of his mind at the moment.'

She closed her eyes, wincing, and knew he was watching her, calculating the effect of what he had just said. Opening her eyes again, she looked at him with a mixture of bitterness and regret. Why was he such a swine? His features held such strength: lean and hard-boned, with that firm jawline and beautifully shaped mouth, those cool, intelligent grey eyes. What sort of mind lay behind them? He was using a cruelly effective blackmail, enlisting her own emotions against her, how could he bring himself to do it?

'You're ruthless, aren't you?' she whispered, and he shrugged.

'If I have to be.'

'Why do you want to humiliate me?' she cried out, her voice shaking, and Daniel's brows jerked together, his features all tightened, his mouth levelling, his cheekbones angular, a tiny muscle jerking beside his mouth.

'If it humiliates you so much, I'm prepared to marry you first,' he said, and laughed, but it was a humourless laughter. 'I know how you insist on that wedding ring,' he added. 'That was what you held out for last time, wasn't it? And you got it, but even that wasn't enough, was it? You still couldn't bear being touched, you bolted. You're a psychological mess, do you know that? When I'm touching you, you burn. It drives me insane to feel that response one minute and the next have you freeze on me and push me away. What happens inside your head to make you ice up like that? Is it guilt? Are you afraid of sex?' His voice held an impassioned pleading now, Lindsay looked at him in shock, her eyes wide. He took a step closer, putting out his hand, and she flinched involuntarily.

'Don't move away from me like that!' Daniel snarled, then he turned away and walked to the door in three strides. 'I said I'd give you until Thursday—I will, but remember, Stephen is waiting for your answer just as much as I am, so don't prolong the agony.'

The front door slammed and Lindsay sank on to the couch, trembling, her thoughts in chaos. Daniel had come strangely close to the truth in his accusation that she was afraid of sex, but it wasn't sex she feared, it was love. Sex was merely the symptom of the disease, love was the sickness itself. Her love for Daniel had been too intense, too devouring: she hadn't been able to control it, she had wanted him too much, been jealous of everyone who came near him, and her jealousy had taken over her whole life in the end, she hadn't slept, hadn't thought about anything else, it had been a permanent torture.

She had thought Daniel knew. Had he forgotten her constant probing, her questions about what he had done, where he had been and with whom? She had thought she was so obvious—hadn't he realised, after all?

She sat in the darkening room, a slender white statue on the couch, unmoving. Daniel seemed to see their marriage from an entirely different angle—he remembered everything in a totally different way. But he had one thing right—she was a psychological mess, she couldn't deny that. Her jealousy was a desire for total possession, she had long ago faced that, and that was abnormal; she had had to leave him to escape the endless maze of that bitter, unrewarding emotion. She did not want to be drawn back into it, but if she allowed herself to love Daniel, she was afraid that she would.

CHAPTER EIGHT

'YOU'RE looking rather wan,' Chris told her next morning, eyeing her through half-closed lids as he lounged back in his swivel chair in his favourite position, feet on the desk and arms behind his head.

'The heat,' Lindsay lied, and looked out of the window at the blue, blue sky that floated overhead, unconcerned that London was suffering, far below, from the remorseless heat of the sun. 'Another scorching day,' she added. 'You're lucky I came to work at all, I was thinking of going off to the local swimming pool.'

'Poor little dear,' said Chris, and nudged a pile of reports with one beautifully shod foot. 'Take these and skim through them for me, will you? I'd like a brief résumé by lunchtime.'

'Yes, boss,' she said with venom. 'Anything else I can do?'

'Not just now,' he decided, settling back for a nap with his eyes shut, and she left the office with a crash as the door banged behind her and the glass shook in all the windows on that floor.

'Temper, temper!' Chris yodelled after her.

Her secretary grinned as Lindsay passed her. 'Pleased with himself, today, isn't he?'

'As Punch,' Lindsay agreed, going into her office and dumping the reports on her desk with a groan. That lot would take her all day, Chris could wait for his résumé.

She rang Stephen before she began work on them. Alice answered the phone and told her Stephen had gone to work. 'He insisted, I couldn't persuade him to stay at home any longer.'

'How is he?' Lindsay couldn't get out of her mind the haggard face of her brother last time they met.

'Quiet,' Alice said flatly. 'I think he worries more about the staff at the factory than he does about us, all he keeps saying is: Where will they get other jobs if I have to shut down? He isn't worried about us.'

'Of course he is, you know that isn't true. He was so worried about you that he couldn't face telling you.' Lindsay was indignant on her brother's behalf, Alice was being unfair to him. Lindsay could understand why her sister-in-law was upset, Alice had two small children to think about, she must be very unhappy about losing her home, but that was no reason to be so unkind to Stephen.

'He was so worried about me that he let me go through hell thinking he might be dead,' Alice muttered.

'Oh, Alice!' Lindsay said on a sigh, and heard Alice draw a shaky breath.

'I know,' she said suddenly. 'I'm so angry with him I can't bear it at times, he hurt me, I feel insulted because he didn't confide in me, he rang Aston Hill and he barely knows the man. I feel so small, being left out like that. I'm his wife!'

'Daniel may help him,' Lindsay said on

impulse, and Alice broke into the sentence with an eagerness that hurt.

'Did he tell you that? Do you think he meant it? Has he talked to Stephen?'

'Daniel's cautious, he takes his time to think these things through,' Lindsay told her. 'He won't have talked to Stephen yet, not until he's sure of his plans.'

'It would be marvellous,' said Alice, her voice much lighter now. 'It would take such a load off Stephen, he doesn't know which way to turn.'

Lindsay rang off a moment later and sat staring at the wall. Then she slowly picked up the phone and dialled again, her hand shaking. She found herself counting the rings, and when they stopped and a voice spoke she almost jumped out of her skin.

'I want to speak to Mr Randall,' she said, and the voice took on a tone which had the texture of icecream, frigidly smooth.

'I'll put you through to Mr Randall's secretary.'

Lindsay waited another half a minute, then a woman spoke politely. 'Can I help you?'

'I want to speak to Mr Randall,' Lindsay said again. She hesitated, and before she could decide which name to use the other woman said: 'Who is it speaking, please?' in a distant voice that put her back up so much that she said tersely: 'Mrs Randall.'

There was a silence, then the secretary said: 'Mrs Randall?' again, and Lindsay told her: 'His wife.' When the woman spoke again her voice was very different.

'Would you hold the line for a moment, Mrs Randall? I'll see if I can find Mr Randall, I don't know if he is in his office at the moment.'

Lindsay made grotesque faces at the phone as she waited, and a full minute elapsed before Daniel's voice murmured in her ear.

'Lindsay?'

'Yes,' she said.

He waited, then said: 'What did you want?'

'Yes, I said,' Lindsay muttered, and a long silence fell, then he breathed audibly close to the phone.

'We'd better have lunch today. I'll pick you up outside your office at twelve-thirty.'

'I can't . . .' she began, only to find that he had hung up, the phone had gone dead. Lindsay replaced it, her skin tight around her jaws. She was aching with tension. Did he have to be so brusque? It had cost her a great deal to make that call, he might have been more responsive than that.

She forced herself to turn her attention to work, concentrating on the pile of reports to such an extent that when the door opened she didn't hear it and Chris's voice made her start violently.

'Jumpy today, aren't you?' he observed, staring down at her.

'I was working,' she retorted. 'You could try it, surprise yourself.'

'I'm just off to lunch,' he said, looking amused. 'Coming?'

Lindsay looked at the time, incredulous as she saw that it was twenty to one. 'Oh, no,' she said. 'I'm going to be late.'

He lifted his eyebrows enquiringly. 'Got a date with Aston?'

'No,' she said, unforthcoming. She got up and started towards the door with Chris in hot pursuit. 'I'm going to the cloakroom, where are you off to?' she asked him without turning round.

'Is it a client?' Chris asked, and she ran into the cloakroom, letting the door swing shut in his face without answering.

In front of a mirror she brushed her hair, renewed her make-up and inspected her reflection. She was wearing her white silk blouse with a lightweight green linen skirt tightly belted at the waist with a thin gilt belt. She looked cool and efficient, she did not look exactly sexy, but she decided that that was probably a good thing.

She hadn't escaped from Chris, he was waiting for her at the lift and gave her a beatific grin as she joined him.

'Going my way?'

She walked into the lift and they travelled down together. 'You aren't going to let me expire of curiosity, are you?' Chris asked.

'Definitely,' she told him.

'How can you be so hardhearted?'

'Easily, it's a gift.' The palms of her hands were perspiring, she pulled a tissue out of her bag and wiped them while Chris watched, his face speculative.

'He's obviously someone special,' he guessed aloud. 'You're in quite a state.'

Lindsay walked out of the lift and halted seeing Daniel standing in the foyer talking to a laughing receptionist who was looking at him as if Santa had just delivered him, gift-wrapped. Lindsay had never liked the girl, she decided.

'I'll ring the office,' the receptionist said as Daniel smiled at her. 'She may have left.'

Lindsay started towards the reception desk, her high heels clicking on the stone floor, and Daniel swung in her direction. His grey eyes shot over her and she gave him a curt nod.

'Sorry to keep you waiting, I was delayed.'

He was in a formal, striped suit and crisp white shirt today, his tie a lustrous maroon silk; he looked oddly remote, unfamiliar. His lean, brown face had a controlled smile in it, but the smile did not show in his eyes, they probed her face as though she was an enemy he faced across a minefield. That was how she felt, too. She looked at him coldly because she needed all her armour, all her weapons. This time she was not going to face him empty-handed and already in a losing position.

Daniel glanced past her at Chris, who was hovering behind her shoulder. Lindsay reluctantly introduced them, aware of Chris's curiosity in every nerve, and the two men shook hands. Chris had a coaxing smile on his face, Daniel didn't smile at all, he eyed Chris assessingly from head to foot in one smooth look.

'We must rush, I'm afraid,' he said to him. 'We're late already. Nice to have met you.' Taking Lindsay's elbow, he steered her out of the building and she heard Chris wandering behind them, gloomily guessing that when she got back to work she was going to face a barrage of questions from him. Chris had no sense of shame,

if he wanted to know something, he asked and
went on asking until he was satisfied.

'Good looking guy,' Daniel said without
pleasure, watching her out of the corner of his
eye. 'How long have you been working for him?'

'Oh, ages,' Lindsay said blithely.

'You seem to get on well with him.'

'I do,' she said, and halted as she saw the
gleaming limousine waiting for them at the kerb
with a uniformed chauffeur standing beside it.
The man whisked open the passenger door and
Daniel slid Lindsay into the car, joining her a
second later. Lindsay saw Chris standing on the
pavement, watching them in fascination. She
resisted the temptation to put her tongue out at
him, keeping her profile turned towards him.

'Where are we going?' she asked Daniel. The
chauffeur got into the driver's seat and started
the engine, the car moved off.

'To have lunch,' he told her with a quick,
sideways look. 'You look very businesslike, do
you like working at Vivons?'

'Love it.'

'What exactly do you do there?'

'Public relations,' she said. 'Publicity, advertising . . . we all come under the same department
and I've worked on all three.'

'Will you be sorry to leave?' He sounded so
casual she didn't realise what he had said for a
few seconds, then she did a double-take.

'I'm not leaving Vivons.' She sat up, turning to
stare fixedly at him. 'No way, don't even think that
for a second. I enjoy my job, I'm going to keep it.
I'd be bored out of my skull doing nothing all day.'

'Don't get aggressive with *me*,' Daniel muttered, frowning. 'You gave up your job at the bank.'

'Who wouldn't?' Lindsay retorted. 'It was dead boring, but working at Vivons isn't. I'm good at my job and I get a kick out of it.'

'The idea's ridiculous,' he said. 'You won't need a job.'

'Who says I won't? I'll decide what I need.'

'You'll decide?' he echoed slowly, staring at her, the bones in his face locked tight in grim impatience, and Lindsay outfaced him, her eyes defiant.

'That's right. It's my life and my job.' The car was slowing and she looked out of the window vaguely, her mind set on the little argument they had been having, only to jerk awake as she realised where they were. They had entered the curved drive-in of the block of Mayfair flats where Daniel lived, and she flung him a suspicious look.

'What are we doing here?'

'We're having lunch here,' Daniel told her coolly as the limousine stopped. He got out and came round to hand her out of the car. The chauffeur stood there, his face blank, and Lindsay didn't feel like arguing with Daniel in front of him, she had no choice but to allow herself to be led into the building, and he knew she wouldn't be able to do much about it. He had kept her mind on their row while they drove here, looking back she suspected that he had deliberately trailed his coat for her to pounce on—he was a devious swine.

In the lift she turned on him, her hands curled into fists at her sides, anger flaring in her green eyes. 'You knew I thought we were going to a restaurant! You deliberately didn't tell me you were bringing me here.'

'That's right,' he agreed lazily. 'You wouldn't have come otherwise.'

'You . . .' Words jammed her mind as she tried to find a description vivid enough to make clear how she felt about him, she looked at him in helpless, seething fury, and he laughed.

The lift doors slid open and Daniel took her arm and half led, half thrust her towards the front door of his flat. He had two homes in London, this spacious penthouse flat where he lived himself and a house a quarter of a mile away where his mother lived but where he often stayed, usually when he was entertaining visitors, since the house had far more room. The flat only had three bedrooms, and was a short walk from Daniel's office headquarters, so that he could be immediately available night or day in a business crisis.

Halting at the door, he glanced down at her with mockery in his smile. 'Try to look pleasant for Mrs Henshaw.'

Lindsay opened her mouth to answer that and he put a hand over her lips. 'No backchat,' he warned, and she felt like biting the hand, then he took it away and rang the bell. The door was whisked open and Mrs Henshaw stood there, smiling.

'Oh, Mrs Randall, it's good to see you. How are you? You look very well.'

'I'm fine,' said Lindsay, smiling back. Mrs Henshaw was a short, thin, neat woman with a slightly harassed expression at times and pale blue eyes that dominated her otherwise unmemorable face. They were protuberant, enormous, always glazed as though she might be going to cry. 'How are you, Mrs Henshaw?' Lindsay asked her, and the other woman shrugged cheerfully.

'Mustn't grumble.'

It was embarrassing to face her; Mrs Henshaw had been an onlooker during the months when Lindsay was left alone night after night while Daniel was supposedly working. The other woman must know far too much about Daniel's private life, Lindsay was uneasy with her, and she sensed uneasiness in Mrs Henshaw, too.

'We'll have lunch whenever you're ready, Mrs Henshaw,' said Daniel, moving away, and the housekeeper gave Lindsay an odd look, saying: 'Mr Randall, could I have a word?'

'Problems?' Daniel asked, half-smiling. 'Don't tell me you've ruined our lunch?' He was looking amused as he waited, but Mrs Henshaw's expression was agitated.

'Oh, sir, it wasn't my fault, I didn't know what to do ...' Her nervous words stopped dead as a door opened and out strolled the blonde Lindsay had seen with Daniel the other night.

'I thought I heard your voice,' she purred, and linked her arms round Daniel's neck, smiling into his eyes. 'I just had to talk to you, darling.' She appeared not to notice Lindsay, she ignored Mrs Henshaw, all her attention on Daniel. She put on a good act, Lindsay thought sourly: lashes fluttering, her full pink mouth lifted as though for a kiss, the lipstick moist and glowing, her body deliberately arched against him.

'What's the matter, Carolyn?' Daniel asked coolly, his hands going up to unlock her arms and pull them down.

'I'm not happy,' the blonde told him, pouting. 'A promise is a promise—you can't say you didn't give me your word I'd get everything I want, but now Harry tells me your people are being awkward.' She came just up to his shoulder; a tiny, curved creature whose every movement shouted sex appeal, and Daniel looked at her with amused indulgence.

'Mrs Henshaw, would you give Mrs Randall a drink? I won't be a moment.' He put his arm around the girl's waist and walked her away to the room he used as a study. Lindsay watched, her teeth meeting. Somehow she hung on to her smile, she wasn't going to let Mrs Henshaw see her real feelings. She walked into the room which the blonde had emerged from, her head held high and her expression unconcerned, aware of the housekeeper scurrying at her heels.

'What can I get you, Mrs Randall? Will you have a sherry?'

'That would be nice,' said Lindsay sitting down in one of the deep, smoothly upholstered chairs. The room had been newly decorated, and recently; she had a shock as she realised that, she had expected it to look exactly the same, and finding that it didn't was disorientating. The furniture was all covered in blue suede, the material clung softly to her hands as she touched it, the feel of it sensuous. The carpet was new, too, a deep-piled white on which were laid some Persian rugs whose colours glowed vividly; red and green and blue.

'Sweet or dry?' Mrs Henshaw asked, and Lindsay told her: 'Sweet,' smiling politely. She was feeling numb, it was stupid to feel hurt because Daniel had redecorated the home they had shared together. What had she expected? That he would keep it exactly the same? Reason told her she was being stupid, but she resented it, she felt he had betrayed her all over again by altering their home.

Mrs Henshaw handed her a delicate glass of warm, golden sherry and hovered. Didn't she like to leave Lindsay alone? Or was she trying to say something? Lindsay pretended not to notice her, she sipped her sherry, her eyes lowered.

'If you want anything . . .' Mrs Henshaw mumbled, and Lindsay looked up, nodded.

'Thank you.'

Mrs Henshaw went out and Lindsay looked around the room taking in everything, recognising nothing. What had he wanted to do? Erase all memory of her?

The door opened and Daniel came in, wariness in his face. 'Sorry about that,' he said quickly, his glance skimming across the room towards her.

'I'm sure you are,' Lindsay smiled, ice in her eyes.

'She was uptight about the contract she's signing with us,' he said, pretending not to notice the glacial nature of the smile.

'Just business?' she asked, her tone sarcastic. 'It looked pretty personal to me.'

'Carolyn calls everyone darling,' he shrugged, getting himself a glass of whisky. 'She's an uninhibited girl.'

'So I noticed, she must be very popular.' With men, Lindsay added mentally; the blonde girl had apparently found other women invisible, she hadn't so much as glanced in Lindsay's direction.

Daniel turned, smiling drily. 'I must be crazy,' he said, looking at her with raised brows, 'getting involved with you again—red hair, green eyes, a temper like blazing oil, and a nasty, suspicious little mind.'

'I didn't imagine the way she hung on your neck and oozed sex appeal,' Lindsay snapped, then thought back over what he had just said and added tersely: 'And nobody asked you to get involved with me again.'

He drank some whisky, watching her over the glass, his eyes brooding. 'When I eat lobster I come out in a rash,' he said irrelevantly, and she stared, lips parted in bafflement, until he added with a wry grimace: 'But I can't resist the stuff, although I know what will happen if I give in to temptation.'

Lindsay coloured, her throat beating with an over-rapid pulse. It wasn't very flattering, being compared to lobster, but what he had actually said hadn't mattered so much as the dark, brooding stare with which he had said it.

He took a step towards her and she shrank, trembling, afraid of the expression in his eyes.

There was a light tap on the door and a second later Mrs Henshaw came in, smiling, to tell them that lunch was ready. Over the meal, Lindsay asked Daniel: 'Have you talked to Stephen yet?' and he nodded.

'It's all settled. I'm becoming his partner, he'll still be running the factory, but he'll be answerable to me. My people will work out the details. I'll put somebody in there to work with Stephen, my accountants insist on that, we're investing a lot of money and they want safeguards.' He gave her a brief, dry smile. 'But your brother's pride won't suffer too much, I promise you. Anyone who bailed him out would insist on similar terms.'

Lindsay kept her eyes on the plate in front of her, she was having trouble eating the delicately flavoured Chicken Bretagne which Mrs Henshaw had served with saffron rice and fresh peas. It was a dish which Lindsay had always liked; Mrs Henshaw's memory was good.

'Have you told Stephen ...' she began, faltered, then added: 'That I ...' And broke off again, unable to think of a way of phrasing it.

'That you're coming back to me?' Daniel asked softly, and she felt his eyes on her flushed face. 'No,' he said. 'I thought we would be subtle about that, it might look suspicious if the two pieces of news came together. We'll wait a week or two before we tell him, I think.'

'How tactful,' Lindsay said bitterly. 'Is that for your sake or mine? Stephen might be angry if he knew how you'd blackmailed me.'

'He's stiff-necked,' Daniel said. 'I'm sure he'd

refuse my help if he found out.' His voice taunted
her. 'Of course, if you choose to tell him . . .'

'No!' she exclaimed with violence.

'Somehow I thought you wouldn't,' Daniel
murmured.

'That's what you're relying on,' she flung back
at him. 'You wouldn't want anyone to know how
low you'd stoop and you're banking on the fact
that I'd hate my brother to know what you've
forced me to do!'

'Everything has its price,' he said, his voice
cool, but there was nothing cool about his eyes,
they glinted like hot metal, because he had not
liked what she said, he hadn't liked the voice she
used as she said it. Daniel might be using
blackmail remorselessly, but he did not want her
to keep underlining that fact. He preferred the
truth kept out of sight.

'Our deal is just between the two of us,' he
said. 'Nobody else is involved.' He watched her,
his fingers curled around his wine-glass, their
tips lightly tapping the stem of the glass. 'And
that includes Aston Hill.'

'I don't intend to tell Aston! I'd hate him to
know, too. He would be horrified, I'd feel sick if
I had to tell him.'

Daniel frowned, his mouth straight, dark red
running along his cheekbones. Lindsay kept her
eyes on him, hoping her pointed remarks were
making him angry. She wanted to hurt him, to
prick that thick skin of his, she was still raw from
the memory of seeing the blonde actress hanging
round his neck and calling him 'darling' in those
honeyed tones. Last time she had run away

because loving him hurt so much, and she couldn't live in a ceaseless atmosphere of doubt and jealousy. Nothing had changed, Daniel was still the same man, she had to be stupid to let history repeat itself. Somehow she had to keep a wall between them, she had to learn not to care what he did, who he was with, how he felt. During their separation she had built up a satisfactory life of her own, she had learnt so much about herself and about life since she left him and she was determined not to make the mistake of letting her emotions take control of her, not this time. She would just have to keep him at arms' length.

Mrs Henshaw served their coffee and Lindsay glanced at her watch. 'Look at the time! I'll have to be going soon—I've got a mountain of work to get through before I can leave tonight.'

'Drink your coffee and I'll drive you back to your office.' Daniel looked at his own watch, shrugging. 'I'll have to get back to work myself.'

In the car, he asked: 'Dinner tonight?' and Lindsay shook her head.

'I'm having dinner with Aston.'

She felt him stiffen. When he spoke again his voice held a muffled snarl of temper. 'That's over now, you know that? You're not dating him again. We're getting remarried, the press would have a field day if you were seen with another man.'

He couldn't speak too loudly because he was afraid the chauffeur would hear him. Lindsay gave him a sweet smile. 'Aston's an old friend.' The car had stopped, she opened the door and quickly fled before she got any reaction from Daniel.

Of course, Chris was waiting for her, buzzing with questions. She regarded him wryly. 'Oh, well, you might as well know—we're getting married again.'

His jaw dropped. 'You and Daniel Randall . . .'

'Me and Daniel Randall,' she nodded. 'Happy now? Can I do some work?'

'When?' Chris demanded, and she looked at her piled desk.

'Now might be a good time before I get buried alive in paper.'

'No,' he said impatiently. 'When are you getting married again?' Then he laughed and said: 'You knew what I meant.'

'In a fortnight,' Lindsay told him. 'We just spent an hour planning it—that gives his damned sister time to buy a new hat, let's hope it hides her face.' Daniel's sister had never liked Lindsay. Meriel was a feline, self-important woman with too much money, too much time on her hands and too little to do with either.

Chris stared at her, wide awake for once. 'I didn't know you were still seeing him,' he said slowly. 'I thought it was Aston . . .'

Lindsay shrugged and couldn't think of an answer for that. Chris ran a hand through his glowing, honey-blond hair, frowning.

'I hope you'll be happy,' he said in a dubious way, looking distinctly worried, then he wandered away and Lindsay sat looking at nothing. So did she, wasn't that what everyone wanted? To be happy? Marriage to Daniel Randall didn't seem a

likely prospect for finding happiness, though.
Heartache, perhaps, she had had enough of that
last time, he was good at that.

She got home late that evening and had to rush
to shower and change before Aston arrived. She
was just brushing a little rouge along her
cheekbones when the doorbell went. She ran to
open it, smiling, but it wasn't Aston, it was a girl
in a T-shirt and jeans who grinned at her and
handed her the enormous cellophane-wrapped
bouquet she was holding.

'Mrs Randall?'

'Yes.' Lindsay said. 'Thank you.'

They were beautiful. She walked slowly into
the kitchen cradling them, deep red velvety roses
with long stems, frilly white carnations, yellow
gladioli. Lindsay stripped off the cellophane and
began to put them in vases. The doorbell went
again and this time it was Aston. He looked at the
rose she held, smiling.

'For me?' he asked, his mouth crooked.

She laughed, walking back into the kitchen. He
stood at her shoulder, staring at the flowers,
watching her finish the arrangement.

'Randall?' His voice was quiet, it held no
particular intonation.

She nodded without looking round, nerving
herself to tell him she was remarrying Daniel, but
before she could say anything, Aston's hands
gripped her shoulders, he moved closer, his
mouth moving against her neck.

'He's chasing you again, isn't he, Lindsay?'
She felt the pressure of his lips, heard him
breathing quickly. 'Don't let him too near you,

have you forgotten what he did to you last time? It was a year before you could bear a man near you, you were a human iceberg.' His hands slid down her arms and round her waist, she felt them warm and firm below her breasts. 'I've waited too long,' he said unsteadily, and she was disturbed by the note in his voice. 'I should have turned a blow-torch on you long ago.'

'Aston——' she began, but he was spinning her round to face him and as she looked up into the rugged, humorous face she saw a new expression, one she had never seen before; a fierce excitement, a passion, that silenced her in shock.

His arms went round her, pulled her close in a convulsive, demanding movement, and he kissed her hungrily, with desire, with pleading, and the sheer naked need in that kiss sent her spinning off balance, everything female in her responded to Aston's unhidden need of her. He pressed her even closer, a hand gripping her back, and his mouth was warm and sensuous. He had never kissed her like this before, and she yielded to him without being able to think.

It was always dangerous to think you knew someone, she thought; had she been so wrong about Aston? Her heart was going inside her like a steam-hammer, crashing wildly, she couldn't breathe. Aston was turning her body to soft, yielding wax in his caressing hands.

He lifted his head, breathing raggedly. Lindsay opened her eyes, dazed by the light, and he said in a husky voice: 'I love you.'

She burst into tears.

CHAPTER NINE

'DARLING!' Aston sounded horrified. He tipped up her face and gently wiped her eyes with a hankie, murmuring soothingly: 'What is it? Lindsay darling, don't, I didn't mean to frighten you—don't cry, love.'

She couldn't stop the tears, they poured out of her like Niagara Falls, she rubbed her hand across her wet face and Aston said: 'You're smudging your mascara, you look like a panda,' which made her giggle hysterically and then hiccup, crying and laughing together.

Aston urged her into the sitting-room, pushed her down on the couch. 'What you need is a drink,' he said. 'I need one myself,' he added in a self-mocking voice. 'A stiff whisky, that's what I need. I seem to have rubber legs.' He went over to pour the drinks, saying with his back to her: 'That was some kiss.' He sounded selfconscious; he was not given to such violent emotion, he was a calm man who liked his life to be under control. Lindsay had never expected him to break out like that, she had thought she had him worked out to the last detail, she had been wrong, and she was dreading the next few moments. How was she going to tell him about Daniel now?

She hadn't expected Aston to be pleased, of course, she had known he would be taken aback, even hurt or angry, but it hadn't entered her head that under his smiling surface there lurked such strong feelings.

He came over and put a glass into her hand, sat down next to her, swallowing some of the whisky in his own glass. He was very flushed, he looked like a man who has surprised himself and isn't sure what to do next. Lindsay glanced at him secretly from under her lashes, pretending to sip her whisky. Grimacing at the taste, she said huskily: 'Aston, I've got to tell you . . .'

'I know,' he said, interrupting. 'Why do you think I haven't rushed you until now? I knew you weren't in love with me, I realised I had to be patient. Don't think I'm expecting an answer right away, I just wanted you to know how I felt.' He pushed and looked down into his whisky, smiling, a quick, secret smile he tried to hide by turning his head away, but too late, Lindsay had seen it. 'I should have shown you sooner,' he said, and she knew from that smile that her response to his passionate kiss had misled him into thinking she felt more for him than she did.

Or was he right? She sat up, jerked into cold self-appraisal. How had she felt? At the time she had been swept away like a straw on a flooding river, helpless to do more than go with the compelling tide. She hadn't been thinking or assessing how she felt, she had given in to him mindlessly. If Daniel had not come back into her life, would she have fallen in love with Aston, sooner or later? She had been telling herself she liked him but nothing more; she had seen him in a different light now and she was no longer so sure.

What was love, anyway? Why did she feel the way she did about Daniel, rather than any other man? His looks? Other men were as good-looking, but they didn't do a thing to her heartbeat. His wealth and power? If he had been as rich as Croesus but hadn't turned her on, she wouldn't have looked at him twice. His personality? She grimaced, drinking some more whisky. Daniel had the personality of a steam-roller; he crushed everyone he met and left them flattened at his feet.

There was a lot of hostility in the way she felt about him, but she couldn't hide from herself the truth that her emotions towards him were complicated, involved, convoluted, like a thick skein of multi-coloured silks, twisted together and almost impossible to unwind without violence. When she was with him she couldn't take her eyes off him, he fascinated her; images flashed through her head now and she felt that betraying weakness she always felt when she was with him. Daniel's wide, firm mouth, smiling, or hard, his lashes lying on his skin like shadows when he looked down, his brown neck, the slow pulse at the base of it, the way he moved suddenly, the long legs graceful. She visualised without thinking, swallowing on a sudden dry-mouthed intensity. How can you pinpoint the focus of so deep an attraction? Perhaps it was none of those things, perhaps it was in herself that she should be looking—her own nature needed something she sensed in Daniel and not in any other man, but she didn't have a clue what it was she needed.

Would she have found it with Aston, though?

She looked at him and he was watching her, his mouth crooked.

'Don't look so worried, it will wait,' he said, and she wanted to cry again because *he* was trying to comfort *her* and that made her ache with guilt.

Self-hatred forced the words out of her. 'I'm going to marry Daniel.'

Aston sat there, staring at her, his glass clutched in his hand. He looked as though he hadn't understood the words. The colour drained slowly out of his face.

'I tried to tell you,' Lindsay mumbled in a low voice.

He leaned over and put down his glass, whisky spilled out of it at the crash as it hit the table.

'Why?'

The word had a raw force behind it. She couldn't meet his eyes, she was pale and she felt sick. What could she tell him? Not the truth, obviously, the situation was explosive enough without that.

'I don't know,' she said helplessly, her lower lip trembling, and in a sense that was the truth, the whole truth and nothing but the truth. On the surface Daniel was blackmailing her, but under that there lay whole layers of reasons for what was happening, subterranean levels of feeling one upon another, so complex she couldn't reach the end of them.

'What do you mean, you don't know?' Aston broke out angrily, and he might well be angry— she knew she sounded fatuous, stupid, she wasn't making sense, to him or herself. 'Are you out of your mind?' he asked, and she grasped almost gratefully at the question.

'Yes,' she said, and began to laugh now, a high-pitched, unbalanced laughter close to tears. 'Stop it!' Aston muttered, and she stopped, dead, swallowing.

'You can't be serious,' he protested. 'After what you've said about him? He's poison to you!'

A sweet poison, Lindsay thought, shuddering, and felt the ache of desire deep inside herself—wasn't that what Daniel had meant when he said that although lobster brought him out in a rash he couldn't resist it? Did he feel the same about her? Were they both aware that it was insanity for them to be together, but far more painful for them to be apart? During their separation she had built up a pleasant life, her days had been busy and painless, her burnt-out nerves had had a chance to heal, she should have been very happy, but since Daniel came back into her world she had felt fifty times more alive, a hundred times more real. He hurt, he drove her crazy, but she needed him.

Aston was looking at her grimly. 'Just now——' he began, and she put her hands over her face. He had good reason to be angry with her, she was angry with herself.

'I'm sorry,' she muttered through her fingers, and he pulled them down, refusing to let her hide from him.

'Why did you let me kiss you like that when all the time you knew you were going to marry Randall again?'

'I didn't mean to ... I'm sorry ... Aston, I like you so much, but ... what can I say? I don't know, you've every right to hate me, I wouldn't blame you if you did, I wish I could love you,

you're a wonderful man.'

He got up in a fierce, aggressive movement. 'I don't want to hear any more. I don't understand you, I don't understand women at all.' He walked to the door and Lindsay sat on the couch, shivering.

Aston stopped at the door, looked back. His hazel eyes were still almost black, his jawline rigid. She thought he was going to say something and waited, not quite meeting that stare, but after a long silence he went without a word, closing the front door very quietly.

Lindsay sat there without moving for a long time, then she got up unsteadily and went into the kitchen, to be met by a wave of perfume from the flowers Daniel had sent her. She looked at them with animosity, as though they were to blame for what had happened. She pulled some of the roses out, water dripping on the floor as she did so, and was barely conscious of the thorns pricking her skin. Half sobbing, she tore the flowers between her fingers. 'Damn you, damn you!' she whispered, and flung them from her. They drifted to the floor in a shower of torn crimson petals and green leaves. Her fingers showed tiny spots of blood, she stared at them with clouded eyes. He was hurting her already.

The phone rang, making her jump. She answered it reluctantly. It was Stephen, sounding almost lightheaded. 'I suppose you know,' he said, and she pretended not to understand, her voice puzzled. 'Know what?'

'You don't?' Stephen sounded disbelieving, but he told her about Daniel's offer and she exclaimed joyfully, hoping she wasn't over-acting and that he wouldn't guess she knew all about it.

'Isn't that wonderful? I'm so glad—are you pleased? Is he giving you a good deal, or aren't you happy with his offer?'

'He's being more than handsome,' Stephen told her in a slightly dry tone. 'I'd be an ungrateful fool if I wasn't relieved and delighted. Nobody loses their job, the firm stays nominally mine and Alice won't have to leave her house. I couldn't in my wildest dreams have hoped for anything like Daniel's offer.' He talked about the details for a while, then said: 'Thanks, Lindsay,' and she protested: 'What for, what did I do? I had nothing to do with it.'

'Pull the other one,' Stephen said bluntly. 'Daniel Randall isn't the quixotic type, he and I were never that close, he wouldn't do this for me. There's only one person who could get him to play Sir Galahad. He was always nuts about you.'

When she had rung off Lindsay slowly went into her bedroom and sat down on the bed, staring at her own reflection with searching eyes. Her skin had a betraying pallor, her green eyes looked too large, too bright, their lids flickering nervously as she stared at herself and saw in the mirror those hints of emotional turmoil which she did not want anyone else to glimpse. She ran a shaky hand through her hair and it flamed in the lamplight, soft, gleaming red curls which clung to her pale fingers. She thought of Daniel, and involuntarily, her eyes shut, she breathed faster, hating herself but wanting him. If only she knew how he felt about her—did he hate her? She knew

he desired her, but how much of that desire was
hatred?

It's so easy, she thought, to hate and love at
one and the same time, the piercing emotional
intensity of both can be mistaken for the other.

She undressed and slipped into bed, turned out
the light and tried to sleep. She was very tired,
sleep should have come quickly, but it evaded
her. It was some time before she felt her body
relaxing and then just as she was falling asleep
the phone rang. Groggily, she groped for it in
the dark and the bedside lamp almost crashed to
the floor. She lifted the phone and mumbled:
'Mmm ...' Even as she muttered that she was
waking up and guessing that Aston had rung, her
face wary as she finally managed to find the lamp
switch and turn on the light.

'Lindsay?' The voice was hard and cool and it
wasn't Aston's—it was Daniel, sounding distinctly harsh.

'What on earth ...' She looked at her bedside
clock in disbelief. 'Do you know what time it is?
It's midnight.' Then fear made her voice rise.
'What's wrong?' Her mind leapt to the obvious.
'Stephen ...'

'Is fine, as far as I know,' said Daniel. 'I was
ringing to make sure you were okay.'

'You were what? You wake me up to ... I
don't believe my ears!'

'I just saw Hill,' he said tersely.

Lindsay froze. 'What? Aston? Where? What
did ...'

'We didn't speak,' Daniel said. 'He was drunk.
It was the most incredible thing—I was with a

party of Swedes over here on a buying expedition, we'd been having dinner and went on to a club. Hill was going out as we went in—he saw me, gave me one look and hit me.'

Lindsay's breathing seemed to stop. She gripped the phone tighter.

'Luckily he was too drunk to connect,' Daniel told her. 'I was his fist coming, side-stepped, and he fell flat on his face.'

'Oh, no!' Lindsay gasped. 'Poor Aston . . . is he hurt?'

'Providence looks after drunks,' said Daniel without apparent sympathy. 'He passed out, but I didn't see any injuries, and luckily my Swedish friends took it as a joke, they thought he'd taken an instant dislike to me because he was stoned.'

'Where is he now?'

'Home, I'd imagine—I called my driver over and sent him home in my car.' He paused. 'Then I rang you to make sure you were safely home. You told him, I presume?'

'Yes,' she said very quietly.

'Took it badly, did he?'

'Damn you,' Lindsay muttered, her voice shaking. 'Mind your own business!'

'Was there a scene?' Daniel asked. 'He didn't hurt you, did he?' He sounded icily harsh, and she hated him.

'Go to hell,' she said, and hung up. She crawled down into the bed and pulled the sheet over her head, but although she kept her eyes tightly shut she could not shut out the pictures Daniel had conjured up for her. Poor Aston! She hated herself, she hated Daniel, and most of all she hated knowing that she had hurt Aston so much that he had gone off to drink himself insensible. She knew how he felt, she wished she could do the same, but she would only be sick if she tried to drink enough to stop her mind from working.

She closed her hands around her head, rocking to and fro in the bed on her knees, like a demented woman. Her mind was her real problem, it wouldn't stop working, telling her home truths she didn't want to hear. Her body was always on Daniel's side—if her mind would only stop interfering, she could forget pain, give in to the heated necessity in her flesh and be oblivious of everything else. She felt like banging her head on a wall until her mind gave up.

Over the next few days she was grateful for the fact that she was too busy to have time to think. The office was hectic, Chris even did some work himself, but he did so with more vigour when the managing director was around. Charles rarely appeared on their floor, he normally summoned Chris to his own much plushier suite, but he was taking a great interest in their campaign to find 'The Face'. Chris's original brainwave had been enlarged—they were launching their new range at the same time as their highly publicised competition to find the perfect girl to represent Vivons, and both newspaper and television advertisements would feature a large cut-out silhouette of a girl's head without features, only a question mark and the words: Are You The Face?

'Clever,' said Charles, nodding approval. He looked at Lindsay. 'He's a genius, isn't he?'

'A genius,' Lindsay agreed, but when he had gone she eyed Chris with wry amusement. 'Stop preening, you look like a half-witted peacock!'

He laughed, then looked at her hard. 'And you look like a ghost—not sleeping? You haven't looked too good all week. Does Daniel Randall keep you awake all night? All play and no work, remember.'

'I work,' Lindsay said. 'A damned sight harder than you . . .'

'It was a joke, a joke,' Chris protested, pretending to be alarmed, holding up both hands as though she might hit him.

'Not a very funny one,' she told him, and he sighed and hung his head.

'No, ma'am, sorry, ma'am, I beg your pardon, ma'am.'

'Oh, get lost,' Lindsay said without heat, and stormed off back to her own office to regret losing her temper over nothing. What was the matter with her? As if she didn't know!

That evening she called in to see Alice and found her very busy cooking Stephen's dinner while Matt and Vicky called plaintively down the stairs for drinks of water. 'They ought to be asleep,' Alice said distractedly, tasting the home-made chicken soup and hesitating about the flavour. 'Is there enough salt in that?' she asked, and Lindsay lifted the ladle and sipped, nodding.

'Plenty, it's delicious.'

'I used the carcase,' said Alice, replacing the saucepan lid. 'Why don't you stay? There's more than enough for three.'

'I'd have loved to, but . . .'

'Date?' Alice asked, and Lindsay nodded, smiling at her, although it was a lie, she didn't have a date, she was simply afraid to talk to her brother for long in case she said too much about Daniel.

'Aston, I suppose?' Alice asked, and Lindsay hesitated, biting her lip.

'Well, no.' Matt's footsteps padded down the stairs and Alice made a wrathful face.

'Back to bed,' she yelled, then looked at Lindsay curiously. 'Who are you seeing tonight?' Her face brightened. 'Daniel?' She stared hard, smiling. 'It is, isn't it? I knew it, I told Stephen so, I guessed from the minute he walked in here that night. If he wasn't still mad about you, he wouldn't have hared over here the minute that reporter told him you were in trouble.'

'Mummy,' Matt said at the door, 'can we . . .'

'I thought I told you to stay in bed? Do you want a smack?'

'No,' said Matt, not surprisingly. He advanced to twine himself round Lindsay's leg, hugging her waist. 'Auntie, tell us a story. We're not sleepy, come and tell us a story, we like your stories, you haven't told us one for ages and ages.'

Lindsay hoisted him up, groaning exaggeratedly. 'Heavens, you're getting heavy! What does your mummy feed you on? Elephant steaks?'

'Take no notice of him,' Alice said crossly. 'He should be asleep, they both should. I put them to bed dead on six, it gets later every night. I can't wait for the autumn, these summer evenings drag on and on.'

'Just a quick story, then,' said Lindsay,

carrying Matt up the stairs. 'I've got to rush, you know, I didn't come round to tell you two stories.' She slid him into his bed and Vicky peered at her through the cot bars, her nose pink in the half-light. Lindsay bent to kiss her on it and Vicky wriggled, chuckling. Lindsay got her to lie down, tucked the cover over her and sat on Matt's bed while she told them a slow version of The Three Bears. Vicky sucked her thumb, eyes half shut. She was quite ready to go off to sleep, it was Matt who was keeping her awake.

When Lindsay got back downstairs Stephen was in the kitchen, sipping a glass of gin and tonic which Alice had given him. He grinned at her. 'Kids asleep?'

'Vicky is—Matt is still full of beans. It's time he had a room of his own, isn't it?'

'You may be right,' said Alice, nodding. 'Drink, Lindsay?'

'No, I must go. See you both soon.' As she walked away Stephen said: 'I'll give you a lift home,' and although she tried to refuse he insisted. 'It won't take me ten minutes,' he said, and Alice joined him in persuading Lindsay to agree. It was obvious that Stephen wanted to talk about Daniel, and Lindsay was reluctant to do that, but she had no choice but to give in to their combined pressure. At the moment, Daniel was their favourite person, Stephen knew how much he owed Daniel and he wanted to impress on his sister that Daniel was a terrific guy. It wasn't selfish of him, it was only human. Stephen had been overwhelmed by Daniel's rescue operation and he wanted to show his appreciation. He thought Daniel was doing it for Lindsay's sake and Stephen was very fond of his sister, he would do a lot for her himself. He already had, Stephen was an unselfish, loving man with a strong sense of family and a deep sense of responsibility. He had placed his own interpretation on what Daniel was doing. Stephen knew that in Daniel's place he would be acting out of love, and it had made it much easier for Stephen to accept Daniel's help since he worked out why Daniel was doing it. He wanted Lindsay to be kind to Daniel, he made that as clear as crystal.

'I feel as if a great load was off my mind,' he told her as he drove her back to her flat. 'It was unbearable, knowing there was no way out. I've never felt so desperate in my life. I was going crazy!'

She listened, her face sombre. 'I'm glad things have worked out,' she said, and Stephen quickly said: 'Thanks to Daniel, he's being terrific. He's already paid off the bank, and his accountants are working to get the business back on a good footing.'

'You will be careful,' Lindsay said hesitantly. 'Daniel is a tough businessman, he'll expect a profit.'

'I want the firm to be profitable,' Stephen told her. 'It has to sell what it makes. I'm not a fool, Lindsay, I'd have let him have the whole firm for a song just to keep the factory open. We were right down the drain, I hadn't got a hope, and all those men and women would have been out of a job. I felt so guilty about them, about Alice and the kids ... it was my fault. I overreached myself, tried to expand too fast, borrowed too much money and then couldn't pay it back—I meant well, but that's a weak excuse.'

'Don't sell yourself short,' Lindsay said crossly. The car stopped outside the flats and she turned and kissed him lightly. 'You're not a bad brother,' she said with a slightly crooked grin.

Neither of them was over-demonstrative. Stephen grinned and looked uneasy. 'Thanks.' He was a grown man with two children of his own, but for a second or two he looked like a pink schoolboy. Hurriedly he said: 'And thanks for being so good to Alice. She was worried sick, I know. I wish to heaven I hadn't put her through that—believe me, I wasn't myself, I'd never have done that to her otherwise.'

'She knows that, we both do.' Lindsay gave him a little punch, smiling. 'So stop apologising, buster. You don't need to, nobody blames you.'

'I do,' Stephen said soberly. 'Alice was as mad as hell for a while, but she's come out of that now. I should have told her—she's right. I just wanted to protect her, I wasn't trying to insult her by keeping her in the dark. I'll never keep anything from her again.' He gave Lindsay a wry grin. 'I didn't know Alice could be so belligerent—she threw things at me, imagine that! I was dumbfounded. Alice! She never even raised her voice to me before.'

Lindsay laughed. 'It sounds as though your marriage is going to be more exciting in future! Let's hope she doesn't take boxing lessons, that's all.' She got out of the car and waved to him as he drove away, then went into the building slowly.

She was tired, she would have a bath and an early night. The flat was dark and empty, and she stood in the little corridor listening to the silence, hating it. It was absurd, she could have stayed with Stephen and Alice that evening and relaxed in a warm, family atmosphere, but she had insisted on coming back here to be alone and now she was feeling lonely and abandoned, she was wallowing in self-pity. How stupid could you get?

She had her bath, soaking herself in warm, luxurious water generously sprinkled with rose-scented bath crystals, lying back listening to the radio with closed eyes, occasionally wiggling a foot to make the water swish around her body, and now and then sipping a glass of Martini. She wasn't in a hurry, she had nowhere to go.

It wasn't until the water was almost cold that she reluctantly stepped out of the bath, dried herself lightly and slid into a robe. She rubbed the mist off the steamy mirror, and peered at her reflection; she looked pink and clean, her red hair curling in the steam, her eyelashes clustered damply. Making a disgusted face at herself, she wandered off to the kitchen to get herself a snack. She looked into the fridge and didn't fancy anything she saw. In the end she fell back on scrambled eggs and toast, but just as she was beating the eggs with a fork the doorbell rang and her hand jerked in surprise.

Aston? She hesitated, biting her lip, not sure if she felt up to facing him tonight, and while she stood there trying to make up her mind the bell rang again with a sharp, peremptory note. Clutching the lapels of her terry-towelling robe, she opened the front door a fraction, looking through the gap warily. Daniel looked back at her, his mouth indented impatiently. He didn't say anything and after a moment Lindsay fell back and let him walk into the flat. She closed the door and leaned on it weakly, her pulses accelerating.

The cold, empty flat was suddenly alive; she was alive, too. Daniel stared at her and smiled suddenly in a way that made her tremble, and then sent a wave of pure rage through her at her own folly. He was looking pleased with himself, his eyes touched her, lingering, and she knew what he was thinking, there was a quality of satisfaction, complacency, in that smile. He thought he had got her, in a moment he was going to kiss her, his lean body was poised to make a move, and she resented every inch of him.

'I'm tired,' she said coldly. 'I've had a difficult day and I'm in no mood to deal with you, Daniel, so whatever you've got to say, say it and go, please.'

He lost the smile and the grey eyes cooled and hardened; anger came from him in icy waves. 'Don't talk to me like that! I won't stand for it!'

Lindsay dug her hands into her robe pockets, hunching her slender shoulders in a shrug, angrily enjoying the new tension in his face. He had come here tonight with one thing on his mind; she had known that the minute she set eyes on him, but he could think again, she wasn't going to be the push-over he expected. She had some self-respect—not much, she thought grimly, but some!

'If it isn't important, could it wait? Ring me tomorrow,' she said, calmly opening the door.

Daniel charged towards it, his wide shoulders tense under the smooth grey suit he wore, his face harsh, every line of it set fiercely in rage. Lindsay hurriedly got out of his way; she had the feeling he might knock her down and trample on her if she didn't.

The door slammed with a violence that made the flat echo, but Daniel hadn't left, he was still on her side of that door, and Lindsay gulped in alarm as he turned a menacing glare on her.

'Now!' he said without any hint of a smile anywhere, and her heart dived down with sickening dismay as he moved towards her.

CHAPTER TEN

'KEEP your hands off me,' she stammered, backing against the wall and Daniel advanced remorselessly, pinning her into the corner. He put a hand on either side of her, his face inches away, a grim, shadowy mask she watched nervously, her eyes very wide and alert to every move he made. She wasn't expecting what he did say, it took her totally by surprise.

'Why did you leave me?' The question had explosive force in it, his voice was harsh, he held her stare fixedly, refusing to let her look away.

'I ... I'm not going over old history,' Lindsay said in a shaky little voice, wishing he wouldn't stand so close, his nearness was doing drastic things to her heartbeat.

'Oh, yes,' he said, 'you are. I want to know.'

'Too bad,' she muttered, looking down to escape that hypnotic stare and his hand came up to grab her chin and force her face upwards. Her lashes flickered uneasily, she moistened her dry mouth with her tongue-tip. 'If you manhandle me ...' she began, and Daniel laughed shortly.

'What will you do, Lindsay? Hit me? I told you what would happen if you ever hit me again.'

'Oh, you'd like that, wouldn't you? That turns you on, does it? I didn't have you down as a man who got his kicks from hitting women, but it figures. Force is all you understand!'

'I sure as hell don't understand you,' he said bitterly

'Have you ever tried?' she threw back, and the grey eyes flashed.

'I'm trying now, in case it had escaped your notice.' His hand came down on her wrist, locking it tightly in a vice; he turned and walked into the sitting-room, pulling her after him, struggling to break free. Daniel sat down on the couch and yanked her down to him, she tumbled helplessly across him and before she could sit up his arm clamped over her so that she lay on his lap, her head on the arm of the couch. Her hair escaped from the pins holding it and flew in all directions, a damp sweet-smelling cloud of fiery red-gold, a few strands drifting across her eyes. Daniel brushed them back, she felt his fingertips lightly touch her lids and shivered.

'Try again,' he said softly. 'Why did you leave me?'

'I was sick of sitting around at home while you made it with other women,' Lindsay said viciously, angry again because she knew her body was throbbing with a deep, aroused, erotic heat. Daniel had her at a disadvantage, she couldn't get up, she couldn't get away from his dangerous proximity without a humiliating struggle, and he was far too close, she could feel his body warmth under her back, she could see the faint blue vein in his neck where his blood beat under that brown skin.

His brows came together. 'What?'

'Did you think I wouldn't guess what kept you out so late night after night?' She sneered, laughing angrily. 'I may have been young, but I wasn't that stupid!'

'I was working,' he said, staring at her, and she laughed again without any humour.

'Oh, sure. And I bet you worked hard, too.'

Daniel was staring at her as though he didn't know her, and she wasn't surprised; she didn't know herself, her jealousy was blackening everything she saw, her face was hot with rage and her voice had the sting of a scorpion. She had hidden her jealousy for so long, now that it was escaping she couldn't control it.

'You thought I had other women?' Daniel sounded incredulous, if she hadn't known better she would have thought his blank expression held innocence, but she did know better. He was acting and doing it brilliantly, but he couldn't fool her.

'I didn't just think,' she said bitingly. 'I knew! Someone was getting your attention, it certainly wasn't me. When we first got married you made love to me every night, then everything changed—some weeks you didn't even kiss me, let alone make love to me! I might as well have been a piece of furniture for all the notice you took.'

'You never said a word,' he protested. 'You didn't tell me you suspected I was having an affair.'

Lindsay curled an icy smile at him. 'Where was the point? You'd either have lied or admitted it—either way, I didn't want to get into that sort of discussion. I was humiliated enough already.'

'So you were judge and jury, you found me guilty without even telling me what I was

supposed to be guilty of . . .' He sounded hoarse,
little spots of dark red had come up in his face
and his mouth was unsteady. Lindsay felt nervous
as she looked up at him, she shifted uneasily.

'You stupid bitch,' Daniel muttered, and his
hand shot out to curl round her throat. She
tensed, her nerves jumping with fear. 'I ought
to . . .' He broke off again, swallowing, she saw
his throat move convulsively. 'Not even to ask
me! My God, your opinion of me must have been
rock bottom! You couldn't even be bothered to
talk about it, you went around secretly accusing
me and didn't utter a syllable.' His hand
tightened and she flinched. He saw the fear in her
face and his lips drew back from his teeth in a
snarl. 'Yes, you're right to look nervous! The way
I feel at the moment I might just lose my temper
and give you what you deserve!'

'Don't threaten me,' Lindsay said as firmly as
she could. 'You're not frightening me.' She was
lying, he *was* frightening her, but she was not
going to admit that even if he had already realised
it.

'Then you're even more stupid than I thought,'
Daniel muttered. 'You ought to be scared, you're
very close to being strangled.' The long fingers
flexed on her throat, making her even more aware
of their power. 'Who did you think I was seeing?
Or didn't that interest you?'

'You had plenty of casual girl-friends before
you met me,' Lindsay said with a pretence of cold
indifference. 'You told me as much yourself, you
never hid your past love life—I knew you used to
pick girls up all the time, look at the way you

picked me up. Old habits die hard, don't they say?'

He said something she didn't hear, the words choked.

'You can't deny it,' she persisted. 'I wasn't your usual type, was I? You went for more sophisticated ladies and your interest in them wasn't limited to giving them dinner or a night at the theatre. Well, go on—deny you slept with them!'

'Why should I?' he said angrily. 'I was free, adult and normal—why shouldn't I go to bed with an attractive woman if she was willing? But that was before I married you, you aren't accusing me over the distant past. If you thought I was carrying on like that after we were married, why didn't you come out with it? Why hug it to yourself without a word?' He bent down towards her and she shrank, a hand up to keep him at bay. 'Unless, of course, you were looking for an excuse to leave me!'

Her flush deepened. 'That's right, make a counter-accusation! I didn't need an excuse, you handed me a reason on a plate.'

'I didn't do anything of the kind! There *were* no other women,' he said, and she smiled, angrily incredulous.

'No?'

'I'll make you believe me if I have to beat you black and blue,' he muttered, and took hold of her shoulders, twisting her forcibly while she struggled and kicked, until she was lying across his knees face down. She couldn't believe he meant it, she gave a gasping cry of shock as she felt his hand come down.

'I wasn't unfaithful to you,' he snapped, and hit her hard. 'There wasn't anyone else.' He hit her again and she writhed furiously, throwing herself backwards, so that she slid off his lap and tumbled to the floor, her red hair spilling over the carpet. Daniel was on top of her a second later and she hit him, with all the force she could muster, across his face. He took hold of her wrists, anchoring her to the floor by his knees, and she heaved upwards, panting breathlessly, trying to wrench free. One hand broke from his clasp, she flailed at him with it, flinging herself sideways again. Their bodies rolled over and over in confused, violent struggling. Lindsay punched and kicked and felt Daniel's hands trying to hold her, the heavy weight of his body forced down on her.

'Keep still, damn you,' he muttered, finally holding her down.

Through tousled masses of hair her eyes glared up at him, and unbelievably he started to laugh.

'You look like an old English sheepdog,' he said.

'I bite like one, too,' she threatened, showing him her teeth.

'I know, I've the toothmarks to prove it,' he said, and she reddened.

'That's a lie—I didn't bite you.'

He turned his head to one side, a finger touching his neck, and she saw the tiny mark in his skin and was taken aback, she couldn't remember doing it. 'What's that, then? A love bite?' he mocked, looking down at her, then his head swooped down and she caught her breath as she felt his mouth at her throat, his teeth gently nibbling her flesh. 'Tit for tat,' he whispered, then his lips pressed warmly, deeply, along the throbbing vein in her neck. 'You're crazy—there wasn't anyone else. Lindsay, believe me—there wasn't anyone. The last few months before you walked out, I was up to my ears in work. I didn't have time to eat or sleep, let alone go to bed with anyone else.'

'Or me?' Lindsay asked bitterly, and he held her face between his hands, staring into her eyes.

'You froze up on me, I didn't know why, did I? I was working flat out, all I knew was that suddenly I was getting cold looks from you, if I came near you, you went rigid and obviously didn't want to know.' He gave a rough sigh, his expression grim. 'We both leapt to conclusions. You decided I was sleeping around—I decided you'd either fallen out of love with me or were just plain frigid. Is that so surprising? Before we were married you jumped six feet in the air if I so much as tried to touch you.'

'I wanted you to,' she muttered, her face uncertain and flushed. 'I wasn't frigid, I was just nervous.'

'Inhibited,' Daniel said drily.

'Yes,' she said, because that was it in a nutshell. It had seemed so important then, the first time she would ever sleep with a man, it had looked like a unjumpable fence, she hadn't been able to make it. Angrily, she said: 'I wasn't very old, remember. It was the first time for me, and you scared me, you were so ...' Expert, she thought; he had been too experienced, it undermined her, she felt gauche and stupid when she thought of all the other women he had had, the sexy, exciting, sophisticated women from his own world who knew precisely what they were doing and made love with an expertise which matched his own. Lindsay had blushed and stammered and felt awkward and clumsy.

'I felt so boring,' she finished, and Daniel stared at her intently.

'You were lovely,' he whispered. 'Young and shy and adorable—I was almost afraid to touch you, I wanted you so much I was afraid of scaring you.'

'I was scaring myself,' she admitted. 'All the time—putting up barriers in my mind when what I really wanted to do was . . .'

'What?' he asked as she broke off, and she lifted her head and kissed him with a raw, open passion she had never shown him before. She felt the barriers in her head go down with a crash and the floodwaters poured over them, her arms went round him and her hands touched him the way she had been longing to touch him, her palms pressing into his body, her fingertips caressing and exploring along his spine, his nape, his shoulders. Daniel's hands slid under her and lifted her, held her so close they became one. Her robe fell open, he looked down at the smooth pale flesh and she heard his breathing quicken.

He stood up and the next second she was in his arms, carried close to him as he walked out of the room. He was looking at her every step of the way, he wasn't walking steadily, she felt him trembling and his deep chest heaved as if the air had no oxygen, he was snatching at every breath raggedly, while his eyes leapt over her naked body.

She felt as if it would be the first time, she was shaking as though in terror; but it was not fear, it was desire turning her limbs to water, tearing at her until she ached with longing.

Daniel put her down on the bed and began to pull off his clothes, his hands shaking. She watched, ice-cold suddenly with shock and piercing excitement, huddling in her robe to stop herself shivering. His body had a male power which her female instincts both recoiled from and were drawn towards, she couldn't stop looking at him, she was pale and at the same time feverish, her lips were dry, her breasts ached. She couldn't have spoken to save her life, and she didn't want him to speak, her whole being concentrated on a need to be part of him.

He knelt on the bed in the darkness, his eyes moving with nerve-racking slowness over her. His hand parted her robe, and she allowed it, her own hand falling back on the bed, palm curled upward, and Daniel stared as if he had never seen her, his pupils dilated, darkening his eyes and he breathed with parted lips, audibly. Lindsay couldn't move, she lay trembling, while he looked from the hollowed pallor of her shoulders to her warm, rounded breasts where the nipples had firmed, their pink surrounded by a darker circle, then down over her midriff and the flat, smooth stomach to her hips and slim thighs.

He was looking at her deliberately, it was an act of possession as much as would be the lovemaking which would follow, and Lindsay looked at him in hungry exploration in the same way.

When he put out his hand she tensed, watching. His fingers trailed softly where he chose to touch her, so light, so fleeting a contact, all the way down her body and a smothered gasp broke from her, she put up an arm to pull him down to her, the long-deferred desire too fierce to be borne. As he came down on her she shook violently and moaned in satisfaction, her arms round him, holding him locked to her.

Daniel lifted his head and caught her face in one hand, held it while he kissed her, but as if there was still anger somewhere in him it was not a gentle, tender kiss, it was a kiss of devouring intensity, bruising her mouth, forcing her head back against the pillow until her neck ached. She met it with fire, her lips clinging to his in burning response, and at last his mouth softened and warmed, he whispered: 'I love you, love you, you stupid little bitch, there hasn't been anyone else, only you. I didn't want anyone else—I've tried to, but it didn't work, all I thought about was you.'

There was too much she wanted to say. I'm sorry, I've been stupid, I believe you, I love you, I'm such a fool.

She didn't say it, she said over and over again: 'I want you, I want you . . .'

'God,' Daniel muttered hoarsely as her body moved against him, her hands touching his shoulders, his chest, his strong thighs.

'I love you,' she said a second later on a wild

moan of pleasure as he entered her. 'Daniel, oh, Daniel!'

Words couldn't make the bridge on which they had to cross to become one being, their flesh melted and dissolved together, she felt the hair on the back of her neck prickling, her spine arching to meet the hardness of his body, and there were no inhibitions, no barriers left, because her fear had gone, taking them with it. She no longer feared other women, or her own inexperience and nervous shyness. Desire burnt them all out, both her own and his—she felt the agonising need in him as he took her, his breathing tortured by moans of intense pleasure. He had always been too strong, too sure of himself. Now he was neither; he was, like her, a human being drowning in sheer need, for the first time she felt they were on the same ·level, equal, moving together to the same goal.

No longer aware of what she was doing, she held him, her fingers digging into his back, her nails in his flesh, and Daniel groaned as though the pain delighted him, the urgent thrust of his body hurting and exciting her in turn.

She felt herself opening, the warm, receptive clamouring of her body engulfing him; the intensity rose to an unbearable peak, her deafened ears beat with her own cries, she did not hear the cries he gave, she moaned with closed eyes like someone dying and almost blacked out, her heart, brain, lungs seeming to cease their functions for an instant of time that seemed to stretch for ever.

Daniel's face was buried between her breasts

when she began to think again. He was hot,
flushed, trembling violently. 'Darling, darling,'
he kept saying, but his voice was low and hoarse,
she only just heard him.

She put a trembling hand on his hair, it was
damp with perspiration and clung to her fingers.
'I love you,' she said, stroking it, and he turned
his head on her body, his lips brushing her skin.

'Do you believe . . .' he began, and she put a
finger on his lips.

'I love you,' she said again, what else mattered?
She had never understood the words before, she
had mouthed them without knowing what she
said, now she did, nobody in the world had ever
said them or understood them as she did now.
They were elastic, they contained whole dic-
tionaries of meanings, when you loved you
trusted, believed, accepted everything. She had
wanted Daniel to prove himself, his love, she had
greedily asked for all of him without giving all of
herself; bargaining like a market stallholder,
beating him down, when if she had really loved
him she would have given to the end of the world
without asking in return. She had set boundaries
on her love and walled herself up inside them,
now they had been smashed down and how she
felt had washed over the whole world. She held
the world in her arms when she held him. She
was no *part* of him—she *was* him, and he was her,
there were no divisions, no rights or claims
between them, they were one being.

'I was crazy about you from the minute I saw
you,' he said in a husky voice, kissing the finger
muffling his words.

'I was too young,' she said. 'I didn't understand love. I do, now.'

'You do,' he agreed, and laughed. 'My God, you do! I thought I was flying!'

There was that gentle mockery in his voice, and she smiled in the darkness, a hand running down his back and fingering the little indentations in his flesh where she had dug her nails into him without realising what she was doing. 'Daniel!' she exclaimed. 'Did I do these? I'm sorry, did I hurt you . . .'

'Mmm,' he said, kissing the little valley between her breasts. 'I loved it.'

'Wicked,' she said, laughing. 'That will teach you to blackmail people!'

He sighed, his body shifting so that he lay more easily against her, their bare legs entangled, his head still on her breasts but his weight not lying heavily on her. Lindsay felt him glancing up at her, his lashes flicking back.

'It seemed an irresistible opportunity,' he said wryly. 'I knew how much Stephen meant to you, you've always been very close, I figured you wouldn't be able to turn my offer down and I wanted you back at any price. When I saw you again, I knew I had to have you back, even if you hated me for it. You were lovely when you were five years younger, but now you're gorgeous.' His hand ran down her body from breast to thigh. 'Your figure was never this good before, you've rounded out beautifully. I couldn't take my eyes off you.'

'Or your hands,' Lindsay said in teasing dryness.

She felt him laughing. 'Or my hands,' he admitted without apparent shame. 'And when I kissed you I knew you were responding. I started to hope you still felt something, too. When I realised Stephen was in real trouble, I thought I'd use it to get you back. I wasn't sure exactly what was going on between you and Aston Hill.' He watched her sideways. 'I didn't think it meant much but I didn't like having him around. He was in love with you, wasn't he?'

'Poor Aston,' she said, frowning. 'Don't talk about him, it isn't fair to him.' She liked Aston far too much to discuss him with Daniel; Aston would hate that, it would be a betrayal of him, and Lindsay would hate to add insult to the injury she had done him.

'He didn't hide it,' Daniel told her. 'That night I bumped into him at the nightclub, he looked at me as if he'd like to kill me. I knew you must have told him something, I wasn't sure what, and I was afraid he might have hurt you, he seemed a very angry man and angry men get violent. That's why I rang—I'd have come round myself if I hadn't been with those Swedish guys.'

'Aston isn't the type to hit a woman,' Lindsay said, and Daniel grimaced.

'Not like me, you mean?'

'I shan't be able to sit down tomorrow,' she accused, but with a smile.

Daniel put a hand to his shoulder. 'I'm pretty black and blue, myself. You're a very violent lady.' He paused. 'If I hadn't turned up again, would you have married him?'

'Hypothetical questions are a waste of time,' Lindsay said.

'Would you?' Daniel pressed flatly, and she sighed.

'I don't know. I was never in love with him.'

He was quiet for a moment, then he said: 'I'm lucky I came back when I did. Another year and I reckon you'd have been married to him.'

'I didn't love him,' she insisted, and he nodded.

'Maybe not—you might have married him, all the same, and then all three of us would have been as miserable as sin.' He lifted his head, moving, and kissed her mouth possessively. 'Because you're mine and always have been, and sooner or later we would have met up again and once we saw each other we wouldn't have been able to stay apart. Hill may be as sick as death at the moment, but sooner or later he'll realise it was inevitable.'

'You were quite ruthless in the way you used Stephen against me, though,' Lindsay told him. 'That wasn't very nice, Daniel.'

'Lindsay, bailing Stephen out is a stupid undertaking, believe me—financially, I need my head examined. It will take years before his firm shows a profit—if it ever does. My accountants smile politely, but they look at me as if I'd gone mad. If they didn't know Stephen was your brother, they'd probably have me in a straitjacket by now. The accounts speak for themselves.'

'It was still completely immoral to blackmail me!'

'I'd have committed murder to get you back,'

he told her. 'A little blackmail seemed mild by comparison with what I wanted to do to Hill when I saw you kiss him at Stephen's house.' He looked at her, eyes glinting in the darkness. 'I love you,' he said, and she was silenced, the emotion in his voice held its own message, then he yawned and she began to laugh helplessly. 'Sorry,' he said. 'I'm used up, totally dead.' He yawned again widely and she pulled the covers over them, her arm cradling his head.

'Go to sleep then,' she said, feeling the warm, heavy weight of his body relaxing against her. This was how she had always wanted it; Daniel was hers, he belonged to her, and she belonged to him, but she had always been afraid of exposing herself by admitting the depth of her love because she could not have borne it if he left her once he knew. It would be different now. She was older, more sure of herself, more aware of what love meant. If there were problems ahead she would stand and face them, not run away, as she had before. If she had told him what was on her mind instead of walking away with her head in the air, they would never have parted. They hadn't known enough about each other, they hadn't talked enough, been honest enough. They had to learn so much, but they had already learnt the only vital thing—they loved each other.

Daniel was breathing in the regular rhythm of sleep, his naked body warm and slack in her arms, vulnerable, human, given up to her for safe keeping through the night. Lindsay let her own eyes close, a faint smile lingering along her mouth, and slowly drifted into sleep.

DESPERATION

BY
CHARLOTTE LAMB

WORLDWIDE BOOKS
LONDON • SYDNEY • TORONTO

First published in Great Britain in 1988
Reprinted in Great Britain in 1993
by Worldwide Books, Eton House,
18-24 Paradise Road, Richmond, Surrey TW9 1SR

© Charlotte Lamb 1988

ISBN 0 373 58953 0

99-9309

Made and printed in Great Britain

CHAPTER ONE

MEGAN CARR slid out of the open french windows on to the raised stone-paved terrace and stood there, her pale face, framed in long, dark hair, lifted to the rising moon. It was a calm, clear night in late September during one of those unpredictable spells of warm weather that can make autumn one of the loveliest of seasons. Behind Megan buzzed the noise of the party: loud music, laughter, insistent voices trying to be heard above the rest. Everyone in there was having a great time, but she had come out to escape the gaiety. It grated on her own mood. Tonight she was melancholy.

'What are you doing out here? You haven't got a headache, have you?'

The deep voice behind her made her stiffen, but she did not turn. She didn't need to; she knew who had followed her out here, and perhaps she had been hoping that he would, although torture wouldn't have wrung the admission out of her.

'No, I'm fine. I just wanted to . . .' Her husky voice died away as Devlin Hurst came up close behind her.

'Get away from that racket?' he asked, a smile in that deep, dark voice of his, and Megan pretended to laugh.

5

'Well, it is more peaceful out here!' Although
the tranquillity had been blown to smithereens
the moment Dev had come out here and sent her
temperature climbing, had made her pallor
become a burning flush.

'A full moon tonight!' he said, his hands
resting lightly on her bare shoulders. Megan
shivered at the brush of his skin on her own.

'Cold?' he asked with concern. She hurriedly
shook her head, but he turned her to face him,
lifted her chin so that her blue eyes had to look
up at him. He was a head taller; a man of commanding height who would have been daunting
even if he hadn't had such incisive features.
Megan had only known him for a couple of
months, but she was already in love with him,
and the explosive mixture of pain and passion
showed in her flushed face.

'What's the matter, Megan?' he asked, and
she started to speak half-way through the question, her voice unsteady.

'Nothing! Don't bother about me, go back to
the party and your friends.'

'I've talked to them all,' Dev said, grey eyes
cool. 'There's nothing more to say to them.'

'You're impatient to be on your way to South
America, I suppose,' Megan said, trying to
sound light-hearted.

'Yes and no,' he shrugged. 'I am looking forward to reaching the Amazon. This extended
trip is the fulfilment of a lifetime's dream. For
years I've wanted to explore the river from the
source to the river-mouth.' He looked down into

her eyes, his mouth crooked. 'But there are some things I'll miss, and I'll be away for a whole year!'

Her lip trembled for a split second and she looked away. 'A year's a long time.' When she thought of the next twelve months, they seemed endless. 'You're going to miss your family,' she said, then over his shoulder she saw the house. Hurst Manor had been in his family for nearly two hundred years, and had all of the solid, comfortable elegance of the eighteenth century.

'I'll miss you!' Dev said, and Megan caught her breath, her face rigid with shock and incredulity.

Dev laughed suddenly at her expression, then stopped short, his hands coming up to frame her face.

'I mean it, you know. I am going to miss you.'

She couldn't speak, only stare, and after a charged silence he bent his head to kiss her. Her eyes closed, her arms went round his neck, a fire between them as their mouths mingled. It wasn't the first time he had kissed her, but this time it was different; this time she was dizzy with pleasure, and Dev's lips were so fierce they almost hurt.

She felt his fingers winding through her long, fine, black hair. From the beginning her hair had seemed to fascinate him; he had stared at it the day she lunched with him that first time, for the TV chat show on which she worked as a researcher. As they left the restaurant Dev had taken a white rose from the vase of flowers on the table and gently pushed it into her hair. 'I love long hair,' he had said as they shared a taxi later. 'It's so sexy; all those amazing swirls and strands floating around your face every time you turn your head.' She had been breathless; no man had ever said such things to her, but then she had never met a man like Devlin Hurst before. Perhaps she had begun to fall in love at that moment.

Dev's mouth reluctantly released hers, and she leaned on him, shuddering with feeling.

'I didn't mean to let go like that,' Dev said thickly. 'I'll be away so long! It wouldn't be fair to ask you . . .' His voice broke off, his white teeth clenching.

'What?' Megan shakily whispered. 'As me what, Dev?'

His eyes moved over her face and her knees turned to water at that look, then Dev shook his head grimly.

'No, I've no right!'

Megan knew she should accept that; of course it was stupid to get seriously involved with a man who was about to go away for a year, especially as they had known each other so short a time anyway, but she knew, too, that she loved him and that time wouldn't change that; neither time nor absence.

'Ask me, Dev,' she said huskily, everything she felt in her blue eyes, and he looked down at her, his face full of conflict. 'Oh, Dev, I love you,' she whispered, and then he began to kiss her again, holding her so tightly she could scarcely breathe.

It seemed a long time later that he asked her. 'Will you marry me when I come back, Megan?' And she felt so happy she wanted to cry.

'Yes,' she said, although it wasn't necessary to say it because he knew by then how much she loved him; she had told him, over and over.

'A trick of fate,' he said. 'Meeting you just before I leave—why couldn't we have met a year ago?'

'I wasn't working on Johnny Fabian's show a year ago,' she pointed out, laughing and feeling a little light-headed. 'I was still at college.'

He frowned. 'At college . . . yes, you're so young, I keep forgetting.'

Her heart constricted. 'I like older men,' she pretended to tease, to cover her fear. He was thirty-five; the difference in age didn't honestly bother her but she had already sensed that it made Dev uneasy, especially when his friends made stupid, envious jokes about it.

'They'll say I'm cradle-snatching,' he said now, so he, too, was thinking about his friends.

'I'm hardly a child,' Megan said, wishing she was taller and looked older; but her build was against her. She was slight and fragile-looking; a tiny, pale girl to have such a heavy weight of hair and such great, wide-open eyes. She wasn't pretty, and found it puzzling that Dev should be attracted to anyone as unglamorous as herself when he must have plenty of pretty and glamorous women to choose from. It scared her, too, because it might be a passing fancy, a whim;

and what if he changed?

'You've been working for Fabian for six months, and that would age anybody!' Dev agreed, his tone dry because he didn't like Johnny, but then men rarely did. Johnny Fabian was a woman's man; his own sex resented him.

'I'm old enough to know what I want,' Megan said, then blurted out, 'Dev, couldn't I come with you?'

He stared, his face tight. 'Up the Amazon? Are you crazy?'

'Lots of women have been there, Dev!'

'On holiday trips in and out of the more populated region, maybe—but that is the whole point of this expedition: we're going to the largely unexplored region, and we're going to stay there for months on end. God knows what you could pick up—we've all had the most horrific courses of injections against the more common diseases rife out there, but then there are the snakes and the insects, any of which could give you a bite that would make you very ill indeed, if it didn't actually kill you. We can't inoculate you against snake bite or any of the microscopic things swimming in the river. We can't save you from the humidity or the sticky heat or the terrible rainy season, not to mention some of the more unpredictable human inhabitants.' He pushed her away to arm's length, still holding on to her, shaking her slightly. 'If I could take you, don't you think I'd have suggested it? It's impossible, Megan.'

'I'd take the risk,' she said eagerly.

'Megan, I couldn't concentrate on my job if I

had to keep worrying about you! I've visited South America before; not the Amazon, but other parts of the continent which have similar terrain. To some extent I'm ready for what I'll come up against. You wouldn't be. You've hardly been out of England before, have you?'

She lifted her chin, her big eyes defiant. 'Of course I have! I travelled all over Europe on a train two years ago! Some friends and I spent the whole summer vacation touring around. It was a cheap holiday, and great fun. People told us then that it was risky, but we came through without a scratch. We didn't run into anything we couldn't handle.'

Dev groaned. 'The Amazon basin isn't Europe! There are no roads, let alone trains. We'll be using the river; canoes, living in them for safety half the time. No, Megan, it's out of the question for you to come, but whenever I can I'll write, and I'll let you have a string of addresses and dates so that you can write to me and I can pick your letters up at intervals.'

'Oh, but Dev . . .' she began, and then the french windows behind them opened and his sister, Emma, confronted them.

'Dev, what on earth are you doing out here? There are a lot of people still wanting to talk to you.'

'Let them wait,' he said with his typical ruthless indifference to what other people wanted.

'Dev!' his sister protested. 'There are some very important people in there!'

'There's a very important person out here, too,' he said with wry amusement, deliberately encircing Megan with is arm.

His sister's pale eyes narrowed and she stiffened. Megan had only met her for the first time tonight, and she knew that Emma Stansfield hadn't really noticed her. Dev's sister looked oddly like him; the same colouring and features but in a more feminine mould, which yet had far more arrogance and pride of family than Dev had ever shown Megan. The Hursts were wealthy and had a long pedigree; they even had a remote connection with royalty some generations back. Emma had married one of her brother's oldest friends, Graham Stansfield, a member of the banking family; no doubt it had been viewed as a very suitable marriage when it took place, ten years ago, and from the look on Emma's elegant face now she was not going to see Megan as in any way suitable to marry into her family!

'Megan and I just got engaged,' Dev said. Megan wondered if it was her imagination that there was a ring of defiance in his tone.

'Engaged?' his sister repeated slowly, as if querying the word.

'There isn't time to get married before I leave, but we'll fix the date as soon as I'm back.' Dev was watching his sister, those grey eyes disturbingly chilly. Megan had seen that look on his face once or twice before, when someone angered him, and she shivered, hoping he would never turn that stare on her. 'Aren't you going to congratulate us, Emma?' he drawled, and there was something in his voice akin to a warning.

His sister's face tightened, her red mouth a thin

line. At last she said, 'Of course!' then added coldly, 'Congratulations.' She wasn't looking at her brother, though, or speaking to him; the word was drawled at Megan and it was dripping with sarcasm. Megan felt sick as it dawned on her that Dev's sister suspected her of ensnaring him. He was highly eligible, there was no denying that, and Megan hated the idea that people might think she was marrying him for his money or status. She felt Dev's body tighten; the fingers holding her waist curled, then released her.

'Megan, I'd like a word or two alone with my sister—why don't you go in and get us both a drink? I'll join you in a minute.'

Flushed and distressed, she gave a hasty nod, without saying anything, and hurried towards the open french windows, glad to get away. It should have dawned on her that Dev's family might not welcome her, but his proposal had come as a blinding surprise to her, she hadn't been expecting it, so she had not ever considered his family's reaction.

She closed the french window behind her, but in her haste she didn't click the lock home, and the window suddenly blew open again. Megan went back to shut it and heard Emma Stansfield's voice raised in cold mockery.

'You can't seriously intend to marry that plain little nobody!'

'Oh, but I do, and I shall expect all of you to be kind to her!' Dev's voice was angrily commanding, but his sister wasn't overawed.

'Why her, though? For heaven's sake, Dev, why

someone like that? She's so . . . so . . .' Emma Stansfield paused and Megan heard her breathing, then she said loudly, 'So ordinary!'

'That's why,' Dev said flatly, and Megan flinched, her blue eyes wide in pain. Was that how he saw her? As ordinary? A plain little nobody, his sister had called her, and Dev hadn't argued with that judgement; he had merely said be nice to her—or else!

There was a silence outside on the terrace, as if Emma Stansfield and her brother were staring at each other and communicating without words, then Dev spoke again in the same calm, quiet voice.

'I want children, a family, a home, and she'll give them to me.'

Emma's voice was different now, softer, almost pleading. 'Dev, not all beautiful women are like Gianna. You don't have to pick a boring little mouse to get a loving wife! This girl won't fit in, you know!'

'That's up to the family,' Dev said with hard emphasis. 'If you make friends with her . . .'

'Make friends with her!' Emma repeated, sounding outraged, and Megan very quietly closed the window and stood there, fighting with tears.

She had known about Gianna Montesi, of course; it had been much written about in the Press, that affair. The gossip columns had really gone to town on it, and when Megan was researching Devlin Hurst before he appeared on the Johnny Fabian show she had had to read her way through acres of print on the subject. It had happened a long time ago, though, she remembered, and, although Dev was frequently seen at parties or out at dinner with other women during the years following Gianna's sudden marriage to an American oilman, there had never been another 'big' affair, nothing that hit the headlines or seemed likely to end in a wedding.

Had Dev been deeply in love, and badly hurt? She bit her lip, closing her eyes in a spasm of jealousy.

From what Emma had said, he obviously had, and Gianna's rejection had left him determined never to fall for a woman of her kind again. Megan swallowed, the pain so intense that she had to clench her teeth not to cry out with it. She had been amazed that he showed such interest in her, hadn't she? Amazed and stupidly grateful, because a man like Devlin Hurst so much as looked twice at her! And all the time he had been picking her because she was just ordinary; a plain little nobody who would give him the children he wanted, make a home for him, be adoringly devoted all her life because he had chosen her!

'Oh, there you are, Megan! I was beginning to think you had gone home! What have you been up to?'

Johnny Fabian's light, amused voice broke in on her mood like a sudden blow, and she started, eyes wide in shock.

'Hey! Don't jump like that! What's up with you? Your nerves are in a hell of a state!' Johnny stood close to her, staring, while she fought to get herself under control again.

'You startled me, that's all.' Her voice wasn't quite steady, though, and Johnny's shrewd, dark eyes watched her curiously. 'Were you looking for me? What did you want?' Sometimes it worked to distract him with questions, and the last thing Megan wanted was to make Johnny curious, because he had the nose for secrets of a highly trained truffle-hound. That was what made his show so popular: Johnny found out things people wanted to keep hidden, and he loved to deflate the pompous, bring down the over-confident.

Of course, there were other reasons why his show was one of the top-rated chat shows on TV—and all of them began and ended with Johnny himself. He came from an extraordinary family; had a French grandmother and a Russian grandfather, an English mother and an American father; spoke six languages fluently and could get by in heaven knew how many others, and added to his undoubted brains an unfair amount of good looks and charm. Women couldn't resist him when he gave one of his sudden, wicked smiles and made one of his famous little gestures—pushed back his thick, curly auburn hair, looked sideways with narrowed eyes, gave one of his wry, resigned shrugs. They were such practised movements, but they never failed to gain their effect. Johnny could do no wrong in the eyes of his adoring fans. Anyone who wasn't a fan usually loathed him, but that didn't bother Johnny. He knew which side his bread was buttered, and he ignored his enemies, concentrating on pleasing his fans.

'I've been talking to someone interesting, that's

all, and I wondered if he might do for the show so I was going to ask you to check him out some time next week, only I couldn't find you, could I? So I wondered where you could have got to . . .' His voice faded as the french windows opened and Dev walked into the house. Dev paused, seeing Megan, then realised that she was with Johnny and walked on, his brows dark.

Johnny caught that look and stared at Megan, whistling softly. She had kept quiet about her dates with Dev since he'd appeared on the show. She hadn't wanted any gossip about them and had not wanted to be teased, or questioned, either.

'Don't tell me you were with him?' Johnny asked incredulously. 'Are you out of your mind, honey? The two of you don't have a thing in common and, anyway, he's off up the Amazon in a couple of days. I thought you had more sense.'

Megan's face was white and stiff, but she tried to sound normal. 'Who was it you wanted me to check out?'

'And you know it isn't wise to get involved with any of our guests; it can cause all sorts of complications, and it's a habit I don't encourage.'

'I don't make a habit of it!'

'Glad to hear it,' Johnny said, still watching her out of those shrewd, dark, beautiful eyes. 'Megan . . . Meggy . . . I don't want you to get hurt!'

'I'm in no danger of getting hurt,' she said, crossing her fingers behind her back in the age-old gesture of protection, and Johnny shrugged, grimacing.

'OK, honey, if you say so! Mark Bond.'

She stared blankly. 'Sorry?' Sometimes Johnny's gnomic muttering baffled her.

'The possible guest I want you to check out. Mark Bond.'

The name was totally unknown to her. 'Who is he?' Megan moved to where she could see most of the other guests in the enormous room in which the party was being held. Her blue eyes flicked from face to face, but she couldn't guess which of them had caught Johnny's attention.

'By the fireplace,' directed Johnny, and Megan's eyes moved sideways to where a man in an evening suit was leaning against the lovely Georgian fireplace.

'Who is he?' He wasn't elegant, in spite of his well-cut clothes; the body underneath them was far too muscled; shoulders broad, chest deep, legs long, it was the body of an athlete or a wrestler.

'I gather he's a sculptor.'

'Sculptor?' Megan stared even harder. 'Sure he isn't pulling your leg? If you'd said all-in wrestler, I'd have believed you.'

Johnny grinned. 'That's why I want you to check him out. He may be selling me a line, but if he's on the level he would be fun to have on the show. He's very funny about his work. Doesn't take it, or himself, too seriously. Might be interesting to have him bring whatever he's currently working on . . . he could maybe . . . what's the operative word, sculpt? . . . on the show. What do you think?'

'Sounds interesting, so long as he doesn't do massive figures, like Henry Moore! Have you told

Fanny?'

'It's my show!' Johnny was quick to take offence
if he thought you took more notice of the
producer's opinion than his own.

'Of course, Johnny,' soothed Megan at once. 'I
just wondered what she thought. She collects
garden statuary, doesn't she? I wondered if Mark
Bond was in that line, that's all.'

Distracted, Johnny said, 'I'd forgotten Fanny
and her garden statues. Yes, I must have a word
with her, but meanwhile go and chat Mark Bond
up, would you? Ask him to lunch, see if you can
get into his studio or whatever. Get a look at his
stuff and ring round the various dealers to get an
idea how good he is—or isn't, as the case may be!'

'OK,' Megan said, watching the stranger on the
other side of the room. She was rather grateful for
the excuse to keep out of Dev's way; she needed
time to think, and a chat with Mark Bond might be
the perfect cover. Megan couldn't believe that
Johnny was serious about this, though. He often
met people at parties whom he thought might
make good guests, only to change his mind in the
morning when he was sober, but as far as Megan
could judge he didn't appear to be drunk tonight.

'Not yet!' Johnny said, glancing at his watch.
'My car should be here by now, shouldn't it?'

'I'll go and see if it has arrived.' Johnny's
chauffeur-driven limousine always arrived to
whisk him away in good time so that if he wanted
an excuse for leaving a party one was at hand; but
the chauffeur just waited outside, knowing that if
Johnny was enjoying himself he wouldn't want to

go back to his luxurious but empty flat. Unless Johnny took someone home with him, of course. That had been known to happen! Johnny usually had a problem keeping women away, rather than attracting them, and that was why Johnny lived alone, in fact. There had always been too many women eager to vie for his attention; he was spoilt and hard to please.

'Aren't you enjoying yourself, Johnny?' Megan asked him with a sympathetic little smile.

'This isn't the greatest party in the world, is it?' he replied discontentedly. He caught her hand. 'Why don't you and me go and have a late, late supper together somewhere with a better atmosphere than this?

She gave him an indulgent smile. 'Not tonight, Johnny, thanks.' Gently disentangling herself, she hurried off to see if his car had arrived, and only then did she realise that Dev was watching them, his face coldly expressionless. Megan's eyes met his briefly, then she looked away because she could not face him just yet. She did not know what to do. She was deeply in love with Dev, but whatever his reasons for proposing to her she no longer believed that he was in love with her, not now that she had heard him discussing her with his sister in that cool, distant fashion. That hadn't been the voice of a man in love, had it? She had to think long and hard. Wouldn't it be madness to get engaged to him, knowing why he really wanted to marry her? Yet if she told him she had changed her mind, if she said goodbye and never saw him again, could she bear that, either?

The alternatives facing her were equally unbearable, and Megan's heart ached as she went to find Johnny's chauffeur.

The limousine was parked under the lime trees lining the long drive up to Dev's beautiful family home. The chauffeur was sitting inside, smoking; Megan saw the glowing red tip of a cigar, saw him flick ash, then start the engine as he noticed her on the stone steps under the portico of the house, waving to him.

She went back into the house as the long, black car smoothly slid up the drive to wait right outside for Johnny.

The party was as noisy as ever, the guests a swirl of colour and noise under the beautiful swags of crystal chandeliers. Megan stood in the doorway looking around for Johnny, and took a moment to locate him, only to have her nerves jump in alarm when she saw him with Dev. Their faces were tight and angry; they faced each other like duellists. Megan took a deep breath and hurried over. What had Johnny been saying, for God's sake, to make Dev look like that?

'Your car's here!' she said quickly as they both looked round at her.

Johnny nodded, then gave Dev a hard look. 'I hope you got the message!' he said, took Megan's arm and pulled her away with him, saying, 'Now, go and chat up Mark Bond, and stay away from Hurst after this.'

'Johnny, what did you say to him? Her voice was angry and upset, but he was too pleased with himself to care, grinning at her in satisfaction.

'I just told him that you were my property; that should keep him at arm's length.'

'Johnny!' She was appalled, going red then white. 'How could you? Oh, how could you?'

CHAPTER TWO

MEGAN might have known that it would be useless to reproach Johnny, who was convinced he knew best about everything. He patted her shoulder soothingly.

'You'll thank me for it before too long. After all, he'll be gone soon, and a year is a lifetime. Believe me—I know.' Johnny had never kept up a relationship that long; no doubt he did think a year was a lifetime, but Megan didn't want the sort of self-centred life Johnny led. It would be far too lonely. He didn't care for anyone but himself. He might be rich and famous, and some people might envy or admire his way of life, but she thought it was sad. She often felt sorry for Johnny, but not at the moment. She was blazingly angry with him, and it showed in her fierce blue eyes.

'That's just it—you don't know! You're not me, and you had no business interfering in my life! Don't ever do it again!'

Johnny looked amazed. She had never spoken to him like that before; few people ever did. He was too important, and Megan, like everybody else, usually took care not to offend or annoy him, but even at the risk of losing her job she wasn't going to let him come between her and Dev.

She glared at him, then turned on her heel and looked around for Dev, to tell him not to take any notice of Johnny. Dev was by the door, but he wasn't alone. His sister was talking vehemently to him, and Megan couldn't face Emma Stansfield again, so reluctantly she went over to talk to Mark Bond. He was talking to one of the camera crew going to South America with Dev, who recognised Megan with a grin, putting a lazy arm around her. 'Hi, Meggy, how are you?' He was slightly tipsy, but very cheerful, and she smiled back at his thin, lively face.

'I'm fine, how are you, Charlie?'

'Fine; can't wait to get on that plane.' His hazel eyes shone with enthusiasm. Charlie had once worked on the Fabian show, for a few weeks, and Megan had got to know him then. He had confided to her that he hated studio work, and longed to get into outside broadcasting, or location work in films. He was thrilled to have got this job with Dev.

'I bet you can't!' she teased, amused. 'You're going to have the time of your life for the next year! Just steer clear of snakes and poisonous insects.'

'I like snakes,' he said seriously. 'Used to keep them when I was a kid; I had half a dozen at one time until my mother got hysterical and made me get rid of them all.'

'I once did a study of Medusa,' said Mark Bond thoughtfully, staring at Megan. 'I had quite a job talking my model into holding a perfectly harmless grass snake; she wouldn't be convinced that it wouldn't give her a lethal bite!'

'Most people are like that; my mother, for one,'
said Charlie, then stopped, noticing the obvious
way the other man was watching Megan, and
said, 'Bad-mannered of me; I didn't introduce
you—Megan, this is Mark Bond, the sculptor.
Mark, this is Megan Carr, one of the researchers,
on the Fabian show.'

Mark Bond held out his hand, smiling. He had a
leonine head; thick, silvery blond hair swept back
from a distinct widow's peak, narrowed blue eyes,
a very strongly moulded face.

'Hello—oddly enough, I was talking to Johnny
Fabian himself earlier.'

She smiled back. 'Really?' She didn't tell him
that Johnny had mentioned him; it wouldn't do to
raise his hopes in case Johnny changed his mind
about having him on the show. 'Charlie said you
were a sculptor; what sort of work do you do?'

He looked impatient, running a wiry hand
through his smooth, pale hair. 'People will ask
that, and I never know what to say. I sculpt in
stone and wood . . .'

'Wood?' she queried, and he nodded.

'You can call it wood-carving, if you prefer, but,
although the techniques are different, the aim is
the same. You're bringing out of the material
whatever you see in it. Before you ever touch it
you start to see the hidden shape inside; I often
buy a block of stone or a piece of wood because I
want to create what I think I can see in it.'

'Do you have a buyer in mind before you start
work, or do you sculpt something and just hope to

sell it when it's finished?'

'Well, both. If someone offers me a commission to do some specific piece of work I'll do that, if it appeals to me—but if not, I just work on whatever occurs to me.'

'I'd love to see some of your work,' Megan said, aware of Charlie's watching eyes and the amusement in them. Charlie probably guessed that Johnny had asked her to check out Mark Bond, and it made her self-conscious to have him watching her.

She frowned at him sideways, and he got the message, saying to Mark, 'Will you excuse me? I've just spotted a terrific blonde who looks as if she needs some friendly company.' Grinning at Megan, he added, 'I'll leave you in our Meggy's capable hands; nice to have met you, Mark.'

Mark cheerfully said, 'Have a good trip up the Amazon! I wish I was going with you.'

Charlie laughed and pushed his way into the chatting throng while Megan smiled at Mark Bond.

'Would you really like to go up the Amazon?'

'Love to, but I've never managed to clear enough space in my life. Time is the big problem, isn't it?'

'I hope you can find time to let me see some of your work, at least!' she smiled, feeling devious and not too happy about it, but Mark looked pleased.

'Any day you like; it will be a pleasure. I never have any difficulty talking about my work. In fact, you'll have to stop me when I start boring you.'

'I'm sure you won't,' said Megan, mentally crossing her fingers behind her back. She had been bored out of her skull for the sake of the programme more times than she could remember; she thought she would survive another hour or two of it. It all depended how good a sculptor he was, of course!

'Tomorrow?' he said, and, knowing Johnny was capable of expecting her to have a portfolio on him by dawn tomorrow, she nodded.

'Wonderful.' From the look in his eyes, she realised that he must think she was using an interest in his sculpture as an excuse for meeting him again, which was a nuisance, but that couldn't be helped. Anyway, he didn't look the type to make a heavy pass right away.

A few minutes later, they were joined by another friend of the Hursts, a well-known politician who wanted to talk to Mark about having himself immortalised in stone. 'A bust,' he elaborated. 'Not my idea, of course; it was suggested by my constituency people.'

Megan met Mark's wry glance and smiled a trifle mischievously. 'Will you excuse me? I've just seen someone I must say hello to . . .'

Mark gave her a pleading look, but she abandoned him to his fate. At least he would get a commission out of it, and she had to find Dev!

While she was talking to Mark, she had occasionally glanced towards Dev, to check that he was still with Emma, but when she looked for him now both he and Emma had gone. Megan soon saw Emma, talking to a little group of people, but

Dev wasn't one of them.

She began to hunt through the ground-floor rooms of the lovely old house without catching sight of him anywhere. People kept trying to talk to her; friends of the Hursts, of course, mostly from an easily recognisable tribe, glossy and assured. The people she worked with had another sort of glamour, but the men and women whom she was meeting tonight had that patronising look, meant to convey their tolerant contempt for her world, for television and all who worked for it; in particular the Fabian show.

She smiled indifferently; it was all water off a duck's back, especially as she knew that they would jump at an invitation to appear on the show.

That was something else her job was all about, recognising the difference between what people said and what they really thought. She would hate to become cynical, but it was hard not to be, at times.

She was in the hall when she heard Dev's name and paused to eavesdrop shamelessly on two guests. 'I haven't seen him all evening, I suppose he actually came to his own party?' one man said, laughing.

'Oh, yes, he's around. I saw him go into the library a while ago,' said the other.

Her long, pale oyster silk skirts rustling, Megan opened the double oak doors of the library, then paused on the threshold of the long room in some surprise because the room was in darkness. Dev couldn't be in here, after all! she thought, sighing, and then his voice spoke harshly from the other side of the room.

'Who's that?'

'Dev?'

There was a silence, then he said in the same grating tone, 'Go back to the party, Megan; go back to Fabian.'

Closing the door, she went towards him, talking hurriedly so that he shouldn't stop her. 'Dev, you mustn't take any notice of what Johnny said! He thought he was protecting me from getting hurt; he doesn't think I should get engaged until I know you better. He meant well, but it was all nonsense. You know there isn't anything between me and Johnny!'

Again silence, then a movement as he leaned over and switched on a silk table-lamp, throwing a warm, roseate glow on to the muted gleam of her oyster silk dress with its full skirts and tight waist.

She blinked in the sudden brightness; seeing him through her lashes in a golden auriole. He looked so unfamiliar; hard and remote. So was his voice. 'Perhaps he was right, all the same. I had no business blurting out a proposal at the last minute; giving you no time to think, taking you by surprise.' The harshness was gone, but the chill in his voice was somehow worse.

She was getting used to the light; she looked at his strong, grim face and hesitated, remembering that overheard talk between him and his sister. Did he love her, or had he proposed cold-bloodedly because she would be satisfied with having his children and making him a home, whereas more beautiful women might want more?

Dev looked back at her, his brows lifting at her silence, and her heart seemed to turn over inside her. It was shameful to admit it; she knew she should hate herself, but she couldn't help loving him and she didn't care whether he loved her or not, she wanted him too much to care why he had chosen her. It was enough that he had.

She knelt down beside his wing armchair while he watched her in an unreadable silence.

'You certainly took me by surprise,' she said, smiling shakily at him. 'But I didn't need any time to think. I love you, and I want to be your wife more than anything in the world.'

He didn't move, staring at her, and she wished she knew what he was thinking, then she was glad that she didn't. Dev looked oddly lonely in here, in these shadows; he needed her, whether he loved her or not. People always said that you liked people who liked you—didn't that apply to love, too?

'Megan, it wouldn't work,' he said heavily, his hands gripping the arms of the leather-upholstered chair.

'Oh, Dev,' she whispered, and put her cheek against the nearest hand, closing her eyes and letting the peace of his closeness flow into her.

He stiffened and for an instant she thought he would snatch his hand away, then his other hand moved, she felt his fingers on her hair, stroking and winnowing. Pleasure held her captive, she hardly breathed as his hand slid under her hair, caressed her bare nape, making her whole body weak with the erotic glide of his fingertips.

After a few moments, he said flatly, 'Marriage is a big step, especially as I'm going away for so long. We won't get engaged, Megan . . .'

'But . . .' she began and he cut in tersely,

'No! You may change your mind once I've gone, for a start!'

'I won't!'

'You can't possibly know that, Megan. At the moment you may think you love me . . .'

'I don't think I do. I know I do. How young do you think I am? I'm not a child, Dev. I'm an adult woman and I know what I want.'

He laughed shortly, that hand closing on her throat, lifting her face towards him. 'Do you?' His voice was lower, deeper; sending a long shudder down her spine. One thing had always been undeniable: the physical drag between them, a sensual attraction she read in Dev's eyes now, darkening his gaze, dilating his pupils.

He bent very slowly, still watching her until the moment when his mouth caught hers. Megan's eyes closed and her lips parted, thirsting for the taste of his kiss. Dev's arms went round her, tightened, pulling her up on to his lap, her body yielding warmly. Everything she was flowed out to him in that kiss; she put her arms around him and held him close to her. This was how it would feel to hold his child, she thought suddenly, and she ached to have Dev's child, to hold it in her arms. It was a thought that had never occurred to her before in her life; her whole being seemed to be shaken up and thrown about as if in a kaleidoscope, coming down in an entirely new pattern.

She had just told him that she knew what she wanted, but until now she really hadn't known. She knew now; she understood herself and life better than she ever had before.

Her long, cloudy hair surrounded them both, making a tent for them in which they kissed, while Dev's hands explored downwards, warm on the oyster silk, far warmer on her bare skin, making her draw a sharp breath and shudder, although not with cold—on the contrary, it was the burning heat between them that made her shake.

Dev might not be in love with her, but she had no doubts abut his desire for her. That side of their marriage would work, anyway!

He suddenly broke off the kiss, breathing roughly as he lifted his head. His face was darkly flushed, his eyes smouldering. 'We'd better stop now, while we can,' he murmured thickly, and she laughed shakily, very flushed.

Dev looked at her with a crooked smile. 'A pity we didn't meet a year ago; we could have been married by now!'

She was so moved she couldn't hold his gaze; she looked down, trembling.

She felt him watching her for a moment, then he said quietly, 'If you change your mind you'll write and tell me honestly? We won't get engaged, Megan; not yet, not until I come back. I don't want to burden you with guilt if you meet someone else while I'm away.'

'I won't,' she said quickly, but Dev just shook his head ruefully.

'Promise me!' he insisted.

She gazed at him, wondering if he was using Johnny's interference as an excuse for doing what he really wanted to do—back out of his proposal? Had he asked her to marry him on the spur of the moment, only to realise when he talked to his sister that it would be a mistake to marry a girl his family thought of as a 'plain little nobody'?

'If I ever do meet anyone, I'll tell you,' she said at last, and he gave an audible sigh. Was that relief or regret? she wondered, her disturbed blue eyes hunting over his face for clues to his true feelings, but Devlin Hurst was a past master at hiding his thoughts and emotions. He looked back at her, his features masked and unreadable.

Then they heard the raised voices outside the double doors, and froze, turning to look in alarm across the room, but the doors didn't open, the voices moved further off. Dev laughed wryly.

'This isn't the time or place, is it?' He kissed her hair, his lips moving softly. 'Sexy hair! In Victorian times, men used to wear a lock of their true love's hair around their necks in a locket.'

Megan sat up a little and leaned over to pick up a pair of scissors from the desk; offering them to him with a sideways little smile. 'Take your pick.'

It was half a joke, but Dev took the scissors slowly and ran his fingers into her hair, staring at it, before snipping off some long, curling strands. He took his wallet out of his inside jacket pocket and slid the lock of hair into it. Megan watched him, entranced; the action had been mesmeric, oddly ritualistic.

She could almost believe Dev loved her, and that gave her the courage to ask, 'Can't I come and see you off at Heathrow?' Dev had said firmly that he did not want her to be there to wave goodbye, but she thought he might weaken if she asked him now.

He looked down at her and shook his head, though. 'No, Megan! I told you—I'd hate saying goodbye in front of half the world, especially with the Press there. I'm going to be very busy from now until we leave, so we'll say goodbye tonight.'

Megan went pale, her body wincing. 'Can't we see each other again one more time?' She hadn't been expecting this and was not prepared for it.

'No,' he said, and although she pleaded for some time he would not give in; he had made up his mind and would not budge. Megan looked at him helplessly. Why on earth had she fallen in love with someone so immovable?

Next day, she got to Mark Bond's studio on time but there was no answer when she rang the bell. She was about to leave when she saw him jogging along the road towards her. He waved, and she waved back, smiling.

'Hi!' he said, a little breathless. 'Am I late? Sorry, I thought I'd be back by now, but I saw someone I know and had to stop and chat.' He was wearing a plum-coloured tracksuit and matching track shoes, and managed to make the outfit look a million dollars.

'That's OK, I haven't been here long!' said Megan, as he opened the front door and waved her through. 'Do you always jog in the mornings?'

'Usually. You need muscles in my job.'

'I suppose you would!' agreed Megan, thinking of some of the vast statues she had seen.

'While I'm showering and changing, why don't you make us some coffee?' Mark said, gesturing to door. 'Kitchen's through there. I won't be long.' He vanished into another room and Megan wryly went into the galley-style kitchen; impressed by the very well-thought-out layout with everything within easy reach. No doubt he had had a first-class kitchen design firm to install the handsome cream and maroon fittings. She made the coffee and stood for a moment looking out of the window at a long, lawned garden which led down to the river Thames. She could just glimpse the steely shine of water through willows. Mark Bond must be successful to afford this flat in this house; it was a very desirable residential neighbourhood.

What was Dev doing this morning? she wondered, sighing. He was busy, of course, getting ready for that year-long trip, but surely he could have made time to see her? Perhaps he would ring tonight? Talking to him for a few minutes would be better than nothing! Lost in thought, she gave a choked gasp as warm, silky fur brushed her leg.

'Don't you like cats?'

Laughing, she looked round at Mark Bond, who was now wearing a conventional white shirt and smooth grey trousers.

'Yes, but I wasn't expecting one just then!' She bent down to stroke the delicate little Siamese with the strange blue eyes, but it undulated away from her hand and stalked off, offended, tail in the air.

Megan made a face and Mark Bond laughed, then inhaled the scent of the coffee.

'Do I need this! Shall we take it through into the studio?' He picked up the tray and Megan followed him across the corridor into a long, spacious, light-filled room with the end wall entirely made of glass through which she saw the same view she had seen from the kitchen: grass and trees and distant river.

'Sit here,' Mark said, laying down the tray on the floor. He curled up next to it and began pouring coffee. Megan hesitated beside the only chair; a Victorian balloon-backed chair covered in deep red velvet. Mark gave her a grin. 'Go on, sit down. I keep that for visitors. My grandmother gave it to me; she swore it had once belonged to Dante Gabriel Rossetti, but I don't believe a word of it.'

Megan sat down, took the cup he held out to her. 'It's a romantic thought, though, isn't it?'

He studied her. 'Ah, you're romantic, are you?'

She flushed. 'And you're not?'

'I keep it, so maybe I am,' he mocked, pulling a tray full of large sheets of cartridge paper towards him. Picking out a sheet, he began sketching, his eyes on Megan. 'You don't mind, do you? I feel ill at ease with idle fingers.'

Megan wasn't sure she didn't mind, but didn't like to object, so to cover her uneasiness she looked around at the high-ceilinged, white-walled, rectangular room. There were several sheet-draped objects in it; she tried to guess what they were. That one must be a woman, she decided—

what other shape had those particular curves? Had he draped them to hide them from her?

'Those sheets look like veils,' she said. 'They're making me curious about what's underneath.'

He grinned. 'Isn't that always the way with veils? I sometimes think women should never have stopped wearing them.'

Megan laughed. 'I'm glad they did! How boring, going around in a veil all day.' She watched his deft fingers and wondered what the sketch of her would be like; she couldn't remember anyone ever drawing her before.

'Want to see?' He offered the sheet of paper to her and she stared at the sketch, taken aback by it. 'Well? What do you think?' he asked, and she looked at him uncertainly.

'It's very good.' Yet it was alarming, too. She felt he had shown her things about herself she hadn't known; it was not the Megan Carr she knew, and yet she had to recognise the truth of it, and that was disturbing.

There was an uncovered and powerful clay head on a turntable nearby, so to cover her uneasiness she looked at that. She didn't recognise the sitter but the force of the thing hit you from across the room; it was as dominating as any living human being, and it made her eager to see more of his work.

'I am going to see your work, aren't I?' she asked, as she finished her coffee, and Mark Bond laughed.

'That's why you're here!'

She smiled uncertainly, wondering if he guessed

the reason behind her sudden fascination with his work.

'Give me a hand with these sheets,' Mark said, rising, and she got to her feet to help him. He looked down at her, his eyes very bright and intent, and Megan stared into them in faint bewilderment. Why was he looking at her like that? She soon found out. He bent and kissed her, taking her by surprise before she could move away. His lips were warm and coaxing, and she might have enjoyed the experience if she hadn't been in love with another man. Stiffening, she pushed him away, and he lifted his head to look down into her eyes in a long, searching stare.

'Whoops!'

That wry exclamation threw Megan. 'What?'

'In case you didn't notice, I just made one hell of a mistake,' he drily said. 'Obviously, I put two and two together and made it five. I thought you invited yourself here because you fancied me.'

She flushed. 'Oh!'

'Which you clearly don't!'

Megan looked unhappily at him; she had been afraid that he would jump to some such conclusion!

'OK, no need to look tragic,' he drawled, mouth crooked. 'So if it wasn't my fatal charm that brought you here, what was it? You scarcely seem to be a sculpture buff. I don't think you know anything about sculpture.'

She sighed. 'I'm not, no! I am interested in it, that is—really! But . . . well, Johnny asked me to check you out, you see. It's possible he might ask you on the show, but first . . .'

'Fabian told you to chat me up?' he interrupted, brows heavy. 'Does he always send you to flirt with possible guests for his show?'

Hot, angry colour ran up her face. 'I'm one of his researchers. It doesn't make me part of the deal, Mr Bond, and Johnny doesn't require me to flirt with anyone.' She pushed past him and headed for the door. 'Forget it. Thank you for your time.'

He caught up with her before she had finished speaking. 'Megan! I'm sorry! That was damned rude of me. No excuses, but I suppose I found it hard to take the fact that you hadn't come round just because you liked me.'

'That sounds remarkably like an excuse to me!' she said, but already softening, because Mark had a charm she couldn't help responding to; his smile was that of a naughty little boy: guilty, yet still hoping that he would be forgiven. He probably always was! She shook her head at him.' I should go now while I'm ahead!'

'Please stay!' he coaxed. 'Can't we start again?'

She could hardly refuse, so she accepted the hand he held out. 'Friends?' he asked, and she laughed and shrugged.

'Friends.'

'Good. Now, let's get the drapes off these things.'

Of course, it wasn't enough that he should be good at his work, or respected by the art world—he had to be able to talk if he was to appear on the show, and Megan listened intently as Mark showed her the sculptures in the studio. She had done some homework on him before she came and knew that he had sold pieces to several cities for public display, but the statues in the studio at present were all privately commissioned.

'I'd like to see one of your bigger statues,' she said thoughtfully.

'There's a vast shopping mall in North London which has one of my biggest pieces. The central hall of the mall has a fountain; they asked me to sculpt Neptune but I did something a little less obvious: sea-horses, fifteen-foot-high sea-horses thundering along in a cloud of spray—that's the fountain, not me, of course.'

'It sounds wonderful,' she said, watching his face intently; it was so alive, so vibrant, especially when his eyes glowed like that. Yes, he could certainly talk well, on his own subject.

'I have to go there tonight, to one of those city hall dinners. Back-patting affairs! You know, Councillor this and my Lord Mayor that, all telling each other how wonderful they are! I'm invited for the official unveiling of my sea-horses.' He suddenly stopped, looking at her with his head to one side. 'Why don't you come along? My invitation card says bring a guest and I wasn't planning to . . . but you could see the fountain and it might be fun.'

Megan hesitated; half drawn to the idea because she would like to see the magical sea-horses he talked of with so much excitement, and half reluctant to go anywhere in case Dev rang her.

But she knew, in her heart of hearts, that he wouldn't. Dev had made it crystal-clear that he would be too busy to see her; he had virtually cut her off and she was only fooling herself if she hoped to hear from him again before he left the country. Maybe in a couple of months she would get a postcard from some remote little town on the Amazon. Oh, Dev had promised to write as often as he could, and he might write now and then, in between more vital jobs, or when he had nothing else to do, but he was obsessed with this project of his, and Dev was a ruthlessly committed man. Once he was out there he would often be out of touch with civilisation for weeks on end. He might as well be going to the moon.

If she stayed at home she would brood over Dev all evening—perhaps it would be wiser to go out?

'Thank you, I'd love to see your sea-horses!' she said, and saw from Mark's face that he was surprised, had not expected her to accept.

That evening, while she was waiting for Mark to pick her up, she rang Dev, but his voice was recorded; she could only talk to his answering machine; which she was tempted to do, pouring out her feelings as she heard his living, yet already distant voice. Of course, she didn't; she didn't even leave a message, she silently hung up. It seemed an omen, especially when it began to rain. She sat by the window, in the half-light, listening to the hypnotic sound of water washing down the glass, swishing along the gutters in the street, drumming on roofs and cars. She was haunted by the knowledge that Dev was somewhere in the city and within reach, yet had already said goodbye to her.

She didn't understand him. If she could, she would spend every precious minute of these last few days with him—why didn't he want that? Did he really love her? A fierce stab of pain inside her made her want to curl up in a foetus-like ball of misery. Dev was a strange country whose maps she could not read, and in which she was always lost.

The doorbell buzzed; it was Mark, a few minutes early and very striking in formal dark evening clothes.

He smiled down at her, his brows lifting as he whistled admiration. 'You're looking very special tonight! I love that dress.'

'Thank you.' Megan was pleased with his reaction; she liked the dress too; it was one of her favourites, not new, but one in which she always felt wonderful because she knew it suited her. The rich, gentian blue of the taffeta brought out the colour of her eyes, and the tight waist and low bodice gave her figure more impact. She had altered her hairstyle, brushed back her black hair and pinned it up with diamanté stars so that it glittered and swished around her face when she turned her head.

'We make a great pair,' Mark said, taking her hand and drawing it through his arm on the way out to his car. 'Now, you're going to enjoy yourself tonight, and that's official.'

She laughed. 'Yes, sir, certainly, sir.'

'You aren't going to be bored, and if you go to sleep during the speeches I'll kick you under the table, and you'll do the same for me, which could be vital, as I'm one of the speakers and if it's me making the speech when I fall asleep someone might notice.'

'Unless they're all asleep, too?' she suggested, and he nodded as he started the engine.

'Knowing the power of my oratory, that is more than likely.'

'What do I do then?'

'Just let us all sleep, OK?'

In fact, he made a brilliant speech, funny and fascinating. Megan was very impressed; there was no doubt that he would be a big hit on the Fabian show. He was a big hit with the audience that night—and a big hit with Megan. She was just as struck by his incredible fountain; the horses took your breath away as they seemed to thunder towards you through the flying spray. An imaginative local council had lined the edge of the pool with water fern and water lilies. It gave the rather stark, windy mall a beautiful and tranquil centre, as Megan told Mark while he was driving her back to her flat.

'An improvement on some places I've seen,' he agreed, his eyes on the almost empty road. It was almost midnight, still raining, and most people seemed to be staying at home. Megan yawned convulsively.

'Tired?' said Mark, shooting her a glance. 'Never mind, we're nearly at your place.'

That was when the car began jerking and coughing, and Mark sat up, swearing. 'Oh, hell!'

'What's wrong?' Megan asked anxiously.

He slowly drew into the side of the road and

then stopped. Turning to look ruefully at her, he said, 'I'm out of petrol.' He watched her mouth open, then curve into amusement. 'Don't laugh, damn you! Unless a taxi happens by, you're going to have to walk home from here in this rain!'

She peered out and recognised the street. 'It's only a block from where I live, don't worry.' She huddled inside her short black velvet evening jacket, wryly realising that her clothes were going to get soaked.

'Could I use your phone to ring for a taxi?' Mark said. 'I'll have to leave my car here and come back for it tomorrow.'

'Of course.'

They ran through the rainy street, and laughing and breathless, almost fell into her flat, both of them dripping wet; their hair plastered to their heads and their clothes damp.

'The phone's in the sitting-room,' said Megan. 'Take your jacket off and dry it in front of the electric fire while you wait for the taxi. I'll make us some hot chocolate.'

'Mmm, you're an angel.' Mark stripped off his jacket while she switched on the fire, then she went to find him a towel for his hair, put on the milk for the chocolate and took off her wet dress, replacing it with a loose purple caftan. She had to hurry before the milk boiled over.

When she carried the mugs of hot chocolate into the sitting-room she found Mark sitting on the floor in front of the electric fire, listening to a jazz record and glancing through a glossy book about Renoir which someone had once given Megan for

Christmas.

'I hope you don't mind; I've made myself at home,' he said, giving her an impish grin. 'The taxi won't get here for twenty minutes. They said they were very busy tonight because of the rain.'

'No problem. So you like jazz, too?' Megan handed him his mug of chocolate, and curled up on the floor next to him, her own mug clasped between her cold hands.

'Love it! You must come and hear my collection some time . . .' The sudden clangour of the doorbell stopped him mid-sentence and his brows rose. 'Who can that be at this time of night?'

Megan had turned pink and was already on her feet. She didn't answer, but Mark's eyes narrowed at the look in her face as she rushed to the door, entirely forgetting him.

She ran, because she was afraid that if she didn't get there fast Dev would go again. She knew it was Dev, who else could it be at this hour?

He stood there in a short black leather jacket, the collar turned up, his hair darkened with rain, smiling at her.

'I was driving past when I saw your light come on and I thought I'd drop in to . . .' His voice died away as his eyes moved past her to the open door of the sitting-room through which he had a clear view of Mark in his shirt-sleeves, sprawled on the carpet by the fire, sipping his hot chocolate.

Slowly Dev looked back at Megan in her loose caftan, her hair tousled and fluffy where she had dried it with a towel hurriedly without afterwards running a comb through it.

She went scarlet as she suddenly realised what he was thinking. 'Dev, I . . . we've been . . .' she stammered, so upset she couldn't get out a sensible explanation.

'Sorry to have interrupted your cosy evening,' Dev said curtly before she could pull herself together, then he turned on his heel and strode off too fast for her to have a chance of catching up with him.

CHAPTER THREE

SHE tried to get in touch with him at his flat later, but there was only the answering machine at home; she left a husky message but Dev did not ring back. She didn't sleep, and went in to work heavy-eyed and unable to concentrate.

'What's the matter with you?' Johnny asked. 'Coming down with something nasty? Don't come near me, I don't want it.'

He wouldn't catch it, she thought. Johnny was immune to love; had he ever been a victim or had he been born immune?

'In fact, you'd better go home to bed and stay there,' he said from a safe distance. 'And don't come back until you're over whatever it is . . .'

She went home via Dev's flat, but he didn't come to the door when she rang the bell, and there was no sign of his car in the usual space. She put a note through the letterbox, explaining why Mark had been with her in her flat the night before, and asking him to call her. When he hadn't rung by lunch time, she tried again to ring him, but this time there wasn't even an answering maching. All she got was the steady whine of a disconnected phone. Dev had had his phone cut off.

Feverish and desperate, she paced the floor, watching the clock inexorably tick through the hours until Dev went. Surely he wouldn't go

without seeing her? He must have got her
messages. He must know now why Mark was at
her flat at that hour, and he would realise how
unhappy this misunderstanding had made her. He
couldn't just fly away for a whole year without
telling her he believed her, he knew the truth?

For a second night she went without sleep;
even though she tried to relax in bed she
couldn't, her brain was too active and she was
too miserable.

Dawn found her white and shivering, almost
hallucinating because she had had no sleep for
two days. There was only one chance left, she
thought, looking at her watch for the hundredth
time. She had to go to Heathrow. Dev had
insisted that he didn't want her there; there
would be photographers and reporters there to
see the team off, and Dev didn't want her
involved in any of the publicity ballyhoo.

The situation had changed, though. She
couldn't let him go without seeing him, even if
only for a moment. She had to be sure that he
knew he had jumped to the wrong conclusion
when he saw Mark in her flat. Dev must not go
off to South America without knowing the truth.

When she reached the airport she parked in
the short-term car park and walked to the
terminal building, but just as she got to the
check-in desk she saw Dev and the rest of the
team walking through the control barrier on the
way to the departure lounge.

Running, she called his name; the others went
on but he stopped and looked round. Megan

waved, calling again, 'Dev!'

His cold grey eyes briefly met hers, then he walked on, out of sight. She skidded to a halt, feeling sick. He had gone. She couldn't believe it; Dev had seen her and he had known very well why she was here, but he had turned his back on her and walked away.

Slowly she walked back to retrieve her car and drove back into London, without really being aware of what she was doing, acting like an automaton. She was trapped inside a nightmare. Lack of sleep, emotional stress, fever and weariness made the world seem totally unreal to her. She kept moving because he couldn't think of anything else to do. She could not break down in the airport, in the car park, in the street. She couldn't cry or lie down in public. She had to get home, to be alone; only then could she give way to what she felt.

She was only a mile from her flat when she ran into the back of a lorry and the world disintegrated into chaos for her.

It was days before she knew anything about what had happened to her; time had become a seamless garment of pain and sleep. She woke from one to the other only to retreat again. Her parents were dead and she had been an only child, so she had no relatives visiting her, but somebody sent her flowers; enormous bouquets which the nurses showed her excitedly.

'Get well soon, I need you here, love, Johnny,' they read from the card. 'Johnny Fabian! His secretary has rung up twice to find out how you are!'

Megan had gazed at them with blank indifference. In the place where she was, Johnny had no real meaning. Nothing but pain had any meaning, including herself, for a long time; the drugs the nurses gave her could take away the pain, but they took away all the significance of memory, too. It wasn't that she forgot, so much as that she did not think of anything outside those four pale walls and the threat of the pain.

When she did start the slow drift back to life, Johnny was her first visitor. She and her little room were prepared for his visit as if he was royalty; by then Megan was capable of sensing the air of excitement pervading the whole ward. Johnny Fabian was a national figure; his show was always close to the top of the TV ratings. The nurses chatted in low, elated voices while they waited for visiting hours to start. They seemed shocked that Megan was so calm about it all.

When Johnny did arrive, he brought more flowers. A basket of exotic fruit, too, and magazines, a couple of fat best-sellers, several get well cards from the programme team, scrawled with personal messages and signatures. The nurses were impressed; Megan knew he had most probably asked his secretary to go out and buy everything, but all the same she was touched by his thoughtfulness. Johnny had more than charm; he had a kind heart. When he kissed her cheek, he tried hard not to look shocked at the sight of her.

Megan knew why he was avoiding her eyes; she

had seen herself that morning, and for the first time discovered both how very ill she had been and how gaunt and haggard she looked.

'I can see you're on the mend,' he said in a bright voice. 'You're looking great, kid.'

She smiled wearily at him. 'Thanks, Johnny.' It was nice of him to lie.

She asked him how everyone else was and he told her in a lively way, trying to boost her mood with his own energy. He didn't mention Devlin Hurst and she didn't ask about him. She wasn't yet strong enough to think about Dev; instinct made her protect herself from the pain of it. For the moment she was just concentrating on getting through each long, long day.

'When they let you out of here,' said Johnny before he left, 'we're going to send you to a convalescent home in the Cotswolds. You'll love it; it was a big manor house set in a park before they turned it into a nursing home. It's got a gymnasium, jacuzzis, indoor swimming pool, saunas—you name it, they've got it, and if you get bored with that lot you can always just take a walk in this beautiful parkland. More like a good country hotel than a hospital, really.'

She tried to laugh. 'I shall be too exhausted to come back to work after a few days there!'

Johnny gave her an odd look. 'Your job will be open for you whenever you come back,' he quickly said.

After he had gone, she wondered about that— the strange glance and the hurried reassurance. How ill was she, and how long would it be before she was back to normal? Worry kept her awake, and when her specialist came to see her he noted the insomnia marked on her daily progress report and asked about it.

She frankly told him what was bothering her and he sat on the edge of her bed, lifting the tails of his spotless white coat first and apparently quite oblivious of Sister's flared nostrils. It was a ward rule that nobody—nobody at all—ever sat on the side of a bed, but Sister didn't utter a syllable. She just took a deep breath and tightened her lips.

The doctor took Megan's hand and patted it. 'I think you're up to hearing the facts now,' he began ominously, watching her pale face. 'I'm afraid you will not be going back to work for quite a while. You have some plastic surgery ahead of you when you're strong enough.'

Her free hand involuntarily flew to her face and the doctor half smiled, half sighed, shaking his head. 'No, not your face, your body. At the moment you have some scarring after the operation we had to perform when you were first brought in. A good plastic surgeon, however, should be able to disguise all that—you may even be able to wear a bikini again in time.'

He watched her face quivering, and frowned. 'You know, you're lucky to be alive, Miss Carr. You could easily have died from your very serious injuries. Our operating team worked like demons to save you—you have a lot to be thankful for.'

The ward sister stared at her, gimlet-eyed,

daring her not to be grateful.

'I am very grateful, Mr Oliver,' Megan said huskily, and he waved the words away with a peremptory hand.

'I did my job, now I want you to do yours—and fight your way back to normal. It won't be easy, I am not going to promise it will be—you'll get tired, dispirited, depressed, but if you make yourself hold on, in time you'll get there.'

She forced a smile, nodding. 'Thank you.' Sister's stare made it clear that the great man has spent more than enough time on her, and she should let him go.

He rose, smiling properly. 'Good girl. I'll see you again in a few days and then we'll discuss a date when you can move on to this expensive convalescent home! I know the place; only wish I could spend a few weeks there myself!'

Laughing, he walked on, with his attendant entourage of students and nurses, escorted by Sister every inch of the way.

It wasn't until his next visit that Megan discovered the full consequences of her accident and the following operation. The specialist hadn't allowed her to be told until then because he wanted to be certain she was mentally strong enough to stand the shock of the news.

He told her himself, quite gently. Megan stared blankly at him as it sank in, and he frowned.

'You understand?'

She was white, her skin ice-cold. She slowly moved her lips and heard her voice saying casually, 'Yes; I will never be able to have a baby.'

He looked disturbed, and picked up her wrist. 'Sister!' he snapped and Megan heard the flurry of movement, the prick of a needle. She felt annoyed because she had been very calm about it, hadn't she? She hadn't screamed or begun to cry. But they hadn't given her a chance to protest; she already began to feel light-headed. She closed her eyes and sank into the strange, muffling sleep she now recognised: drug-induced and disorientating, it was nothing like real sleep, and she never woke from it feeling fresh and restored. This time she did not even want to wake from it at all.

A week later, she was driven in a small, private ambulance, out of London to the Cotswolds convalescent home. By then, she was allowed up for most of the day, although she still had to rest a good deal. Physically, she was healing. Her state of mind was something else again; she was silent and withdrawn and often sat by a window, staring out across the parkland, her face blank.

'You aren't mixing with the other patients—why?' asked one of the nurses, a large girl with a horribly cheerful manner.

Megan frowned. 'I prefer to be alone. When can I go home? I'm fit enough now.'

'There's a good film on tonight, everyone will be watching it in the video room—why don't you come down?'

'No, thanks. I want to finish the book I'm reading.'

The place was run like a hotel; the nurses were only there in case of emergency, but they still kept a watchful eye on everyone and Megan was always glad to get away from that sensation of being watched. She had her own room with a lovely view of the lake and of woodland beyond the edge of the park, and she liked to stay there, rather than mix with the other patients. Only when pressed did she use the facilities available: the indoor pool, the saunas, the gym. She was perfectly well, she kept telling Johnny. 'Once I'm back at work I'll be fine! That's what I need—normal surroundings!'

The truth was, though, that she had no energy or spirit. Something inside her had broken with the news that she could never now have a child.

She had spent days brooding over what to do about Dev. No letter had come from him yet, but then he had warned her that it might be weeks before she heard, because he would be very busy before setting off on this great journey along the Amazon and might only have time to scribble her a note at the last moment.

He had been angry with her when he flew from Heathrow, and she didn't really have a clue how Dev felt about her any more, but one thing was crystal-clear to her—she had to end their engagement, anyway.

Dev was getting married because he wanted children; a home and family. She couldn't give him that now and so she couldn't marry him. If she told him the truth, Dev might feel obliged to lie out of pity or kindness. He might deny that he wanted children, or suggest they adopted, and, ironically, if she had not heard him talking to his sister she might have believed him, because she loved him enough not to care whether he could give her children or not. If the position were reversed, she would always have preferred to have Dev and no children than a chance of children with any other man, but how did Dev really feel about her?

She didn't know, and she couldn't tell Dev that she had overheard him and Emma talking. He must not know how much she guessed.

He had told her to write and let him know frankly if she changed her mind, if she found someone else while he was away, so that was what she did, at last, when she had nerved herself to do it. She wrote to Dev and told him she had met someone else, she was sorry, and ended the short letter, 'Goodbye, Megan.' Those were the two hardest words she had ever used; she agonised over them before she wrote them, and once the letter was in the post on its way to South America and Dev she spent a lot of time alone in her room, crying.

By the time she left the convalescent home she had used up all her tears and had learnt how to smile again; with the lips, at least, if not the eyes.

Her most frequent visitor throughout those weeks was Mark Bond. He had turned up one day, soon after she arrived in the Cotswolds, bringing an armful of flowers: roses and white iris and feathery gypsophila.

'I'd have come sooner, but Fabian told me you

weren't allowed visitors yet.' He dropped the flowers on her bed and stood back to stare assessingly.

Megan knew she was pale and lifeless, but she was too weary to smile. '*La Belle Dame Sans Merci*,' Mark murmured, and, incredulously, she laughed—the first time she has laughed spontaneously since her accident.

'What?'

' "Her hair was long, her foot was light, and her eyes were wild",' he quoted, a glimmer of teasing in his eyes.

'You're crazy,' Megan said, a faint pink rising in her cheeks as she remembered the rest of the poem.

Mark was remembering it, too. ' "I shut her wild, wild eyes with kisses four",' he quoted, sitting down next to the bed.

'Sister wouldn't approve,' she assured him, shifting on her pillows.

'She doesn't like Keats?' he blandly enquired.

'I doubt if she knows anything about him or his *Belle Dame Sans Merci*, but if she did, she wouldn't approve. There's a lot Sister doesn't approve of!'

He roared with laughter, which brought a capped head around the door, 'Not too much noise, please,' Sister said stiffly. 'Some patients are resting at this time of day.'

'Sorry,' Mark got out in a choked voice, and she nodded and vanished again. When she had gone Mark began laughing again, less noisily, and Megan couldn't help laughing, too.

Later, when she was alone, she realised that his visit had lifted her. She was glad he had come, and as the weeks passed looked forward more and more to his arrivals. By the time she was back home and able to start work again, Mark had become part of her life. They weren't lovers, they were friends, and the warmth between them made the loss of Dev more bearable.

Autumn had passed into grey winter long ago; she has missed all the rich warm colours of the falling leaves and the transitory sunshine. Megan came back to a cold city; to a quiet Christmas and a New Year which she found far from joyous. She has never been a creature of sharp mood-swings; in the past she has usually been even-tempered and contented, but that was before fate struck and deprived her both of the man she loved and any hope of ever having children or a normal marriage.

Before leaving the convalescent home she had had to go through several interviews with a psychiatrist. Meagan hadn't wanted to see her. 'I'm not sick,' she had said obstinately, refusing to keep the first appointment, but she had been persuaded to agree. The woman was middle-aged; thin and watchful with shrewd dark eyes. Megan had not liked the way she looked sideways, or the funny, superior little smile she wore when she did not like the answers Megan gave her.

'You ought to talk about your feelings; express them more openly. If you lock it all up inside yourself, you may have problems later. It's quite natural to feel bitter and angry. Anyone would, in your place; there's no shame in that.'

Megan had nodded without saying anything, and had been given that little smile again.

'You do feel bitter, don't you?' coaxed the other woman.

'No,' Megan said, smiling sweetly. Of course she felt bitter; she was angrily resentful of the trick life had played on her. She dreamt sometimes that it had not happened, and woke up in the darkness of night, face wet, listening to the indifferent breathing all around her. Life went on, whatever happened, but she felt her life had ended. She did not know how to cope with what had happened. She felt empty, desolate. She felt she wasn't a woman any more; she felt betrayed. But she wasn't going to talk about it to this woman. Why should she? She would never tell this woman how she felt. She did not like her. She wouldn't tell her the time of day. She hated the gleam of curiosity; the brightness of the eyes. Show me your pain, the other woman said; let me see it. But Megan wasn't telling her anything, and after she left the convalescent home she did not keep the further appointments that had been made for her. She ignored letters and phone calls, and in time the psychiatrist gave up.

Megan's own doctor saw her several times but did not get past the high stone wall she had erected to keep out all curious strangers. She might have talked about her feelings to someone close to her, but none of her friends were close enough, and she had no family. She had never realised until then how alone she was, or how much she had secretly wanted to build a family life for herself one day.

The pain of her situation was so intense that she could only cope with it, and Mark helped her there, without being aware of it, by being light-hearted, always fun to be with, which allowed Megan to forget what she wanted to forget and laugh as though she had no troubles in the world.

One day in his studio he gave her a ball of clay and told her to try her hand at making something while he worked.

'Making what?' she asked, taken aback, and he shrugged, grinning.

'Whatever you fancy.'

'But I don't know how.'

'It doesn't matter how; just play around with the clay until you get an idea. You'll find it soothing, like making mud pies when you were a little kid.'

She laughed, but he had hit the nail on the head. It *was* soothing, she found. Her hands instinctively felt the clay; squeezed it in her palms, smoothed it with her fingertips, rolled it round and round, drew it out, gave it shape and new dimension, screwed it up again into a ball, and while she played with the plastic stuff she was absorbed and calmed, and smiled at Mark when he winked across the studio at her.

'I like it.'

'I knew you would,' he said quietly, and Megan wondered how clever Mark really was and how much he understood of what she had been going through.

As the days passed, his company meant more and more to her, although it still had no romantic or sexual hang-up. They were friends, nothing more.

She should have known that people would misunderstand the situation, but it didn't occur to her until she went back to work and rapidly realised what everyone was thinking.

It was Johnny who came out with it bluntly. 'Is it serious?' he asked and when she stared, at a complete loss, added wryly, 'You and Mark, I mean, don't pretend you didn't know that!'

'Mark's a buddy of mine, that's all!' Megan snapped, and Johnny laughed.

'Oh, yeah? Platonic, you mean? I don't believe in platonic friendships between a man and a woman. Between the sexes there's only one sort of relationship.'

Megan narrowed her eyes at him, smiling angrily. 'So what is there between you and me, Johnny?'

'I'm just waiting for my cue,' he claimed, grinning unashamedly. 'Is this it, Megan? Are you giving me a green light?' He put both hands around her waist, pulling her towards him, and bent to kiss her, but as his lips touched her mouth she pushed him violently away.

Johnny looked down at her, amused by her angry reaction. 'How about dinner after the show tonight?'

'No thanks,' she said through her teeth before walking off. She was having dinner with Mark, as it happened, and wished now that she hadn't arranged for him to pick her up at the studios, because someone from the programme was bound to see them and that would only add fuel to the gossip.

She tried to hurry off once they were off the air, before any of the team left, but Johnny chose that evening to get difficult because in researching one of that batch of guests she had somehow missed a vital piece of information.

'How could you let me make a fool of myself like that? It should have been in your notes! What do you think I pay you for?'

Johnny was nasty because he had tripped up in public, and Megan couldn't blame him for getting angry. She han't done her job properly; she didn't even know how she had come to miss something so obvious.

'I'm terribly sorry, Johnny, it won't happen again!' she stammered apologetically, and Johnny stared at her, mouth hard, then shrugged.

'I hope it won't! Maybe you aren't quite back to normal after your illness. I'll forget it this time, but for the lord's sake keep your wits about you in the future!'

He walked with her out of the building a few minutes later, his brows rising as he saw Mark in his car waiting for her.

'Now I see why you wouldn't have dinner with me!'

She was flushed and didn't answer.

'Which reminds me, did you know Devlin Hurst is coming back soon?' Johnny asked after a thoughtful pause, and Megan looked at him in shock.

'But he isn't due back for months!'

'He picked up a bug out there and has been ordered home! The rest of the team are going on and if Dev recovers in time he may go back and join them, but I gather they've already shot an enormous amount of film and he may stay here to start the editing and write the narration.'

Megan fought to look calm, but knew Johnny was watching her with a mixture of curiosity and half-malicious enjoyment. He wasn't privy to all the secrets of her relationship with Dev, but he had known that she and Dev were seriously involved before Dev left, and he knew that she had been seeing a lot of Mark Bond over the past few months.

'I'm sure you're longing to see him again,' he said, eyes teasing, and Megan managed a stiff little smile.

'Yes, of course. Well, goodnight, Johnny.' She walked away to get into Mark's car, feeling sick. Dev was coming home too soon; she wasn't feeling brave enough to face him yet.

CHAPTER FOUR

FOR days she was on tenterhooks, expecting any moment to see Dev walking into her flat, into the office or the studio—but time passed and there was no word or sign of him. She decided Johnny had been teasing, or else had heard some groundless gossip. Or perhaps Dev had fought off whatever bug he had picked up, and was not coming home until the full year was up? The relief was almost as unbearable as the tension of wondering when she would see him, and in a mood of euphoria she went to a party with Mark one evening, feeling better than she had for a very long time.

The party was being given to launch a highly publicised new drama series; the director had invited some big stars as well as lots of media people. There was live music, expensive food and good wine, and a threat of several of the stars singing for their supper.

'It should be fun,' Megan had told Mark, tongue in cheek, after telling him the names of the big stars.

'I was once asked to sculpt the lady,' he confided thoughtfully. 'In the nude.'

'Did you do it?' She glanced up at him as they danced, and he gave her a wicked grin.

'What do you think?'

'Did she commission it herself?' Megan could see the beautiful actress in a corner of the room, surrounded by men. She was still ravishing, even at forty-five. How did she look naked, though?

'A lover,' Mark said. 'They split up not long afterwards. I've no idea which of them kept the statue.'

Something in his voice made her look sharply at him. 'Did they fall out over you?'

Mark's brows lifted. 'You're uncanny, do you know that?'

'It wasn't hard to guess! You looked much too smug,' she mocked gently, and he tightened his grip on her slender waist, putting his cheek against her long, richly curling hair.

Megan was still smiling as her blue eyes gazed vaguely over his shoulder at the shadowy, crowded room. A haze of cigar smoke hung in the air, people either danced casually, shuffling close together, or they stood about drinking and talking above the little band playing a medley of popular songs.

'Hey,' said Johnny, looming up in front of her, and she said, 'Hi, Johnny!' smiling, before she saw who he had with him.

'Look who just arrived!' Johnny said, watching her face.

Her skin was icy, her eyes stricken.

'Hello, Megan,' Dev said, and managed to make the greeting sound like an insult. She hadn't expected him to be so angry; it bewildered her.

'Good heavens, Hurst, I thought you were up the Amazon for a year,' Mark said cheerfully, his arm still round her waist although they had stopped dancing.

'I had to come home for medical treatment,' Dev told him curtly.

'That sounds serious.' Mark had stopped smiling, a faint bewilderment in his eyes at the other man's brusque tone.

'It could have been if I hadn't had a course of drugs as soon as possible, but they say they caught it in time and I'm almost back to normal now. I'll probably be allowed to go back to South America next month.'

Johnny frowned. 'Is that wise, Dev? Isn't there a risk of re-infection?'

'A slight one, but I want to finish filming, even so.' Dev's voice was forbidding; he did not want to talk about it and resented Johnny's questioning, which was instinctive, of course. Johnny always asked questions; that was his method of interviewing, particularly when he met up with someone who did not want to answer questions at all. He had the bulldog mentality and it was his great gift as an interviewer. Megan was staring at the floor, but through her lashes she managed to absorb how Dev looked: his face had a new grimness, he had lost a lot of weight, his cheekbones showed starkly through his sunburnt skin and his clothes looked a little too big for him. Her heart turned over. Dev had been very ill and it showed.

'You shouldn't take the chance, should he, Megan?' Johnny said with that typical trace of malice underlying the words. He was having some peculiar fun at her expense, but she wouldn't let him see that she knew as much. She didn't answer, pretending she hadn't heard.

Johnny merely repeated the question. 'Should he, Megan?'

'I can understand it,' Mark calmly answered for her. 'Work comes first, doesn't it, Hurst? Even where our health is concerned!'

Dev's mouth twisted; he shrugged. 'Exactly.'

Megan dared to look up at him while he was looking at Mark, but a second later his grey eyes flashed sideways and she found herself looking into them. It was like looking at a frozen wasteland and she flinched.

Why was he so angry? He hadn't been in love with her; he had more or less admitted as much to his sister. Over and over again he had insisted that Megan should write and tell if she found anyone else; he had seemed quite calm at the prospect, almost seemed to expect it. She had been dreading his return because of the pain of seeing him again, but she had not been expecting Dev to look at her with such bitterness and contempt.

Several other people came over to join their circle at that moment, and the talk became very lively. Megan whispered to Mark that she was just going to powder her nose, and without even looking in Dev's direction hurried away.

The party was being held in a big suite in a London hotel. Megan walked through the crowded, busy foyer and out into the street. Across a traffic-jammed road lay one of London's royal parks; an oasis of smooth green turf and trees. She darted through the traffic, slowing as she reached the safety of the park. It was twilight; a chilly, raw day in February. There were very few people around and those she saw were bent, huddled in their winter coats against the biting wind. The trees were bare, their branches a confused black criss-cross against the pale sky.

Megan walked slowly, hardly aware of having no coat, or of the wintry weather. How dared he look at her like that? She felt as if he had struck her; those cold eyes had been like a blow.

Restlessly, she turned in her tracks to walk back to the hotel, and her nerves jumped as she found herself facing Dev at the far end of the tree-lined walk. Had he followed her out here? Or was it sheer coincidence that he had come to the park, too? Pretending she had not seen him, she swung round and walked hurriedly along a path to the left, but when she reached a bend in the path there was Dev again, coming towards her.

She glanced from side to side, looking for an escape, a way of avoiding him, but she could only get away by turning and running in the opposite direction, and that would be so childish, it would be a confession of guilt she was not going to make. If Dev had loved her it would have been different, but she knew he hadn't, and his resentment made her burn with anger.

'There was no need to run away from me!' he said bitingly as they met. Her darkened eyes seemed to magnify him; he looked very tall, very forbidding. He wasn't anyone she knew any more. Had he ever been? How much had she ever known about Dev? She had thought she knew him, she had loved him, yet all the time she had been living in a delusion.

'I wasn't running away!' She put up her chin defiantly, her long hair blown around her face by the wind.

'That's what it looked like to me.' His voice was as wintry as the weather in the streets. 'When I arrived, you were dancing with Bond happily enough. You certainly looked as if you were enjoying the party, before I arrived. Then you fled. If it was guilty conscience, you needn't worry. I won't make any trouble.' Their eyes met and he smiled tightly; it wasn't much of a smile and it didn't make her feel any easier, especially when he added, 'Does he know about us, by the way?'

She looked down without answering, her fingers twisting and knotting together. She hadn't mentioned any names when she wrote to say she had met someone else, but the one fact she knew for certain about Dev was that he was clever. Seeing her with Mark, he had put two and two together at once. Of course, he wasn't to know she had lied about wanting another man.

'It is Bond, isn't it?' insisted Dev, and she hesitated, then nodded without looking up because if she met his eyes she might find it harder to lie, even in silence.

Dev laughed humourlessly. 'I wouldn't have thought he was your type!' A spasm of pain seemed to tighten every muscle in his face, and Megan watched him, her blue eyes wide and dark with feeling, wondering if he was still quite ill, in spite of his denials. In the thickening dusk he looked even more haggard, his face thinner. Had he come close to dying? The very thought made her heart dive sickeningly.

'I'm sorry, Dev,' she broke out in a shaking, husky voice, her face white. That seemed to make him angrier, the line of his mouth tightened.

'Just tell me one thing!' he said harshly. 'Was it going on behind my back before I even left? That night I went to your flat and found him there I had my suspicions. Were you already sleeping with him?'

'No!' She was incredulous—how could he believe that? Didn't he know her at all?

'It was an intimate little scene, though, wasn't it?' He smiled, but it wasn't a nice smile.

'Are you calling me a liar?'

'Let's say that men have divorced their wives for less!' he drawled, his mouth cynical.

'I do not sleep with Mark and I never did!' she snapped, red in the face. 'Not that it's any of your business. If I chose to it would only be my affair.'

'His, too, I'd have said?'

The cold mockery made her want to hit him, but she bit down on the furious words trying to burst out of her, and fought to stay cool and collected. 'Actually, Mark had taken me to a civic function that night, a very respectable affair, but while he was driving me home his car broke down and as we were close to my flat he just came in to phone for a taxi.'

'And while he was waiting, you slipped into something comfortable and he lounged about on your carpet by the fire in his shirt-sleeves? I see.'

His sarcasm made her teeth meet; through them she grated, 'It was pouring with rain, we got soaked to the skin running to my flat and the taxi couldn't come at once, so I made us some hot chocolate . . .'

'A cosy bedtime drink,' he drawled.

'You've got a very nasty mind!' Megan snarled back.

'Maybe I have, but I didn't imagine that letter of yours, did I? I can't say I was surprised to get it, of course! There isn't a woman on earth who could be trusted to stay faithful while her man was a thousand miles away.'

'That isn't fair!' she burst out, forgetting in the hurt of the moment why she had lied to him about meeting someone else.

'Not fair?' he repeated harshly. 'I hadn't even left the country before you were seeing another man! And you accuse me of not being fair!' He caught her face between his hands and forced her head back, staring into her startled eyes. 'Why the hell did you let me make a fool of myself by proposing? Why . . .' He bit the words back, his mouth snarling. 'Oh, what's the point? Women are all the same; they love to play little games and they can never bear to let any man go, even if they don't really want him.'

'Dev, you've got it all wrong,' she whispered, eyes wide and glazed with unshed tears. It was so long since he had touched her; he was making it hard for her to think straight.

'Have I? I doubt it.' But he was watching her fixedly, his eyes uncertain. 'Did you blame me for going away, was that it?' he asked suddenly.

'No!' The question threw her, perhaps because there was some truth in it. It hadn't occurred to her before, but now she wondered—had she been secretly angry with him because he was going away for so long? But she had known he was going when they first met, she thought, frowning. It would have been stupid to be resentful. She had merely wished he wasn't going. Flushed and trembling, she shook her head. 'No, of course not!' she insisted, and was foolish enough to try to explain how she had really felt. 'I didn't blame you, I'd known from the start that you were going—but, maybe . . . well . . . but . . .'

His lips curled back in a hard sneer. 'But? But what did I expect, you mean?'

She tired to struggle free of his grip and he wove his fingers into her hair to hold her. They were standing very close now, and her heart was shaking her whole body. She couldn't look away from that dark, dominating face, even though it scared her. 'Don't!' she whispered, trembling, and her fear seemed to push him right over the edge, feeding his rage as wind feeds fire.

He swooped down on her. mouth relentless, forcing her lips to part under a kiss that was full of fury. He wanted to hurt her. Megan's eyes burnt with tears behind her closed lids, she writhed in his arms, but he held her too close, and after a moment she grew very aware of the warmth of his body beneath his fine silk shirt. Only then, as she touched him, did it really get home to her how thin he was! Her heart winced as she discovered the new, terrifying austere contours of his chest and shoulders. All bone and muscle, so little flesh. He must have been desperately close to death to lose so much weight in such a short time.

She was so absorbed in discovering what his illness had done to him that she had forgotten to fight, her body limp in surrender, her mouth trembling with compassion and feeling as, with tightly shut eyes, her hands gently explored the changes in his body, unaware at first that her touch was turning his violence into a hot sensuality.

Dev might never have been in love with her, but she had always known he desired her. Whenever they made love there had been this heated abandonment, and although he had never said to her, 'I love you!' the way he touched her was more eloquent than words and she had innocently imagined that only love could make him so passionate.

She would never be that naïve again! She broke off the kiss, dragging her head back and to one side, and Dev let go of her, his hands dropping to his sides as he saw her put a hand to her bruised mouth.

His dark brows dragged together and his mouth twisted with a sort of self-disgust. 'Sorry,' he muttered with a mixture of regret and defiance. 'I lost my temper.' He watched her, his teeth tightly clenched, then reluctantly asked, 'Did I hurt you?'

Megan didn't answer; she was too busy looking at him and worrying about him. His face was darkly flushed, his eyes restless; he looked as if he had a high temperature. 'Are you OK, Dev? It's chilly out here!' She shivered herself as the wind blew through her silk dress.

'I'm fine,' he said, frowning down at her. 'But you're cold—and you aren't wearing a coat! It was stupid of you to come out in that thin dress in weather like this!' He took off his own jacket and put it round her shoulders, and Megan was horrified. She slid it off and tried to give it back.

'I'm fine, Dev! You need this, not me!' Didn't he know how ill he looked? Or was he refusing to admit it?

He firmly clamped the jacket around her, held it there with his arm. 'I'll decide what I need, thank you. You'll have my jacket until we're back in the hotel, so let's hurry!' He made her run, encircled with his arm, and Megan's heart beat a violent tattoo all the way. Once they were in the centrally heated foyer of the hotel Dev halted and looked down at her, an odd expression in his eyes. He still had an arm around her, a fact of which she was fiercely aware, just as she was very conscious of being far too close to him.

Since that kiss, his mood seemed different, gentler and less angry, but, far from making her feel happier, that disturbed her because Dev might have picked up her true feelings, and that was the last thing she wanted. He must not have any reason to suspect that she still loved him. He might try to talk her into going on with their marriage, and she couldn't do that to him.

'We can't really talk here, can we?' he said. 'Have dinner with me tomorrow night, Megan.'

He smiled suddenly, and she saw again, for the first time that evening, the private charm Dev showed to few people. 'I'm sorry for my bad temper. When your letter arrived I was already hatching the bug that stopped me in my tracks out there. I went a bit crazy for a while; hallucinating, seeing things that weren't there—I thought at one time I was seeing snakes! Fever plays weird tricks with the mind.'

She was horrified by the revelation of what he had been through. 'Oh, poor Dev!'

'Don't look so worried!' he said, a fingertip brushing away the frown above her distressed blue eyes. 'I survived, but I came close enough to dying to realise I wouldn't leave much behind me, if I did go! That was one thing that helped me fight my way back—the need to live and get some good work done. I suppose a crisis helps to concentrate your mind. I'm going to work like a dog to put this series together, for a start, but that wasn't the only thing bothering me! I kept wishing I had a wife and children waiting for me! I'd wasted years of my life and maybe I wasn't going to get another chance. If I'd died then, who would have missed me? Apart from a few relatives and friends there was only you—and then you wrote to say you had met someone else!'

She bit her lip, wincing. 'I'm s . . .'

'Don't say you're sorry again! Just say you'll have dinner with me tomorrow.'

He sounded relaxed and much too sure of himself; all the rage had gone, and she stared at him uncertainly. She was tempted to say yes, her body still burned with the fever of that kiss in the park—but she knew she couldn't go. She mustn't take the risk. If she saw him again he would soon guess she still loved him, and once he knew that, she would have to tell him the real reason why she had written those lies to him. But that would make it so hard for him; she did not want Dev to carry the burden of guilt over her.

He had only jut told her frankly how much he wanted to have children—and she couldn't give them to him! She loved him and she wanted him to be happy, but he would never really be happy with her if she could not give him the children he longed for. Sooner or later the day would come when he would regret marrying her, and she would know, even if he tried to hide it. She slowly shook her head, and Dev's face hardened again, but before he could say anything a man's voice spoke behind him, and Dev stiffened.

'Oh, there you are! I've been hunting high and low for you! Where on earth have you been, woman?'

Megan pulled a pretence of a smile into her face as she looked at Mark. 'Sorry, it was so hot in there that I wandered into the park.'

'Into the park?' Mark looked blankly at her. 'On a day like this? You haven't even got a coat!'

'Yes, silly of me—anyway, were you wanting to leave?'

'Is that OK with you?' Mark was frowning as he observed Dev's grim face.

'Fine, hang on while I go to the cloakroom to get my jacket.' Megan didn't meet Dev's stare; she just hurried away, leaving the two men contemplating each other in a hostile silence. She had never talked to Mark about Dev; she had no idea if he had ever known about their relationship. Nobody at the studios had known that she and Dev planned to marry, of course. She had kept her own counsel about that, because Dev had wanted it that way, although she would have loved to tell everyone. She had been dying to talk about Dev and the marvellous fact that she was going to be his wife. She had learnt to keep secrets, though. Her job meant that she had to be discreet, if not actually secretive, and it had stood her in good stead when she had a secret of her own to keep, so she had accepted Dev's decision and hadn't confided in anyone at the studio.

She collected her jacket; but lingered in the pink and gold powder room, which had a cool marble floor and Venetian mirrors along one wall. She had to repair the ravages to her appearance. She contemplated her reflection with something approaching shock. Her face seemed so unfamiliar, almost disturbing. Dev's rough fingers had wrecked her hair, his kisses had smudged her rose-pink lipstick and her skin was shiny with perspiration. She spent quite a time making herself look as good as she had earlier, when she got to the party.

Megan knew she wasn't pretty; her features were too irregular and she was small and skinny. When she took the trouble to dress and make-up with extra care, though, she knew she had a certain appeal to some men, especially when she smiled. She had learnt from her own experience that a smile was a bridge between people; if you met a smile you felt more confident, you didn't have to be afraid you were going to be ignored or snubbed. She had often been a wallflower at parties until she realised that other people were uncertain, too, and since then she had always tried to remember to smile a lot. It still didn't make her pretty, but she had a host of casual friends.

If she had not been so shy and quiet, she might have had far closer friends, but, although she remembered to smile when she met people, she found it far harder to talk to them easily, the way Mark or Johnny did. It was only because Mark did all the work that their friendship had grown rapidly. She made a face at herself in the mirror. Why couldn't she be more like Mark? Laid back, happy-go-lucky, always relaxed?

She did not hurry because she was nervous of confronting Dev again, but Mark was alone when she got back. 'Why do women always take so long to collect a jacket?' he teased.

'Sorry,' she said, fighting down an impulse to look around for Dev as they walked towards the main door of the hotel. Had he gone back to the party or had he left?

'How about a little late supper? I know a great place on the way back to your flat.'

She smiled absent-mindedly. 'No, thank you, Mark. I ate too much at the party.'

'It's early to say goodnight, though!' He sounded wistful, but Megan couldn't bear the idea of talking to anyone just now. She needed to be alone to think.

Reluctantly, Mark took her straight home. 'Coffee?' he pleaded on the doorstep.

'I'm sorry, Mark. Not tonight. I'm half asleep already.' Her mouth moved in a mimicry of a smile, but her eyes were far away and he could see it.

He shrugged and bent to kiss her. Megan turned swiftly so that the kiss landed on her cheek, not her mouth.

Mark straightened, eyes narrowed, staring at her, before suddenly asking, 'Was there ever anything between you and Devlin Hurst?'

Her blue eyes widened, her skin flushed. 'What?'

'Never mind, I just got my answer.' He was frowning, his jaw tense. 'From the way he acted, I guessed at something of the sort, but I couldn't believe you wouldn't have told me. You never mentioned him. Why not, Megan? We've been seeing a lot of each other for months—why didn't you tell me about Hurst? Or was it over before he left for the Amazon?'

Megan couldn't bear any more. She had to get away. Huskily, she said, 'I don't want to talk about it. Goodnight, Mark.' She closed the door on him before he had time to say any more, and heard his footsteps a moment later as he walked away.

Megan shut her eyes on sudden, scalding tears. She liked Mark very much. She had come to rely on him more than she had expected; he had helped her through a bad time since her accident and she did not want to say goodbye to him, but their friendship would never be the same after tonight. She suspected Mark knew that, too. He had strong intuition, almost feminine intuition. Perhaps all artists do, she thought. Seeing Dev had changed everything; it had come too unexpectedly, before she was ready to cope with it. She felt as if she had had a high wind blowing through her life. Everything had been overturned, flung into chaos. She was afraid to look to closely at what had happened, but she was even more afraid of what was to come.

At the programme conference next day, their producer, Fanny Gordon, said, 'I see Devlin Hurst is back. We could have him on the show again, Johnny, what do you think? Interesting to hear how his trip's going, get him to talk about this nasty bug he picked up.'

Megan stared down at her notepad, her face stiff and pale. Please don't agree, Johnny, she prayed, but Johnny seemed quite enthusiastic.

'He's a good talker, why not?'

'Right! Which of the girls wants to handle that?' Fanny looked at the trio of researchers sitting opposite her. Megan didn't look up. One of the others could get in touch with Dev and arrange a return visit to the show. The idea of doing it froze the marrow in her bones.

'Megan knows him, don't you, Megan?' Johnny said softly, feline enjoyment in his voice.

She gave him a furious, sideways look and he laughed out loud.

'Oh, well,' said Fanny, 'Megan had better do it.'

There was no point in arguing; it would only draw attention to her and make them all curious, which was no doubt what Johnny wanted. He loved to amuse himself by teasing people and infuriating them.

Fanny was quite different; if she had had any notion why Johnny was suggesting Megan she would never have gone along with the idea. She was not the malicious type, but was sensitive and clever. It was her mind that gave the show its strength. Johnny was the up-front image; he performed what Fanny planned behind the scenes. They made a brilliant team.

As the meeting broke up, Johnny followed Megan out, saying happily, 'Don't forget to ring Hurst, will you, darling?'

'If you were a woman, I'd call you a bitch!' she muttered, and he laughed, apparently flattered.

Back in her office she contemplated the phone with dread. Would Dev be in his London flat, or at his family home in the country? With any luck she wouldn't find him at either and could just leave a message for him to ring Fanny. It was hardly necessary to do any research on him as he was a return guest; they had his history on file.

She grabbed up the phone and dialled the London number. 'Yes?' Dev's voice was impatient and she took a deep breath on hearing it. 'Hello? Who is this?' he demanded when she couldn't get a syllable out.

Megan pulled herself together. 'Hello, I'm speaking for Johnny Fabian . . .' She used her 'public' voice; calm and assured. It was just as well

Dev couldn't see her face.

It was his turn to be silent, then he said, 'Megan?'

'Yes,' she said brightly. 'Johnny asked me to get in touch and invite you back on the show for tomorrow night. We're sure the viewers will want to hear how your journey is going, and about your illness, of course, and why you've had to come home, and so on——' She was babbling, but she couldn't stop it, because she was afraid of what Dev might say.

'Come over,' he interrupted suddenly, and her voice broke off.

'Sorry?'

'Can you come now?'

She was shaking, but he couldn't see that. He would be able to hear the huskiness of her voice, though, so she tried to sound level and unflustered, without much success.

'Oh, there's no need for us to research you this time, I'm just ringing to ask if you can appear tomorrow night.'

'If you come over here now. Otherwise, forget it.'

'That's . . .' she began, then bit her lower lip.

'Blackmail?' He laughed ominously. 'Maybe, but if you don't arrive, tell Fabian to find another last-minute guest!'

The phone went dead and she looked at it with blank disbelief before slowly replacing it. What was she to do now?

CHAPTER FIVE

MEGAN stopped off at Johnny's office on her way to the lift and found him dictating to his secretary. Johnny was inundated with fan mail every day; replying took up most of his mornings, and he wasn't sorry to stop for a moment when Megan walked into the room.

'Get hold of Dev, darling?' he mocked.

She gave him a cold stare. 'Yes, but he asked me to go over to see him to discuss it, and I'm very busy in the office with the clippings on the Italian fashion model.'

Johnny grinned. 'Too bad, but Devlin Hurst is a priority, and if he wants you to go and see him, you'd better go.'

She considered him with irritation. He was wearing his usual expensive tailoring; silk shirt, silk tie, handmade shoes; all chosen to give the utmost effect to his looks, that auburn hair, those fluid dark eyes. You had to admit he looked terrific. Johnny Fabian lived the good life and loved it. His myriad fans had no idea what he could be like behind that charming façade.

'Off you pop,' Johnny crooned, much amused by her expression.

Without another word, Megan turned on her heel. Behind her, Johnny called out, 'You look simply gorgeous today, darling!'

She felt like slamming the door, but she wouldn't give him the pleasure of knowing he had put her into a roaring temper. Perhaps it was the necessity of being so nice in public that made Johnny often very tricky in private. He could be kind, or charming, or thoughtful, to his staff, when he chose—or he could tease, lose his temper, snarl at people. You never quite knew what to make of him, but one thing was certain. You couldn't afford to make an enemy of him, or you had to leave the team. Megan couldn't remember any of the girls quarrelling with him, but several men had come and gone because they simply could not stand Johnny.

Fanny handled him perfectly; she behaved like a duchess confronting a tiresome child, and Johnny always fell into line. Fanny was, perhaps, the only person in the world he was afraid of.

She had her car in the staff car park outside the studios, and decided to drive to Dev's flat, but got caught in a traffic jam en route. Megan felt an odd relief; she wasn't in any hurry to get to Dev. To occupy the time she switched on her car radio and listened to a music programme on the BBC while she renewed her make-up and ran a brush over her cloudy dark hair, to the amusement of the driver of the car next to her.

'Hey, beautiful! What about a date?' he yelled.

She grinned at him, but didn't answer because just then the traffic began to move again.

She started to feel nervous again as she walked towards Dev's front door. Butterflies fluttered in her stomach and her mouth was dry.

He opened the door almost at once and her heart thudded in her chest, seeming almost to shake her whole body.

'Hello, Megan,' he said in that deep, familiar voice and she murmured something, feeling light-headed. He was in casual clothes: dark trousers, a white ribbed sweater over a dark blue silk shirt. His dark hair was ruffled, his grey eyes brilliant.

'Come in,' he said, standing back. 'I have some coffee freshly made—or would you like something stronger?'

'Do you think I'll need something stronger?' She pretended that was a joke, laughing huskily. 'But no, thanks, I won't have either coffee or anything else.' Dev gave her a sideways glance, gesturing for her to go ahead into his beautifully furnished sitting-room. His home in the country had been furnished by generations of his family, it didn't really reflect his individual taste, but his flat did; he had chosen the furniture and décor, and it told you quite a bit about him. Cool, masculine colours for carpets and the blinds on the windows; golden Scandinavian pine for chairs and tables, highly expensive music desk with the very latest equipment—ultra-modern angled lamps, black ash bookcases crammed with a bewildering variety of books on very different subjects—the place was very classy, and had that lived-in look of a real home.

'Sit down,' he said behind her as she hovered near the door.

'I can't be out of the office for long,' she said, hesitating between the two deeply upholstered leather armchairs.

'Stand if you prefer it,' Dev said, his hard mouth crooked with mockery. She had never noticed before how large his pupils were; they gleamed like black jet as he looked her up and down—from her heavy head of hair down over her slender figure in a demure, pleated cream wool dress. It clung to her breasts and waist and flared out over her slight hips, swirling around her legs as she walked. His stare made her so edgy that she hurriedly walked towards one of the armchairs, but Dev moved too, getting between her and the chair, so that she found herself sitting on the cream leather couch, with no real notion how she had come to be there.

'Pretty dress,' Dev said, sitting down next to her.

'Thank you.' Her voice was rusty; she prayed he hadn't noticed. Producing her notepad from her handbag, she sat up straight, trying to look efficient. 'Shall we start?'

Dev leaned back, an arm wandering along the back of the couch behind her while he eyed her mockingly. 'Start what?'

Her face burned, but she wouldn't let him disturb her. 'Talking about what you're going to say on the show,' she said stiffly. 'Johnny would like some idea beforehand; just the general areas for questions, no need to use any sort of script. But you remember that from the first show.'

'I remember a lot of things,' he murmured, shifting closer on the couch so that his thigh touched hers. At the same moment she felt his fingers brush along the nape of her neck. A shiver ran down her spine and she started up, wild-eyed and alarmed.

'I didn't come here for that!'

He caught her waist and pulled her down again, laughing. 'What did you come here for?'

'You blackmailed me into it!'

'So I did,' he coolly admitted, leaning over her, a little smile twisting his lips.

'Dev, let me go now, please,' Megan begged unsteadily, trying not to look at his mouth because she knew that that would be a bad mistake. She had dreamt about kissing him far too often; that mouth could tempt her into folly.

'You only just got here!' He had a hand planted on either side of her head; he had pushed his fingers into the wild flurry of her long hair against the back of the couch, and she wouldn't be able to escape without getting hurt.

'Don't do that!' Eyes dilated, she stared up at him, her throat pulsing with a growing fever.

'You're in love with another man—why should you be so hyper-tense about being alone with me?' he asked softly, watching her mouth. She knew he was thinking of kissing her, and her lips began to quiver, full and hot already as though he had been kissing her for a long time.

She was too disturbed to answer. She had to look away because she couldn't bear the way he was looking at her.

'Or . . . are you?'

She frowned uneasily. 'Am I what?

'In love with someone else?'

Her lashes flew up again; her blue eyes looked into his and found them closer; far too close. His body was touching hers now; he was leaning right over her, his face inches away.

'You know, I . . . I told you!' she muttered, utterly confused.

'Oh, you told me,' he said very softly, the words murmured out against her mouth. 'I was hundreds of miles away then, but now I'm here, so tell me again, face to face this time.' Their faces fitted like pieces of a jigsaw puzzle, mouth to mouth, hair mingling, breath mingling, and for the first time in months she felt complete, but she must not give in.

'Dev, I can't,' she moaned, shuddering as the tip of his tongue traced the outline of her lips. His hands were wandering intimately, too; her breasts rounded and grew heavy, her body was fiercely sensitive to the feel of his skin on hers. She was aching with a passion more intense than any she had ever felt before, perhaps because she knew she must stop him, yet it was so long since Dev had held her in his arms, and she had thought it would never happen again, and frustration had almost driven her crazy. Saying no this time would be the hardest thing she had ever done.

'Of course you can,' he whispered, smiling. He was sure of her, she could see that. She might be saying no, but her body was saying something else, and Dev's instincts told him so. Megan despised herself for being so weak; she had to stop this before it went too far.

'You're forgetting something!' she protested,

but his mouth went on teasing and tormenting her; lightly brushing her lips, touching and lifting again. He was playing games with her, and his eyes mocked because he knew she was finding it harder and harder to resist him.

'I never forget anything,' he said, his hands sensual, boldly caressing the warm curve of her body.

She was desperate to distract him, to put a stop to this torment. Pushing him away, she stammered, 'You have! You've forgotten Mark!'

Dev went on smiling, eyeing her mockingly. 'What about him?'

'You know very well that I . . . that Mark and I . . .'

'Why are you stammering, Megan?' he asked with a barbed little smile. 'Feeling guilty about something?'

'Guilty?'

He raised his eyebrows. 'Surely you know the word? Shall I spell it for you?'

She had been hot; now she was icy cold. 'Stop it, Dev!'

He pretended to frown, to look thoughtful. 'Oh, are you trying to tell me that you have to be faithful to Mark? Is that it?'

Biting the inside of her lip and tense with nerves, she nodded, and that was when he dropped the mimicry of a smile, the pretence of amusement.

'Why be faithful to him when you weren't to me?' The whipcrack voice made her nerves leap in shock.

'Let go of me!' She tried to sit up, struggle free, but his body was too heavy for her, even though he had lost so much weight. He might be thin, but the muscle and bone beneath his brown skin made him a formidable adversary to wrestle with.

'You must be kidding, sweetheart!' he snarled at her. 'I'm far from finished with you yet!'

She was rigid, utterly shaken as she saw that beneath Dev's smiles and sensual teasing he had been hiding a bitter hostility all this time.

'Don't talk to me like that!' she muttered, but the faint defiance got her nowhere, except that she made him laugh, and the hoarse sound of that laughter made her blench.

'Or what?' he mocked. 'What will you do to me? You can't fight me. You're too small and weak. You're like a bird, trapped in a room, fluttering about trying to get out and just smashing itself uselessly on the walls.' He lifted a handful of her hair and then let it float out around her white face. 'Even your hair is like feathers; soft and downy. When my fever was at its worst, I used to think you were there, with me, your head on my pillow, and I used to turn my face into your hair and let it cover me, like a tent. It made me feel safer.'

His mood seemed to have swung again; to be gentle, almost dreamy. Megan said uncertainly, 'Dev, I'm so sorry you were ill.' She was worried about him; he was so volatile, given to sudden switchback moods, and he had never been like that before he went to South America. What had this bug done to him?

'Are you?' He laughed and she winced.

'Yes!' His smouldering eyes told her that he didn't believe her, and that hurt. She looked at her watch. 'I'm sorry, but I have a lunch appointment at one o'clock. I must go soon.'

His face changed once more. In a businesslike voice, he said, 'But we haven't gone over the topics Fabian wants to discuss tomorrow night!'

'Well, obviously . . .' she began, but he interrupted.

'Look, I don't know about you, but I could use that coffee now.' He got to his feet, and walked away while she bit her lip, fuming. Dev was being bloody-minded, but she couldn't do much about it. Johnny would give her hell if she didn't make these arrangements for the show. Getting up, she followed him out of the room, into the beautifully equipped modern kitchen which faced out into a communal garden planted with well laid out shrubs and trees. Megan remembered vividly how delightful it was in summer; today it looked sad and forlorn in the raw grey weather, matching her mood.

'I really do have to go, Dev,' she said, running a hand over her ruffled hair.

'Not yet.' He was moving calmly, making coffee; he looked so normal that she decided that he had come out of that strange, worrying mood, and so she gave him a placating smile.

'Sorry, but . . .' she began and he turned, lip curling back in a snarl of violence which made her nerves jangle.

'I said not yet!'

She started to shake again and caught hold of the back of a chair; suddenly afraid she might fall down if she didn't grab something.

'Stop talking to me like that!'

'Stop arguing, then!'

'I have a job to do!'

'Then do it,' he coolly said. 'You came here to work out what Fabian would like to talk about—so work it out!'

She sat down at the kitchen table and laid down her notepad, gripped her pen in her hand, trying to look calm and collected and very efficient.

'Right, then,' she said huskily. 'First of all, your illness, of course . . . the viewers will want to hear about that.'

'Black or white?'

She stared, face blank. 'What?'

'Coffee—black or white?

'Oh, black, please.' He ought to know that; or didn't he remember? She remembered how he liked his coffee; she remembered everything he had ever told her about himself—that he always had his egg boiled for three and a half minutes, that he loved any sort of Chinese food, had a passion for hot cheese but never late at night because then it gave him indigestion, that he had once smoked cigarettes quite heavily until a friend bet him he couldn't stop, and was now glad he had taken up the challenge. Those were the little details love fed on, she would never forget anything he had ever told her—but had Dev ever loved her?

He was placing the coffee-pot and cups on a tray. She wrote the date and his name on the top of the page in her notebook. It gave her something to do with her hands; it helped her to feel relaxed.

'Now . . .'

Her voice trailed off as he walked past, out of the kitchen, back to the sitting-room. Megan had no option but to follow him. Dev was playing games with her and she felt like going now while she could, but she had the feeling he would ring Johnny and Johnny would send her back here. For some reason she could not fathom it was amusing Johnny to watch her struggling in the meshes of the net in which she was trapped, and Dev had shrewdly realised that Johnny was for the moment his ally. Or were they conspiring together? She frowned. Surely not? Johnny wouldn't—would he? And if he was—why? What was Johnny up to?

Dev laid the tray down on the coffee-table and sat down on the couch again. 'Will you pour?'

She silently obeyed and then sat down on a chair with her pad open on her knee and the coffee in front of her on the low table. 'Can we get on to business, please?' She didn't give him a chance to change the subject, just began firing rapid questions at him about the Amazon trip, writing down notes on anything he said that might make a good lead-in. This time Dev answered; he wasn't evasive or difficult, and she soon had a string of possible questions for Johnny to ask him.

She finished her coffee, glanced at her watch and got up. 'Then we'll see you tomorrow night; I don't have to tell you the procedure. See you in the hospitality room a couple of hours before the show.'

'Can't make it then,' he coolly said.

She did a double-take. 'But, I thought you had

agreed to come on the show tomorrow!'

'Yes, but I can't get to the studio until later—half an hour before the show starts, OK?'

Megan bit her lower lip, frowning. 'It will be cutting it a bit fine. Johnny likes guests to arrive well beforehand so that he is sure everything will go as planned.' It was one of Johnny's nightmares that one of his star guests wouldn't turn up. They always had someone else on hand, but of course they couldn't ask a 'big name' to hang around in case he or she was needed, and so that meant a second-rate show if a top guest failed to arrive. Johnny hated that idea. He started panicking early, sent his secretary to all the dressing-rooms to check that the guests had arrived. If one of them was late, Johnny went into shock.

'I'll be there!' Dev shrugged, and Megan eyed him with uneasiness.

'I hope you will—I shall get into trouble if you aren't!'

He walked her to the door, smiling blandly. 'Don't worry!' he urged, but Megan couldn't help doing that. Dev was in a worrying mood. It wouldn't surprise her if he didn't turn up for the show. She had not liked the way he looked at her when she said that she would get into trouble if he didn't arrive on time, and he hadn't bothered to hide the glint of menace in his eyes. She was sure, in fact, that he had wanted her to see it. Dev was still angry with her.

'Have dinner with me tonight,' he said, looking down into her troubled blue eyes.

'I'm sorry, I have a date.' She started to walk

away, but he caught her elbow.

'Break it.'

'I can't do that!'

'You will, though.' He sounded amused again, but under the light tone ran a note of threat and Megan looked at him with apprehension. Was she imagining all this? Dev had never been the sort of man to blackmail and threaten a woman—or had he? She had always known he could be ruthless, she had known he had a very strong self-image. He was a high flyer; a man of energy and drive with a lot of ambition and a strong ego. She had hit that ego; she had attacked his idea of himself, and just at a time when he was weak. Illness was always a low point for anyone, and she had unknowingly delivered her blow to his ego while he was very ill. She knew from her own experience how vulnerable you could be when you were ill.

What had it done to him when he got her letter? she wondered, her eyes on his hard face, her face pale between the thick masses of her long, dark hair.

'Oh, Dev, please,' she whispered. 'There's no point . . . it's over between us—can't you just accept that and let it go?'

His face was frighteningly rigid, bones clenched, mouth a white line. 'No.' The word had a volcanic force and she began to shake.

'Dev . . .'

'No!' His voice overrode her low, thready whisper.

She stared at him and he bent towards her. 'I don't let go of anything I still want, Megan, and I don't accept that it's over. It won't be over until I say so.' He straightened again and said in a level tone, 'Dinner, tonight, Megan, or . . .'

'Or what?' she said when he paused. She tried to sound offhand, indifferent, but her voice wavered, and he smiled then; a hard twist of his mouth which was really no smile at all.

'I'll pick you up at seven. My regards to Fabian.' He let go of her and stepped back into his flat. The front door shut and Megan stared at it for a moment, realising the threat he held over her.

Either she had dinner with him tonight—or he wouldn't turn up tomorrow; Johnny would have a nasty big hole in the middle of his show. Of course, Fanny would have a stand-by guest on hand in case of a problem, but the show would not be as good, and Johnny was going to blame Megan.

She liked her job, she was ambitious and wanted to move on at the right time into production. She would do a spell on the studio floor, she had her name down for a course on camera work. She was eager to learn and prepared to work hard to get what she wanted, but being fired by Johnny Fabian because she hadn't done her job well enough wouldn't do her career chances much good.

She drove back to the studio, and walked into Johnny's office to find him cheerfully entertaining a reporter.

'Hi, come in, Megan!' he lilted, holding out an arm and clasping her to his side. 'This is one of my little elves, Mac; God knows what I'd do without them. Megan, this is Mac, say hello to the nice reporter.'

Megan said hello and forced a smile. The reporter was looking nervous; Johnny's remorseless good humour was getting to him. Men never liked Johnny much, especially when he was terribly jolly with them. His women fans loved his whimsy and his jokey moods, but men never quite knew how to take him.

'I'll come back later,' Megan said, trying to look elfin.

Johnny called after her, 'See Hurst, did you?'

'Would that be Devlin Hurst?' asked the reporter, eyes lighting up. 'Isn't he just back from this trip up the Amazon? He coming on the show, Johnny? When? Tomorrow?' He started scribbling a note and Johnny winked at Megan, well pleased with this immediate interest. It told him that his instincts had been quite correct—the public would be fascinated to see Devlin Hurst on his show again.

Megan was not so delighted. She went back to her own office and sat behind her desk in gloomy contemplation of the obvious. Having announced to the Press that Dev was to be on the show, Johnny would be furious if he didn't show up. Even if he didn't fire her, he would make life unbearable for days. Johnny could be very nasty if he felt you had let him down. She had to make sure Dev turned up, and that meant that she must have dinner with him.

As soon as she had taken the decision she felt as if a great weight had been lifted from her shoulders, leaving her light and almost euphoric. She picked up the clippings file on her desk and began to do some in-depth research on the background of an Italian model whose love affairs had made her far more famous than her career had ever done.

It wasn't until much later, when she was at home, in her flat that evening, that she faced the truth about how she felt, her mouth wry in angry self-mockery. Who did she think she was kidding? She wanted to see Dev again. She was only too ready to fall for his veiled blackmail. He had simply given her the excuse she needed. If Dev hadn't made the pace, she would probably have been aching to see him and might have thought up some reason for visiting him. The fact was, she still loved him desperately and she always would. There was nothing she could do about that, but with a sinking heart she admitted that she was giving in to a dangerous weakness, one that could destroy both of them.

She mustn't forget why she couldn't marry Dev. His bitter rage over the breaking of their engagement must not make her forget that she had done it for his sake, and that nothing had changed. She could not marry him, and tonight she had to make that very clear to him.

CHAPTER SIX

MEGAN rang Mark at his studio flat to explain that she had to break their date, but he was out. She had to leave an apologetic message on his answerfone. She said she had to work that evening, which was one way of looking at it, since she was having dinner with Dev to make quite sure he turned up for the Fabian show tomorrow.

At the same time, it was half a lie, because her date with Dev was really entirely personal, and Mark would be very suspicious if he found out who she was seeing instead of him, so she made her message very vague. He had already showed signs of jealousy, without knowing anything about her past relationship with Dev.

He had no right to be jealous, of course. They had never been anything more than friends. Maybe they might have done, if things had been different, but Megan hadn't wanted to have a new romance.

She took ages to get dressed because she kept changing her mind about what to wear. She didn't want to wear anything ultra sexy or provocative because she didn't want to give Dev any ideas, but on the other hand all her female instincts made her want to look her best. In the end she chose a smoky blue taffeta dress cut on simple lines with a scooped neckline, tight waist, full rustling skirt ending at the calf, and the most gorgeous balloon sleeves finishing with a tight-fitting cuff buttoned with mother-of-pearl discs which shone in moony splendour every time she moved her hands.

She had bought it recently for a first night to which Mark had taken her, so Dev had never seen it. She brushed her hair upwards from the temples and fastened it in two wings with art nouveau combs decorated with mother-of-pearl and a silver Celtic maze design. Those she had found herself among a box of assorted junk at a country auction in the Cotswolds. She had bid on impulse and most of the contents of the box had been quite ugly and worthless, but finding the two combs had been a great thrill. They had been dirty and lacklustre; at first she hadn't realised their beauty, but when they were cleaned their real value emerged. They had become her favourite possessions; she loved the way they shimmered when she turned her head. In soft candlelight they were quite magical, especially when she was wearing the smoky blue dress, which matched them so well.

Just as she was putting the finishing touches to her make-up, the doorbell rang. Surprised, she glanced at her watch. Dev was early! She took a final look in the mirror and was pleased with what she saw, which in itself was dangerous. Her skin glowed with warm colour, her blue eyes were too big and too bright. She looked far too excited.

Turning away quickly, she walked to the door, snatching up her short silvery fur jacket on the way so that Dev should have no excuse for coming into the flat. She did not want a repeat performance of what had happened at his flat earlier that day. She was going to keep things low-key this evening.

Pulling open the door with a cool smile on her lips, she did a double-take. 'Mark?'

He laughed. 'Who were you expecting?'

Megan was pink with embarrassment, stammering. 'I'm sorry, Mark, I'm afraid I can't come to the theatre with you tonight. I have to work.'

His smile died as he stared at her. 'To work? What does that mean?'

'Johnny sprang it on me very late—I did try to let you know as soon as I could, but you were out. I left a message on your answerfone.'

'I haven't been back to my place,' Mark said with a frown.

'No, obviously, what a pity. I'm terribly sorry you've had a wasted journey over here, and . . . but you must go to the play yourself, I've heard it's wonderful.' She tried to joke about it. 'You'll be so enthralled you won't notice I'm not there.'

Mark grimaced. 'That I doubt.' His eyes wandered over her and he whistled. 'You look sensational, too! Where are you going dressed up like that? A première again?' The last time she had had to break a date it had been to accompany Johnny, Fanny and a couple of others from the programme team to a film première in Leicester Square.

'No such luck,' she said, evasively looking at her watch. 'If you're going to get to the theatre before the curtain goes up, hadn't you better be on your way? Some time, you must let me take you to a play to make up for tonight.' She was getting very nervous because Dev might arrive at any minute and she did not want Mark to see him.

'Megan, why don't you just skip whatever Fabian had lined up for you?' Mark put a hand to her cheek, stroking it as he stared into her eyes, smiling at her. 'It seems a pity to waste the way you look on that idiot!' He leaned forward and kissed her softly, whispering, 'We could have a marvellous evening, the two of us.'

Megan put a hand on his shoulder to push him away, hearing footsteps coming up behind him. She looked past Mark, her eyes very wide and dark as they met Dev's. His face was hard, unsmiling; he had seen that kiss. His icy grey eyes flicked over her with contempt and she felt like bursting into tears for an instant, before she got angry. Who did he think he was? How dared he look at her like that?

Mark had realised that they weren't alone any more. He turned round, stared and at once began to frown, his face altering.

'Hurst!' he said, his voice thick with suspicion, and slowly looked back at Megan. 'I suppose *this* is your "work" for tonight. I have been slow on the uptake, haven't I? I should have remembered the way Fabian ordered you to chat me up to get me on his show. Your job description may be as a researcher, but there are other words for it!'

Her face burned at the tone, the implication, but before she could react Dev did it for her. 'Don't talk to her like that!' he snarled, and then he hit

Mark. Mark hadn't been expecting that; Dev took him off balance and Mark flew sideways, hitting the wall before sliding downwards.

Megan made high-pitched little moaning noises as she ran and knelt down beside him. 'Mark, are you hurt? Oh, your head's bleeding . . . does it hurt? Let me see . . .'

He gave her a furious look, his face dark red but a white line around his mouth. 'Let me alone, for God's sake! I'm fine.' He staggered to his feet, glaring at Dev. 'That was a lucky punch, mister. I wasn't on my guard, but I am now.'

'Please, don't fight!' Megan protested, trying to make them listen, trying to get between them. 'Mark! Dev!' Neither of them took any notice; Mark had just managed to return the punch Dev had given him and Dev reeled back for a second, only to rush at Mark again. 'Stop it at once! How dare you fight over me, as if I were a squaw?'

They weren't listening, and looking at their set, aggressive faces Megan wondered if she was really what they were fighting over anyway! For some reason they hadn't liked each other on first sight; they were both very masculine and brimming with the competitive spirit, and not only over her, either.

Megan was not going to be used as first prize in a boxing ring. She was sick of the whole situation; sick of both of them, too. She watched them circling each other outside her front door, and then she silently shut the door on them, went into her sitting-room and turned on the television as loudly as she dared with the neighbours in mind. Now she could neither see nor hear them and when doorbell began to ring again she simply ignored it. They could both just go away and she hoped she would never see either of them again.

She should have known it was unwise to underestimate an obstinate man. Ten minutes later, while she was still sitting in front of a blaring television set, Dev walked into the room, and she leapt up incredulously.

'How did you get into my flat?'

'Broke in,' he admitted coolly.

'You can't do a thing like that!' she seethed, flushed to her hairline. 'Breaking into someone's home . . . it's against the law, it's burglary.'

He gave her a mocking look. 'So it is. What are you going to do about it? Call the police?'

'I ought to,' she said angrily. 'How did you do it? If you've damaged my property . . .'

'I haven't. I used a professional technique.'

She stared, dumbfounded. 'Professional technique.'

'I was burgled myself once, years ago. I caught the guy in the act. I should have called the police, but he hadn't had a chance to take anything yet and I suppose I was soft-hearted enough to feel sorry for him, so I let him go, but first I asked him how he had got in, and he showed me. I had burglar alarms fitted next day and new locks, but I noticed your lock was the same as mine had been, so I used the method my burglar had shown me, and it worked like a dream. You really ought to have new locks fitted to that door; and several, not just one. A chain lock would be wise, too.'

'I don't believe I'm hearing this,' Megan burst out furiously. 'You break into my flat and then give me a lecture on security!'

'You need one. Take my advice, call in an expert. It's amazing you've never been burgled before.'

'Get out of here before I do call the police!' she snapped, but he stayed just where he was, watching her.

'Aren't you going to ask about your boyfriend's health?' he drawled.

'Both of you make me sick! Acting like a couple of stupid little boys!'

'I hit him because he insulted you!'

'Nobody asked you to!'

'You're very ungrateful,' he said, smiling wryly, then put a hand to his jaw, as though the movement of his mouth had hurt.

'I hope Mark hit you hard!' She wasn't going to be sympathetic, so he needn't grimace or look sorry for himself.

'Your boyfriend has pretty solid fists. I shan't be able to laugh much for a few days, and I think one of my teeth is loose—but you should see him! Although I doubt it he will want you to until the bruises heal.'

His air of smug self-congratulation was infuriating. 'Will you go away?' she yelled.

'Not until you come with me,' he simply said. 'I must go to your bathroom first and do something about this cut on my cheek, have a wash and tidy my hair.'

'You don't really imagine I'm still going out

with you?'

He strolled to the sitting-room door. 'You'd better.'

'Don't you try to threaten me . . .' she fumed, and he turned and gave her a crooked little smile.

'I'm not threatening you, Megan. I'm making a promise! By the way . . .' His voice lowered, almost to a whisper. 'You look lovely.'

He vanished before she had got her breath back, and she put both hands to her hot face, trembling. It was rare for Dev to say anything like that. She could hardly believe he really had said it, especially in that voice, but she mustn't be weak, she must not let him get to her. It would be dangerously easy to let him coax her into changing her mind; all her own feelings were fighting on his side but her common sense and her honesty kept reminding her that it would be fatal, for Dev's sake. She couldn't tell him why she had changed her mind so she had to stick to her decision, whatever Dev said or did.

She was still arguing with herself when he returned, his dark hair brushed and smooth, the blood washed off his cheek, although there was still an angry mark there, and his beautifully cut suit looking a good deal more elegant than it had after the fight with Mark.

'Ready?' he enquired with that maddening assurance that she would do as he wished.

'I will come to dinner tonight,' Megan said carefully.

He smiled and her teeth met.

'But there are conditions,' she added.

He lifted one brow. 'Oh, yes?'

'You keep your hands to yourself all evening!'

He gave her an insolent look, but still said nothing.

'And this is the last time!'

'Oh, I don't think so,' Dev said, putting out his hand. 'Come along, I'm starving.'

She was still sitting there, her hands in her lap, and refused to move. 'Take me seriously, Dev!'

'Now?' he asked, and she felt her face burn.

'You know very well what I meant!'

He bent and his fingers fastened around her wrist, yanking her ruthlessly to her feet even though she fought against his strength. She was held close to him for a moment; he looked down into her eyes, the darkness in his frightening her.

'Don't provoke me, Megan, which means don't hand out ultimatums when you don't have the firepower to back them up. You and I haven't had our serious discussion yet, but it's long overdue. We'll get dinner out of the way and then we'll talk.'

'There's nothing to talk about, Dev!' She was afraid of talking to him; he might guess something, start putting two and two together.

He put a hand over her mouth. 'You know there is; we have to talk and the sooner the better. Now, come on! They may not hold our table if we're much later. This is a very popular restaurant; I was lucky to get a table at such short notice. I think somebody cancelled.'

The restaurant was small but exclusive and they had a table in a shadowy corner, where they were unlikely to be observed. For such a tiny place, the menu was enormous, and if Megan had had any appetite at all she would have studied the list with greedy enjoyment, but love made her indifferent to food and she just toyed with a game consommé followed by turbot, a fish she liked very much, which the restaurant served with an array of fresh green vegetables. Dev was less abstemious; he chose a rich terrine followed by duck in a wine and cherry sauce.

While they ate he talked about what he had experienced in South America: the terrible poverty he had seen, the charm of the children, the sadness of the old, the vast distances, mind-blowing colours and scents, the riotous confusion of the green forests. Megan listened, enthralled; he was a brilliant reporter even when he was talking off the cuff, his eyes gleaming with excitement, painting a word picture for her of the riot and confusion of the forests and the river's unpredictability. She could see it all—the sudden eddies and whirlpools, the glistening watersnakes, insects dancing always above the surface, birds calling high among the tall trees, hung about with creepers which dangled down into the river, the floating corpses of animals or birds which gave an oily smell to the water at noon, the morning and evening mists. The haunting images filled her imagination, and at last she understood why he had dreamt of going there. He had never talked to her like that before; she saw into his mind and bitterly regretted that this insight came too late.

'When are you returning to finish the filming?'

she asked over their coffee.

'In a couple of weeks, perhaps—I have to take some tests at a hospital, to make sure that my blood is free of the bug I picked up. They aren't sure yet whether or not it's a recurring fever, like malaria.'

She shuddered. 'How terrible! Should you risk going back?' She wanted to beg him not to return, she was afraid that next time he might die, but she had no right to protest; she could only hold her tongue and suffer.

'Unless my specialist tells me to the contrary, I shall go back and finish the job I started.' He smiled suddenly, self-mockery in his grey eyes. 'Anyway, I loved the place and can't wait to get back, for all the discomforts and dangers.'

She sighed. 'Yes, I understand that.'

'Do you?' He leaned over the table towards her, his brown hands resting on the white damask cloth. His fingertips reached out and touched hers and her own hands quivered. 'I had the idea that you wouldn't,' he admitted. 'You never seemed interested.'

'You never talked about it all the way you have tonight.'

He looked struck. 'Didn't I? No, I suppose I didn't. When we met I was straining to get over there; half of me was already there, in some ways. I'd lost all interest in everything else. Nothing but the Amazon seemed quite real to me.'

'Including me,' she murmured, and he looked sharply at her.

'That isn't true!'

'Isn't it? Sometimes when we were together I used to feel that I was just a shadow on a wall to you. You talked at me, danced, kissed me, but I never got through to the real man.' Her voice had a sadness he couldn't understand and she could never explain, because now it was too late and they were fated never to know each other.

His fingers moved again, twined with hers on the white cloth. 'I'm sorry, Megan. It was a crazy time in my life; a pity I met you while I was so obsessed with a dream—but even though it may not have looked like it, I had fallen in love with you.'

Megan's heart squeezed painfully, as if a giant hand had taken hold of it, and she looked down, fighting with tears. Did he mean it? Was it the truth? She couldn't remember him ever telling her he was in love with her; looking back over those meetings before he left for South America, she was sure he had often been evasive, as if afraid to say too much.

'I didn't have the time or energy to give you,' Dev was saying quietly, holding her hands. 'But I knew right away that you were the woman I wanted for my wife. I decided not to ask you to marry me until I got back from the Amazon. I didn't want to complicate matters while I had so much on my mind, for one thing, and for another I didn't think it was fair to you to ask you to give me any promises before I went away for such a long time. You're so much younger than me. I've been around and taken a few hard knocks—you haven't. I was afraid you would meet someone else and I didn't want you to have to feel guilty if you did.'

She kept her eyes lowered, a burning pain behind them. Dev had tried to protect her from the burden of guilt, and that was ironic now when she was trying to save him from the same bitter weight. He had told her why he wasn't asking her to marry him, but she could not be as frank. Honesty was not an option for her; if Dev knew why she had broken with him he might insist on going ahead with their marriage anyway.

He lifted her hands to his mouth and softly kissed her palms. 'But then you told me you loved me, and I knew I couldn't bear to go away without trying to hold on to you.'

She felt grief in her throat, like hot dust choking her. She pulled her hands free and blindly got to her feet.

'Excuse me, I must . . .' She couldn't get another word out and almost ran to the powder-room. It was fortunately empty; she could let the tears come, scalding and bitter, while she sat on a chair and rocked back and forth, her hands over her face.

When she stopped crying she washed her tear-stained face in cold water and renewed her make-up, combed her hair, made sure there were no telltale signs of her misery for Dev to see before she went back to join him. By then there were other women in the powder-room; one of them admired her perfume and Megan stayed for a few minutes to chat, glad of the chance to practise her smile and her small talk.

She walked out with the other woman, still chatting about perfume, and Dev observed her with a wry smile.

'I was beginning to wonder if you'd been taken ill, but I gather you met a friend in there!'

She laughed gaily. 'That's right.' She didn't bother to explain. Looking at her watch, she said with pretended amazement, 'Look at the time! I must go, I'm afraid. I have to be at work early tomorrow morning.'

Dev was frowning, but he paid the bill and they walked along the street to where he had parked his car. Before they drove off, he sat with his hands on the wheel, staring straight ahead.

'You didn't give me an answer.'

Her nerves leapt. 'Answer?'

'I just told you I love you, Megan!' His voice was deep, harsh.

She had hoped to avoid this scene. She didn't feel strong enough to cope with it. She was afraid she was going to cry.

'I'm sorry, Dev,' she whispered, not looking at him.

'Sorry?' He flung round, staring. There was violence in the air; she shrank back in her seat, head bent, her long, dark hair hiding her white face. 'Look at me!' he snarled, but she shook her head.

'Please, drive me home, Dev.'

'And that's it?' He sounded incredulous. 'After all I just said to you, you can only say . . . drive me home, Dev?'

Megan bit down on her lower lip until it bled;

the salt-sweetness of her blood seeped into her mouth, but she felt no pain because her misery over Dev had anaesthetised her.

'You don't love Mark Bond! I don't believe it!' Dev wasn't asking her, he was thinking aloud, and she was afraid of what he might come up with if he started thinking. She had to distract him somehow.

'That night you proposed . . . at your party,' she said in a high, thin voice. 'You told me that if I changed my mind I only had to write and say so, that you'd understand and I wasn't to feel guilty—yet ever since you got back you've been hounding me, accusing me. I'm tired of it. It's over, don't you understand? Now, will you please leave me alone?'

There was a stunned silence, as though he couldn't believe she had spoken to him like that, then he swung round in his seat and started the engine. The car shot away with an angry roar. Dev was staring at the road, his profile jagged with rage. She caught a glimpse of it out of the corner of her eye and winced at the sight.

He didn't say a word all the way to her flat, and when his car screamed to a halt outside he just sat there, his hands on the wheel, his face averted.

Megan swallowed, then huskily said, 'Goodbye.' She had meant to say goodnight in fact, but she must have been thinking goodbye and that was how it came out.

Dev stiffened, his hand tightening on the wheel. She didn't wait for him to react; she dived out of the car and ran.

She didn't sleep very well that night, and in the morning she looked at her reflection with loathing. She was pale and dark-eyed, and even careful application of her usual dark pink blusher could not give her skin any sort of glow.

She knew people at work would notice. In their business, looks were everything, even behind the camera. She would get comments: sympathy, questions, a few catty remarks. If she had been offered odds, she would have bet on Johnny's reaction, and she was right.

He did a double-take when she walked in, and raised his brows at her. 'Darling, what happened to you? Or should I say who?'

One of the other researchers giggled.

Megan kept her temper. 'I think I'm coming down with a cold,' she said. 'Thanks for the sympathy.'

'You poor love,' Johnny said, keeping his distance but blowing her a kiss. 'Don't come near me, though. I can't afford to catch it. I've got a show to do tonight. Which reminds me, where are your notes on Dev Hurst?'

'On your desk,' said Megan with tart emphasis. 'Right in front of you.'

He looked down at the folder. 'Nobody told me.' Megan didn't comment on that.

'Fanny has a copy, of course,' was all she said, as Johnny opened the folder in a desultory manner, but before he had even started to read the door of his office was thrown open and Fanny hurried in, pink and excited.

'Guess who I've just managed to get for

tonight's show?'

Everyone stared at her. Nobody answered and she laughed, her eyes alight with triumph as she told them the name of one of the biggest names in movie history.

'Scrap everything else,' Fanny added, waving both arms as though clearing the room for action. 'We won't have any other guests. We're going to make this special; we'll devote the whole half-hour to her. We'll run several clips from her best films, of course.' She looked at the other researcher. 'Lyn—you can get hold of them from the distributor, and put together a few notes; questions for Johnny to use as lead-ins to the clips. You know what we want. Megan, you can liaise with her people for us. Ring her at the Dorchester—she checked in late last night, she'll probably still be asleep, but her Press agent will be there, or her secretary. Talk to them if you can't talk to her, and you probably won't be able to, but no problem. She's too big a fish for that to matter, so long as we can be sure of getting her here. That could be a problem; she can be temperamental . . .'

'Oh, God,' groaned Johnny, turning green.

Fanny gave him an indulgent look. 'Don't have kittens, Johnny. I'm sure she'll turn up.'

He wasn't reassured. 'I've just remembered what I know about her,' he muttered, running a trembling hand over his auburn hair. 'She never shows up for anything—including her own films!'

'This time I think she will.' Fanny looked smug and Johnny eyed her with a gleam of curiosity.

'Why are you so sure?'

She put a finger to her lips. 'Never mind. Let's just say I have my reasons.'

'Very mysterious,' said Johnny, and Fanny laughed.

Megan had been sitting there in chill disbelief. Obviously, Dev would no longer be needed for the show—and who was going to tell him that he had been dropped? She cleared her throat and Johnny looked at her.

'If we aren't going to need Dev tonight, we ought to let him know as soon as possible,' she said huskily, and Johnny beamed at her.

'OK, you do that.'

Megan bit her inside lip, frowning, very pale. She could not talk to Dev again; she couldn't face it. She had said goodbye to him when she wrote that letter to South America and she had said goodbye to him again last night. She couldn't bear much more of it. She felt as though she was bleeding slowly to death; a coldness seeping through her whole body. She didn't know if she really was ill, but she certainly felt ill.

'No, no,' said Fanny, face thoughtful. 'We may still need him, if she doesn't turn up. No point in telling him that, of course. We'll just keep him as a second string to our bow; a little insurance policy.'

Megan's throat burnt with sickness. It was a ruthless world they lived in; she was coming to think she wanted nothing more to do with it or them. If they got Dev along to the studio and then didn't use him, he would be so angry! He hadn't really wanted to do this second programme; she suspected he had agreed only in order to use it to blackmail her.

Surprisingly, Johnny disagreed, however. 'I think we should tell Dev, Fan. Dev's in the business. He'd understand.'

The producer stared at him, lips pursed. 'He still has an ego.'

Johnny said softly, 'That's just it. He knows too much about how we operate; we couldn't fool him that it was a last-minute decision. He understands the way things work, and he's a very clever guy. Ambitious, too! He's going places. He could be an important man around here one fine day and we wouldn't want him to have a grudge against either of us, would we?'

Fanny pulled a face. 'Now what have you heard, I wonder, that I missed?'

Megan watched Johnny, frowning. She had begun to wonder why Johnny was so careful to please and placate Dev, and now she knew. Johnny thought that Dev was potentially a good friend and a bad enemy to make.

Johnny grinned. 'Never you mind.' He wasn't going to betray whatever secret he had been told; he was far too sharp. Was Dev in line for some really big promotion? wondered Megan, her heart sinking. That would mean that he would be based here in the studio block, perhaps, and she might have to run the risk of seeing Dev every day. What on earth was she going to do?

'OK,' Fanny capitulated. 'So we tell Hurst that he may be dumped, and if he refuses to turn up, what then?'

'We can get one of our tame lions,' said Johnny,

grinning. They had a list of well-known names always ready to step into the breach if they needed someone urgently at the last minute; there would be no problem getting one of them.

'Very well,' said Fanny. 'Megan, ring Dev Hurst now; tell him how things stand, see how he reacts. If he says we can take a running jump, you'd better ring someone else.'

Megan swallowed, throat sore. 'Maybe he would take it better from Johnny.'

Johnny gave her a shrewd look, but Fanny surprisingly nodded. 'Yes, he probably would. Good thinking, Megan. Johnny, it would come better from you—don't you think?'

Johnny was still watching Megan; he gave her a crooked little smile. 'If you say so.' He picked up his phone and dialled. Megan discreetly left the office, her face cold with perspiration. She went to the cloakroom and spent a few moments renewing her make-up. When she got back to her own office she found Johnny there, flipping over the pages of her desk diary. He looked up, an odd expression on his face.

'You don't seem to have anything important down in your diary for the next fortnight,' he said, and Megan stared at him blankly.

'I suppose not. Why?'

'I talked to Dev Hurst,' said Johnny, and she stiffened, suddenly fearing what was to come, although she really couldn't guess what Johnny was going to say, only that from the look in his eye he knew she wasn't going to be too happy about it.

'He wasn't very flattered to be used as a stand-by guest, but he agreed to do it, on one condition.' Johnny paused, quite deliberately, watching her intently.

'What was that?' Her voice sounded very dry, very shaky.

'He is putting together a short programme trailing the Amazon series to be shown next spring, and he's in a hurry to get it done before he goes back to South America, so he needs a good researcher and assistant for a couple of weeks.'

Megan's nerves jangled; she was trembling violently. She knew what Johnny was going to say now and she was appalled. She couldn't do it; the very idea froze the marrow in her bones. Why was Johnny looking so amused, as though this was all a game just for his entertainment? Couldn't he see how it was tearing her apart? And, even more urgently, how on earth was she going to get out of it?

'He asked me to let him have you just for two weeks,' Johnny said, chuckling. 'And of course I said yes. I'm sure you'll have a fascinating time, Megan, working for him; great experience for you. A whole new area for you; you'll learn a lot.'

Megan simply didn't know what to say—she dared not tell Johnny she wouldn't work with Dev, because if she did she would have to tell him why, and she didn't want to do that. She could give in her notice, of course; leave the show—but if she told Johnny she was leaving right away it would be obvious why, and that would make Johnny very curious. She was in a trap and she knew who had laid the trap for her. Dev.

She wished she could hate him; it would be easier for her, but she couldn't. She loved him, and she simply did not know what she was going to do now.

CHAPTER SEVEN

SHE found Dev in a viewing room in the basement. 'He started work this morning,' Johnny had said, telling her where to find him, but, when Megan tapped on the door and was told to come in, she found Dev idly leaning back in a chair, his feet on a desk and his hands linked behind his head while he whistled tunelessly. There was no film running and the lights were blazing.

She stood there watching him with a feeling close to hostility, and Dev stared back with the same look on his face.

'Well, come in and shut the door.'

She didn't close the door, she took a deep breath and said fiercely, 'Dev, I am not going to work for you!'

'Have you told Fabian that?' He smiled mockingly, knowing she hadn't.

'Can't you see how crazy this is?' she broke out, trembling. 'Why are you doing it? It would be so much simpler if . . .'

'Oh, but I've never liked my life simple,' he drawled, swinging slightly in the swivel chair, his long, lean body totally at ease and keeping her eyes riveted, because she might hate him when he wore that insolent smile, but she couldn't help feeling the same old tug of attraction. He drew her as the north draws the magnet; she swung helplessly towards him deep inside herself, and fought it by remembering the pain which still kept her awake at night.

'You may not, I do,' she said, and he shrugged his indifference to that.

'I'm sure you do—but you aren't being given the option. Fabian told you my deal? I could get someone from the temp office people, but the lord alone knows who they'd send. I haven't got time to train anyone and I don't want some resting actress who is only interested in getting in front of a camera. You know this work, you'll at least be useful. The sooner I get this programme put together, the sooner I'll be on my way back to the Amazon, and you'll be rid of me for another six months.'

'Make it for ever and we have a deal,' Megan muttered.

He laughed without humour. 'Who knows? With any luck you may get your wish. I'm not going on a Sunday school picnic.'

She flinched, even paler, and frowning. 'If it's that dangerous, why go back at all?'

'I thought you wanted to get rid of me!' he said softly, and she bit her lip.

'I . . .'

He moved with the lightning strike of the cobra; one moment still and poised, his eyes fixed on her, glittering, and the next getting out of his chair and reaching her in two long strides. She didn't have time to think; she felt his hands clamp down over her shoulders, pulling her up against him, and she gasped, recoiling from the contact with his body as if he was white-hot.

'You look shocked,' he murmured, smiling with satisfaction.

'Why are you doing this?' she protested, looking down because she couldn't meet those grey eyes or they might see what she was feeling. 'You're just making it harder for yourself. It is over, Dev, it's over, please, just let me go, stop this.'

He lifted one of those heavy hands and now it was light, sensitive, his fingertips gently caressing her throat, making the tiny downy hairs on her pale skin shiver and sway in answer to his warm flesh. Her body always betrayed her; she was her own worst enemy, and Dev knew just how to use her sensual weakness against her.

'I told you—it will be over between us when I say so and not before,' he said, his lips stirring the dark tendrils of her hair, making her moan almost inaudibly, her eyes closed.

'I hate you,' she said without any real hope of making him believe her, yet half meaning it, because he was ruthless in pursuit of what he wanted and she felt like a trapped little animal. She ought to fight him with weapons he understood—hit him, scream, turn violent—but she needed all her energy just to fight the terrible drag of her desire for him, and she wasn't, anyway, the type of woman who was forceful. She had never been a dynamic career-woman, although she wanted to be successful in her job and meant to climb the company ladder, if she could. She would have to do it her own way, though—she couldn't play a cut-throat game of politics or cheat or bully her way to the top, any more than she could ever sleep her way upwards, although the opportunities were always there in this business.

She forced her eyes open and made herself stand stiffly, a cold little statue in the circle of his arms.

He was gently kissing her neck, one hand moving down her spine, fondling her back.

'You're so delicate, do you know that? Lovely and delicate; you remind me of Snow White—not the schmaltzy film, she was just a pretty wax doll, that girl. No, the girl in the story, the original story; about the king and queen who couldn't have a child, then the king shot a black bird and it lay on the white snow, a drop of red blood on its breast, and the queen had a child with hair as black as night, skin as white as snow, and lips as red as blood. The first time I saw you, that was what I thought of . . . you had that doomed look.' He laughed, but Megan wasn't laughing; she was standing straight and rigid, her blue eyes wide and sombre.

Dev drew back a little to stare down at her, and his smile died. 'And you are,' he said with a touch of cruelty. 'Doomed, I mean. You aren't getting away from me, Megan, at least for another two weeks.' He put a possessive hand around her neck, as if he meant to strangle her. 'And you can't get out of it because Fabian won't back you up if you make trouble—try it and see.'

'What have you got on Johnny?' she asked angrily, and he laughed.

'I haven't got anything "on" him, as you put it. I'm not leaning on Fabian—I haven't needed to.' His hand moved into her thick, full hair, and tightened in it, jerking her head back.

With a cry of pain, Megan had to look up at him. 'You're hurting!'

'Is Mark Bond your lover?' was all he said, still holding her by the hair.

'That's my business!' She was afraid to pull free in case he really hurt her, and that made her angrier. 'You big bully!' she muttered, glaring, and Dev let go of her but didn't move away, indeed moved closer and bent, his eyes fixed on her quivering mouth.

'Megan,' he whispered, and she ached to kiss him, watching his lips with bitter intensity.

Then the phone rang and they both jumped; eyes startled. Dev swore and swung away to snatch up the phone. 'Yes?' he roared into it and then scowled. 'Oh, yes, this is Devlin Hurst speaking.' His fury had quietened to a flat pretence of courtesy. 'Oh,' he said, listening. 'When? The weekend? Yes, certainly, tell Sir James I'd be delighted, thank him for me. Yes, yes, I'll pass that on, and I'm sure that will be OK. Thank you.' He put the phone down and turned an oddly speculative glance on Megan.

She was afraid he was about to start where he had left off, but instead he asked, 'Doing anything this weekend?'

She froze, hurriedly thinking. 'Yes, I'm visiting a friend,' she lied, when in fact she had nothing planned at all.

Blandly, Dev smiled at her. 'Then I'm afraid you must cancel it. That was Sir James Fordyce's secretary.'

'The chairman?' Megan had never even met the chairman of the board of directors of the company; indeed, she had never even set eyes on the man, although he was very famous, having been a very successful actor before he became a director and then one of the board of the television company. He had become chairman a few months ago, and so far hadn't made any changes in the direction the company had been taking for a long time, but everyone was expecting this new broom to start sweeping away some of the staff any day.

Megan was baffled. What had the chairman got to do with her, or indeed she to do with the chairman? Or his secretary, come to that?

'The chairman,' agreed Dev drily. 'His secretary rang to pass on his invitation for the weekend. He has a little place in Kent and wants us to join him there for a rather exclusive staff conference.'

'Oh,' Megan said, not quite taking it in. 'That should be fun for you . . . it was snowing in Kent, the last I heard.' Then she opened her eyes wide, shock in them. 'Us? Did you say us? What do you mean, us?'

'Us as in both of us,' said Dev. 'You and me, that's what I mean. What else could I mean?'

'I've never even met the chairman!'

'Now's your chance.'

'He doesn't know me, he can't do, we've never met!'

'I think you've established that,' Dev said solemnly. 'You and the chairman have never met, so far, but he wants to remedy that this weekend.'

Megan shook her head slowly, frowning. 'Why

should he? He can never have heard of me, why should he want to meet me?'

'Because I told him about you. He invited me and told me to bring my assistant, even though the last one looked like the Bride of Frankenstein, but I told him I had a new one and she looked like Snow White and he said in that case certainly bring her.'

She looked at him with slow disbelief, blue eyes angry. 'You can't have done, stop kidding.'

'No kidding,' he said, smiling. 'You are invited and you had better be there or the chairman is going to be disappointed, because he loves the story of Snow White too; maybe because he's a dwarf, and that is one part he wouldn't need to wear make-up for.'

Now she knew he was joking and she glared at him. 'Don't be ridiculous!'

Dev sat down again and pulled a notepad towards him. 'OK, the chairman isn't really a dwarf, just an actor, but the invitation is deadly serious, and you'll be there this weekend. It will be very good for your promotion prospects. In this business, it's not so much how good you are as who you know. Haven't you discovered that yet? Now stop distracting me. I must get down to some work.'

Indignantly, Megan said, 'I was not distracting you!'

'Oh, yes, you were,' he said, sliding her an insolent sideways look that made her face burn. 'Put the lights out and we'll either make love . . .' he watched her start to back, her eyes wary, and laughed, 'or we'll start the film,' he said in that soft, tormenting voice.

Megan's teeth were tight. He was enjoying this game of cat and mouse, but it was playing havoc with her nerves. Apparently oblivious of her anger, Dev picked up his scribbled notes and glanced over them, talking without looking at her. 'I'll see it through once, to decide which sections I'm going to use, and after that I want you to run down an old film for me—made some time in the Thirties, I think. I saw it once, years ago—it had some fascinating footage of the Manaus of the period; very grainy black and white newsreel film. I'd love to use a few feet of that for comparison with the Manaus of today.'

Megan groaned silently at the prospect of all the work involved in tracking down this piece of film; he probably didn't even know which studio had made it or who had directed it! But at least if Dev was watching his film footage he wouldn't be concentrating on her, so she crossed to the lights and switched them off, then drew up a chair to watch the film Dev himself had shot in the South American jungle. It was an unbearably vivid film, for her, because she was actually seeing what Dev had until now merely described to her: the heat, the insects, the snakes, the dark, impenetrable trees with their vines and creepers tangling the paths, and, of course, the river. That was always present, even when you couldn't see it, swirling with currents, running limpidly, flat and sullen, but always with that nightmarish quality which was unlike that of any river she had ever known, an air of threat.

Megan tried not to watch Dev all the time, but of course her eyes kept returning to the lean figure in a khaki cotton shirt and shorts, his black hair ruffled, his face daily growing more tanned. Perspiration trickled down his face, made his shirt stick to his body; under the tan she was sure his face was haggard, and his movements were often weary.

'Why do you all wear khaki?' she asked, after a while, and he grimaced.

'You can get very dirty in that jungle; mud, grass stains, sweat . . . you put something on in the morning and inside an hour it can be filthy. On the river you can wash clothes easily enough each evening and dry them on the boat, but white is out. It looks terrible after one or two washings. Khaki is the best colour, we found. It lasts longest.'

When they had run through the film once, Dev put on the lights and glanced at her. 'What do you think?'

'I can see you getting ill in front of my eyes,' she said without looking up.

'I was fine then!' He sounded taken aback. 'I didn't catch the bug until much later.'

'Maybe not, but it's obvious the climate was sapping your energy, and I'm not surprised. It looks terrible there.'

He shrugged. 'It isn't England, no, but I've been to South America before. I could handle the heat.'

'But you picked up a terrible disease!'

'That could have happened to anyone!'

'That's not my point!'

'What is your point, then?' he asked drily, his

eyes impatient.

'You shouldn't go back there!' she burst out, and then wished she hadn't when she saw the look in his face, the triumph smouldering in those grey eyes, the curve of satisfaction to his hard mouth.

'I thought you were indifferent to me, couldn't wait to get rid of me?' he purred, smiling.

Megan was so furious with herself she could have screamed. When would she learn to keep control over her stupid tongue? Hurriedly getting up, she almost ran to the door.

'I'll go and check out that old film,' she said huskily as she escaped, and was even angrier when she heard Dev laughing behind her, but he didn't try to stop her, or call her back. He had given her a difficult job to do; no doubt he realised how long it would take her to track the film down. She had so little to go on—just the subject matter and some vague idea of the period. Film libraries these days were very well catalogued and at least she had a starting point. She could check up on all the film shot in that part of the world during the relevant years, and fortunately it was not an area which had been much used in filming, so that the volume of film material was not as great as it would have been for some places.

She knew the various film libraries pretty well because she had had to use them from time to time for the Fabian show; she had contacts in them all. It was a big help to be on first-name terms with someone who was going to have to work very hard to help you, and she shamelessly sold them a picture of Dev as a remorseless slavedriver ready to tear her limb from limb if she didn't find the film he needed.

'I can't go back without it,' she moaned, rolling big blue eyes, and got immediate sympathy.

'I'll see what I can do,' they all promised and scurried off to search through dusty card indexes or tap their computer files. Megan spent the best part of the day looking for the film which matched Dev's patchy memory, and was about to go back empty-handed when someone came up with a rather poor copy of a film of an expedition along the Amazon. Dev had remembered it as grey and grainy. Since then it had deteriorated further; at times it was like seeing people through a pale pea soup, but Megan was sure she had located the right film.

'No, sorry, I can't possibly let you take the film,' she was told in an apologetic voice. 'More than my job's worth. Tell your ogre to come here and view it for himself, and if he still wants to use it some arrangement can probably be made with my own boss, but it will have to be official. It's quite a valuable piece of film, and it isn't in a good condition at all.'

'OK, thanks,' Megan said, relieved that she had managed to find the film at all. 'Mr Hurst will understand the situation.'

She found Dev in his office, frowning over a thick typed manuscript. Megan paused in the doorway, her heart missing a beat at the pallor and weariness she saw in his face. He hadn't noticed her yet, but he suddenly lifted his head and sighed, passing a hand over his eyes and yawning.

'You ought to be in bed,' Megan said, and he stiffened, looking round at her.

'Is that an offer?' his voice whispered smokily as he smiled at her.

She flushed angrily. 'Will you stop flirting with me?' How many times do I have to say it? It's . . .'

'Over!' he mocked. 'I know, you keep telling me—but somehow you aren't very convincing when you look at me like that, Megan.'

Her face was burning; she averted her eyes from his amused face. 'Oh, for God's sake!' she muttered. 'Can't you see I mean it, or are you so vain that you can't imagine any woman falling out of love with you?'

The silence which followed her outburst seemed to drag on for ever until she was on the verge of breaking down. She didn't dare to look at Dev; she was terrified of what she might see in his face. At last he said flatly, 'Well, did you get anywhere, hunting for the old film footage?'

Still not looking at him, and half sick with relief, she nodded. 'I think so. I've located a film that seemed a strong candidate, anyway, but it's in such poor condition that they wouldn't let me take it out of the library. You'll have to go and view it there, they said, and if it is what you want some sort of arrangement can be made, but it will have to go through official channels.'

'OK, I'll deal with that tomorrow, while you're going through my film again working with this script and looking at where I've marked possible cuts.'

She slowly went over to take the script from him. 'What is it?'

'I've had a typist working all day on the audio recording I brought back with me. I kept a taped diary; each evening before I went to sleep I recorded comments on what we'd done and seen, where we were on the journey, how far we had come and had to go, what film we had shot . . .' He lifted the heavy wadge of script and flicked the pages. 'This is it! The girl did a very good job; there aren't many errors and most of those are in place-names or people's names.' He handed it to Megan, drily saying, 'Careful! It's heavy.'

He wasn't exaggerating; her arm sagged under the weight of it. 'This isn't the script of the actual film, then?'

He shook his head. 'No, but I talked about each section of the journey, and so I've used this to work out a schedule for the actual programme. Working from this damn great thing we can type out a running list and then I'll put together a working script.'

She nodded. 'I see. OK, I'll do that tomorrow, then.' She looked at her watch. 'It's late, I must go.'

'Got a date?'

'Yes,' she lied, walking away, and Dev let her go without another word. Maybe at last he had got the message? she thought, and felt bleakly resigned as she made her way home to her silent, empty, lonely flat. She ate a light salad supper in the kitchen then sat down to watch a rival chat show with a comedian host. Johnny liked them to watch it each week, to keep track of what the other man was doing, and tonight Megan was startled to see Mark on the show. That would amuse Johnny; he loved it when someone he had discovered got picked up by a rival show! The camera focused on Mark's face as he smiled, and she sighed, frowning. She hadn't seen him since the night he'd had the fight with Dev. She should have rung him, written, perhaps—but she simply didn't know what to say and so it had seemed easier not to say anything. Sometimes silence was much wiser.

In the morning, she arrived at the office early and started work on the typed manuscript of Dev's diary. He didn't show up for hours and Megan became utterly absorbed in what she was reading and hearing: Dev's words, Dev's voice, Dev's mind. She hardly noticed the passage of time. What she was doing was far too important for time to matter.

She had known Dev for such a short time before he went away, and she really hadn't known him very well. She had fallen in love with her senses; she had wanted him with painful intensity, but she hadn't found out much about the human being inside the body she desired. A hot flush crawled up her cheeks as that dawned on her. She hadn't realised all this until now, because she had been mistaking naked desire for love.

Dev hadn't helped, of course—he hadn't told her anything about himself; indeed, he had hidden far too much. Now she was beginning to know him. In this copious diary he had recorded everything in a stream-of-consciousness style, putting down whatever came into his head—plants he had noticed and filmed, flowers and ferns and trees, butterflies and moths, ants and termites, birds, toads, snakes, lizards, monkeys and wild cats. Dev seemed to forget nothing, but there was far more to the diary than the fauna and flora he noticed. That was not what fascinated Megan.

It was the insight she was being given into Dev himself—the way he thought, his motives and dreams, what gave him that drive and energy. Perhaps because he was so far away from everything familiar, or because each day he used up all his energy and was half asleep when he began to record, or maybe because after a while he was falling ill, Dev began to be amazingly frank on the tapes. At first, he had been more concerned with mundane stuff like the exact day, weather, distance travelled, what he had done or seen. But then he changed; almost as though he was using the tapes as a confessional, a doctor's couch. He talked about why he had always been fascinated by the Amazon; one of the last unknown places of the earth, he said, a place of secrets and mystery, darkness and untamed nature. It would vanish before too long if something wasn't done to save it, and Dev had wanted to see it before it was too late. It was ephemeral, finite, like everything else, he said.

That was the thread running through everything he said; the ephemeral nature of life. He talked grimly about death, in the jungle, on the river, how abruptly it could come, without warning, the way it had to a friend who had died suddenly in his teens, then mentioned his mother's death while he was still at school, how that had affected him and then he said something about Gianna. Oh, he didn't name her, of course; it was just a brief, sideways comment about women who walked out on you, betrayed you. 'Sex is a little death, of course,' he said. 'Isn't that because even while you're in heaven, you know that hell is just around the corner?'

Megan knew he was talking about Gianna; who else could it be? That icy, bitter tone of voice was painful to listen to—who else but Gianna would he hate so much?

She closed her eyes, her hands over her face. Not me, she thought. He doesn't mean me! Or did he?

It was hard to guess from the diary so far, because, although he talked about his own thoughts and feelings, he never mentioned names or personal events. These were very impersonal admissions; journeys through his mind rather than private gossip, and the occasional mention of someone else was always discreetly veiled. Dev knew very well that his were not the only pair of eyes that would read his diary; he was very careful what and how he wrote.

Had her letter arrived by the time he wrote that passage, though? She read it over again, brow furrowed, but couldn't tell. She thought back over everything that had happened since he came back. Did he hate her? His passion could be violent;

almost volcanic—but desire could spring from hatred too, couldn't it?

She sighed bleakly. Yes, you could hate and desire at the same time; sometimes when Dev was cruel to her she hated him, but she wanted him badly, too.

'Problems?' his deep voice said behind her at that second, and she swung round, her heart missing a beat.

'No . . . not really,' she stammered.

He walked towards her and she felt her face burning. Dev noticed it, too, his grey eyes narrowing.

'So how's it coming?' He perched on the edge of her desk, his leg brushing hers in a casual way, and Megan carefully shifted a fraction to avoid the contact. She wasn't looking at Dev, but she felt him stiffen, felt the sideways glance she got.

'Fine. I'm almost finished, I'll have that running list ready as soon as I can type it up.'

He leaned forward to peer over her shoulder at the script open on the desk. She could hardly breath as she felt his cheek almost touching hers.

'That's great,' he said softly, his arm encircling her. It was deliberate, she knew that. Dev was forcing the little intimacies on her, aware of her reactions, daring her to stop him. It was coat-trailing of a provocative kind, and Megan could have hit him.

She swung her chair sideways so that she could get up without touching him, but Dev moved too. As she stood up she found him in front of her, looking her up and down with speculative mockery.

'Something bothering you?' he drawled, watching her hot face with satisfaction.

All Megan could do was snap, 'No! I'm just going to make myself some coffee—want some?' and walk away, resisting the temptation to run.

That was what it was like all that week. Working with Dev at such close quarters made walking barefoot over hot coals look quite an attractive proposition! He went out of his way to make it hard for her, of course. The way he watched her made it impossible for her to forget that they were alone, and he never missed a chance of touching her, standing close to her, making her aware of him. Her nerves leapt every time he came within a foot of her, and she found it hard to concentrate.

She couldn't even be consistent; she hated him for doing this to her, but every time she saw him her heart turned over. She kept telling herself she couldn't stand it, yet she dreaded the time when it must end.

CHAPTER EIGHT

SHE was even more on edge over the coming weekend. Why had the chairman invited her? Or had he simply asked Dev to bring a girl? Megan wished she had the nerve to refuse to go, but she knew that it would be crazy to pass up a chance to meet the chairman and his influential friends! Dev was right, her career could get quite a boost from spending time with such important people, but Megan wished Dev wasn't going to be there. When it came down to it, it was Dev she was really worrying about. It was bad enough spending all day with him in that office—being with him all weekend under the same roof was going to be a terrible strain.

Dev drove her down there, saying very little at first, and Megan sat staring straight ahead, deeply aware of him sitting there beside her. He was wearing a dark grey suit which made him look thinner and rather pale. His red-striped shirt and dark red silk tie emphasised the formal look of the suit. Dev was out to impress, she thought—the chairman? Gossips in the canteen kept hinting that Dev was in line for a very important executive job, high up in the company—was it all smoke, or was there fire behind that rumour?

'Is it a big party this weekend?' she asked, and

Dev shrugged.

'I doubt it.'

'Any special reason why he's asked you? Is it to hear all about the Amazon trip?'

'No,' he coolly admitted. 'He wants to talk me into taking a job.'

So for once the gossips had been right! Megan gave him a wary, sidelong look. 'In London?'

He nodded. 'But I'd have to take it up immediately, I can't ask him to wait another year until I've finished the Amazon project. He wants me to hand that over to my assistant and take up this other job at once.'

Her throat hurt and she was pale. 'Will you?' she asked huskily.

He shrugged again. 'I don't think so.'

She bit her lower lip, knowing it was none of her business any more, she had no right to comment or even care, and anyway, it would be easier for her if he wasn't always around—and yet deeply afraid of what might happen if he went back to the Amazon.

'Is it a good job?'

'Very.' He was curt, indifferent.

'Is it wise to pass up a chance like that?'

He suddenly swung the wheel and pulled off the road into a leafy lay-by and Megan's throat began to beat with a frantic pulse as he parked and turned to face her.

'What are you doing?'

His grey eyes were glittering with some fierce emotion. Hate or love? she wondered, unable to look away from the heat of his stare. It was like looking into the sun; it blinded her and yet she couldn't stop.

'Give me a reason for staying, Megan,' he said thickly, and she had never felt such pain, because she wanted so much to give him that reason, to beg him to stay, for her sake, and yet she couldn't do that because if she married him she would be bringing him another sort of unhappiness. She stared at him like a dumb animal, cornered and helpless, shaking and close to tears; and Dev waited and watched her, the glitter in his eyes like the lance of a laser now, and it was hate she saw, not love, but there was nothing she could do.

'I'm sorry,' she whispered, and Dev's teeth met, his lip curled back from them in a silent snarl.

He reached out for her with hands that hurt and meant to, and she writhed and fought as silently, trying to keep her mouth closed to him, trying to control the hungry leap of her senses as he touched her. She had never in her life felt such sensual torment; her flesh was melting with the heat inside her body, she was weak with bitter yearning, yet she struggled not to give in to it—struggled not with Dev, but with herself, because she knew she was the real enemy. She knew she couldn't have Dev, it was impossible, forbidden, but she wanted him more now than she had ever had.

At last Dev stopped, gave up, released her, still in the same angry silence, and as he put his foot down with a roar of acceleration, and shot back on to the main road, she turned her head away from him and let the tears trickle out from under her closed lids.

Why on earth had she come? Hadn't she known how it would be if she spent the weekend with him in the country, even at the chairman's house? It was going to be the worst ordeal of her life!

As they shot up the drive towards the place, she pretended to cough, in order to have the excuse for getting out a handkerchief and blowing her nose, managing at the same time to dry her eyes.

She only noticed the house as she was getting out of the car; it was large and imposing, set among perfectly stylised gardens with manicured lawns and beautifully shaped box and yew trees. She saw a soft white blur under some trees; snowdrops, she thought, frowning. It was nearly spring; soon the daffodils would come, taking the winds of March with beauty, and by then Dev would be on his way back to South America.

The chairman himself appeared, all smiles. He was a charming man; smoothly practised in the art of making people like him, putting them at their ease.

'Delighted to meet you, Megan,' he said, holding her hands and gazing at her with apparent admiration.

'Thank you for inviting me,' she said, aware of Dev watching them.

'Thank you for coming,' said the chairman, bland as custard. 'Come in out of this cold weather.'

I wish I could, she thought, following him into the hall, but the weather of her life was far colder than the chilly February day.

His house was glossy and perfect, like himself; not quite genuine, like himself; all things to all men, like himself. Megan viewed it with a jaundiced eye; ready to be critical of everything she saw because she wished she was somewhere else. She was whisked up to her room and told to ring if she wanted anything; the housekeeper would look after her. Megan smiled until her face ached, and when she was alone she sat down on the chintz-draped bed in the pretty, chintzy bedroom, and hated her surroundings.

There were quite a few people staying in the house; mostly company executives and their wives. The men she found boring, the women clannish—they all knew each other already and, although they were not unfriendly, they weren't precisely friendly, either. She got the impression they weren't sure yet if she mattered. If she had been going to marry Dev, they might have been more interested in her, or if Dev had publicly accepted a job on the administrative level, that might have given her status, but as it was she found herself more or less ignored while they talked about clothes, their husband's work, new curtains, their husband's promotion and salary rise, the cost of petrol, the size of their husband's desk, and so on . . .

The chairman was charming to them all; particularly the women, for them he had a special brand of charm which meant gazing into their eyes, holding their hands and calling them honey or lovely. He never used their names, probably

because he never remembered them. He looked as
if he had trouble remembering his own, but to
Megan's surprise, that Saturday afternoon, while
his wife was showing everyone else around the
vast Victorian conservatories, the chairman
hijacked her from the party and took her off alone
with him.

'Come and see my etchings,' he purred, and
when she laughed said, 'I mean it! It's such a
corny line that I simply had to learn how to etch.'

They had been framed and hung in a line on a
stark white wall; all nature studies, black and
white and very striking.

Megan admired them without needing to lie,
and the chairman beamed on her.

'They aren't bad, are they? I should have been
an artist, not an actor. I was a competent actor, but
I would have been a happier painter.'

Megan smiled politely, wondering why he had
really brought her here alone. She hoped he
wasn't going to make a pass at her. She didn't feel
up to coping with a crisis of that sort today.

Suddenly he said, 'Did you know about this job
we've offered Dev?'

Megan started, her blue eyes wide and her face
pale between her soft, dark hair. She nodded
silently after a second, aware of the chairman
watching her.

'Why has he turned it down?' he asked
brusquely, and she took a sharp breath.

'Has he?' It wasn't a surprise, but it still shook
her, and her face whitened still further.

'He didn't tell you that?'

She shook her head, and the chairman frowned at her.

'But you're the reason why he refused it?'

The question was like a knife in her flesh; she looked away, fighting for control, and couldn't answer.

'Talk to him,' the chairman said, after a moment. 'I won't ask any more questions. I don't want to pry into personal matters, but I've had a report on his health and this tropical medicine specialist he's been seeing is concerned about him: Dev shouldn't go back to the Amazon, at least until he has fully recovered, and he's still pretty weak, I'm told. See what you can do, there's a good girl. Surely whatever's wrong between you can be worked out?'

Megan said huskily; 'I'll try to talk to him, but I can't . . . I can't promise anything else . . .'

Dev was with the rest of the party in the conservatories, admiring the ferns and begonias, the hyacinths and hothouse tulips, but as Megan joined them the chairman's wife gave her a quick, shrewd look, and said, 'Look at the time! I think I'll go and have a bath before dinner. How about you, ladies?'

The guests drifted off in her wake, but Dev, his dark brows together, had noticed the way his hostess had looked at Megan. He sat down on a pink velvet-covered love-seat, carefully arranged among the scented flowers.

'Aren't you going to take a bath and dress before dinner?' he asked her, and Megan wandered about, pretending to look at the potted plants.

'In a minute—these blue hyacinths have a very strong scent, don't they?'

'What did the chairman want?' Dev asked curtly. 'Or can I guess? Don't bother to say whatever he told you to say. I'm not interested.'

She swung round, blue eyes distressed. 'Dev, take that job! Don't risk your life again.'

'Don't pretend you give a damn what I do!' His lips barely moved, his voice was icy, but his eyes were molten steel: white-hot and dangerous.

That question must not be answered, so she said miserably, 'Nothing is worth risking your life for!'

'Well, you certainly aren't!' he muttered, and she flinched, meeting the hatred in his stare.

Shaking, she turned and ran, not caring now if he realised she was running away from him. In her room she sat there for a long time, cold and miserable, then she showered quickly and began to dress. She was in her white lace bra and panties when Dev walked in and she swung round, crimson and furious.

'Get out of here, Dev!'

'You forgot to lock your door!' was all he said, staring, and the glitter of his eyes made her heart beat heavily, her breathing thicken.

'Don't, Dev,' she whispered, suddenly paralysed.

He took a step towards her, his grey eyes seeming to burn her skin as he stared at her. Why hadn't she remembered to lock her door? She had known he might follow her, hadn't she? A Freudian slip, she thought.

'A Freudian slip,' Dev said hoarsely, and her

eyes flickered in shock. They were beginning to think alike after all these hours alone together!

'Why, Megan?' he said, his hands sliding down her bare arms, pulling her closer. 'Did you want me to find you like this?'

Shame made her look down; was that what she had wanted? She didn't know, and that was worrying—was her unconscious operating so shamelessly on its own?

He softly cupped her breast and a piercing excitement made her dizzy; she closed her eyes and Dev breathed faster, one arm round her, his hand splayed on her bare back. His mouth was hot; she tried vainly not to respond, but she needed the touch of his lips, the intimacy that had threatened her all that week in the office when they were so close and yet hadn't kissed, hadn't been in each other's arms. It had been on their minds all the time, though. Desire had been in the air they breathed; it had fountained inside her and driven her mad with frustration.

His hands moved and left a track of fire everywhere they touched, and Megan had to touch him, too. He groaned as she did, then suddenly picked her up and carried her to the bed, his mouth burrowing between her breasts.

'No, Dev,' she gasped, surfacing in shock.

'Yes,' he muttered, caressing her naked body with shaking hands. 'I want you so badly I'm going crazy.'

She wanted him too, but she had to stop him before it was too late. 'You aren't making love to me, Dev,' she said, turning her head aside and pushing at his shoulders. 'I won't let you; do I have to make a scene to stop you? If I scream the whole house will hear me.'

He lifted his head, face dark red, those grey eyes hot and raging. 'You little bitch! What sort of games are you playing? You let me go so far and then call a halt, is that it? Just when I'm almost out of my mind? Is that what turns you on—not sex, but teasing a man and then watching him go mad with frustration? Do you know what men call a woman like you?'

His voice made her sick, but she was angry, too. How dared he say such things to her? She hit him hard, across the face, and Dev looked shocked, sitting up, a hand to the livid mark on his cheek.

Megan rolled off the bed, grabbed a dressing-gown and ran for the bathroom. She locked herself into it and wouldn't emerge until she was sure Dev had gone.

She didn't have long to wait; she heard the angry slam of her bedroom door and his striding footsteps, and when everything was quiet again she crept out, shaking.

How was she going to stand the next twenty-four hours? Every time she was near Dev she was going to be on tenterhooks, yet she dared not leave.

Slowly, with trembling fingers, she continued dressing, did her hair and make-up, looked bleakly at her reflection and then in the mirror saw the crumpled bed, the indentations that their bodies had made.

Shuddering, she swung round and pulled off the cover, shook it and remade the bed, erasing all evidence of what had happened, but she couldn't wipe the memory from her own mind, and, when she went downstairs to dinner and found Dev talking to the other guests, she knew it was there, in his mind, too. He gave her a glance icy and remote—and she went to talk to one of the other women, struggling to keep a calm expression on her face.

It was a dreadful evening, and she went to bed early, but lay awake wondering how she was going to get through the next day. To her enormous relief, the chairman chose to hold a conference with his executives throughout the morning, and Dev sat in on it, leaving the women to their own devices. Megan chatted and walked through the gardens and, on closer acquaintance, got on well enough with the chairman's wife.

For the rest of that long, long day she managed to be surrounded by people whenever she saw Dev, but he would be driving her back to London and she could not escape him then. She need not have worried; he did drive her, but he was in a grim, silent mood. He didn't say a word until he dropped her at her flat.

As she got out, he said curtly, 'As we've done all the work necessary for my programme, you might as well go back to Fabian's office tomorrow.'

Megan gave him a quick, startled look, but before she could react he had leaned over, closed his car door and driven away, leaving her on the pavement, staring after him.

Dev had given up, she realised, her face chill and unhappy. It really was over now; he had accepted her decision.

CHAPTER NINE

'YOU'RE in the wrong office!' joked Johnny when he saw her, and she pretended to smile as she explained. 'I see,' Johnny said. 'He got bored and threw you back to me, did he? Well, I've got plenty for you to do, haven't we, Fanny?'

'Pronouns a bit mixed today, aren't they?' Fanny said. 'But we're glad to have you back, Megan. Look, could you ring this lady for me and find out how many films she has made? All the reference books give different figures.'

They were all too busy to care about what had happened between her and Dev, and she meant to push all thought of Dev out of her head, but then Johnny dropped another bombshell half-way through the week.

'By the way, Hurst will be on the next show,' he said, and watched her shaken face with interest. 'Mind you, he wasn't too keen, said he couldn't do it at first, but the chairman spoke to him. I gather he has finished putting his Amazon programme together now, and the chairman wants us to talk about that. They're going to put it out quite soon.'

Megan was dry-mouthed, and could only nod.

'Ring him and check that he'll be there, on the day, won't you?' said Johnny, and then walked off before she could plead an excuse. She was as

nervous as a kitten after that, and on the morning
of the next show she nerved herself to ring Dev,
but he was out. She left a message on his answering machine, then spent the day fretting that he
wouldn't turn up for the programme. When
Johnny grabbed hold of her, though, and
demanded, 'He will be there?' she immediately
tried to look confident and nodded, because there
was no point in making Johnny edgy, too.

'Of course!'

'Great. Got my briefing ready?'

'I'm just typing it now.'

'Well, get on with it. Why are you standing
around chatting?'

She didn't bother to point out that she had been
sitting at her desk working on her VDU when he'd
pulled her out of her chair.

'Yes, Johnny,' she said soothingly, because it
was always the same. As each show approached
Johnny grew more and more paranoid. He was the
lynchpin of the programme; it stood or fell by him
and everyone remembered that when he started
falling apart or bawled them out over nothing.

She was in the green room before they went on
the air, handing out frivolous snippets of food or
glasses of cheap wine to the guests, who looked
askance at their glasses after one sip. 'What is this
stuff?' asked one. 'Paint-stripper?'

'Sorry,' she said, smiling politely, although it
was an effort to smile at all while she was on edge
over Dev.

'Get me some whisky, there's a good girl,' said a
famous actor, sweat on his forehead. 'I hate first

nights.'

She laughed, although he wasn't really being funny, just suffering from nerves in spite of all his years in the theatre. Television was quite another medium, one he was unfamiliar with; they had had a tough time talking him on to the show and Johnny had been afraid he wouldn't arrive, but then Johnny was always afraid his stars wouldn't show up!

There was a flurry at the door, and Megan tensed, her antennae picking up Dev's presence in the room. She smiled vaguely at the famous actor. 'Yes, of course, I won't be a moment.'

She walked over to the drinks table, fighting not to look in Dev's direction. He was being hailed by Fanny; she would get him a drink. Megan picked up the whisky and poured some into a glass, her hand shaking.

'Hey! You trying to get someone drunk?' asked one of the other researchers, looking amused.

Megan realised then what a stiff drink she had poured and grimaced. 'It's for Aidan.'

'Oh! Right!' the other girl said, grinning with understanding, but Fanny overheard and swung round, frowning.

'That man is not getting drunk and wrecking my show! Pour that back into the bottle, Megan, then go and look after Dev Hurst. He's on last.'

Megan swallowed, her mouth very dry, but managed to force a smile. 'He doesn't need a babysitter, he's an old hand,' she said huskily.

'He seems odd this time,' Fanny shrugged. 'When he was on before, he took it in his stride, I remember. Maybe it's his illness, or perhaps I'm imagining it, but he seems different, so keep an eye on him, will you?' She had been muttering as they crossed the room, but as they came up to Dev she raised her voice and said, 'Sorry to love and leave you, but I have a lot to do before airtime, Dev. You know Megan, don't you?'

She vanished, leaving them staring at each other in silence.

'Do I know you?' Dev asked pointedly. He was wearing a dark city suit and white shirt; the formal clothes made him look thinner than ever, his brown skin only emphasising the haggard tautness of his face. He didn't smile at Megan; he just considered her with hostility glittering in his grey eyes.

'Can I get you another drink?' she asked, pretending not to have heard the biting sarcasm.

'No, thanks. You haven't driven me to drink yet.' He looked her over insultingly. 'Very demure; butter-wouldn't-melt-in-your-mouth time, is it?'

Megan looked desperately at her watch. Only a little longer and she could escape from this.

'I'd love to know what really makes you tick,' Dev muttered in a low voice. There were people all round them and she was relieved he wasn't making this a more public scene, but any minute now he might.

'Shall we go, people?' Fanny said from the door and then they heard the laughter and clapping from the audience. The warm-up man was getting them into the right mood before Johnny came on.

The famous actor strolled after Fanny; he was the first guest that night because he was appearing in a new play and would have to be driven across London in time for curtain up. Dev turned to go, too.

'Not yet,' Megan said, huskily. 'You're the last on—another twenty minutes to wait, I'm afraid. We can watch the programme, though.'

The green room had a monitor hanging in one corner; a giant screen on which Johnny's face now appeared, magnified and dominating. The audience whistled and clapped and Johnny beamed.

'Fool!' muttered Dev, and walked away to the window where he stood staring down into the street at the distant lights and cars. On the screen the faces talked; the applause sounded like the meaningless wash of the sea backwards and forwards on an empty beach. Johnny grimaced and winked and the actor preened, stroking back a thinning lock of hair. Megan watched Dev's back and wished she was somewhere else, then thought how stupid she was being because she would rather stand there watching Dev, even knowing he now hated her, than be unable to see him at all.

Dev's call came and he went out without so much as a glance at her. She watched the monitor during the interview and now the talk was not just a pointless buzz; she really listened. Johnny had to work harder than he had on the last interview with Dev; he had a rather puzzled air, even though he smiled as much. What was wrong? his eyes asked, and he sweated in case the interview might go disastrously awry.

'So, are you back home for good or . . .'

'No, I'm flying back to the Amazon tomorrow,' Dev said, and Megan jerked in shock, her blue eyes darkening. Johnny was startled, too; in fact his jaw dropped, because she hadn't had that little titbit in the notes she had typed out for him.

'You're going tomorrow?' Johnny pretended to find it all hilarious, laughing loudly. 'Why wasn't I told? Nobody tells me anything.'

Megan was going to be hauled over the coals next time he saw her, but that didn't matter. The only thing that mattered was that Dev was going back to the Amazon. Her eyes focused on his thin, fleshless features. He wasn't well enough yet. It was stupid, reckless, crazy. He couldn't be serious; what about the tests he was supposed to be having? Had he told the specialist he was seeing? He hadn't been back long and he had said he was staying for some weeks.

'Why the sudden change of plan?' asked Johnny for her, as if their minds had been moving on the same track.

Dev shrugged. 'I'm eager to get on with my filming, and I'm more or less back to normal, health-wise.' He was flat and offhand, but Johnny scented a mystery, a secret, and his eyes glinted. He tried to ferret it out of Dev, using all his charm, his expertise as an interviewer, but he got nowhere, and while he was still prying away at the locked door of Dev's secrecy the music came up and the credits rolled, and Johnny, with an irritated smile, began talking them out, thanking everyone, saying, 'See you same time, same channel, Thursday . . . don't be late, now . . .'

They were off the air and Johnny erupted into the room a few moments later, fire and brimstone spewing from him.

'What the hell went wrong? Why didn't you mention that he was going back that soon? What do you think I pay you for?'

'He didn't tell me!' Megan was talking like an automaton, her eyes on the door. Was Dev coming back in here? 'I'm sorry, Johnny, I had no idea . . .'

'The whole interview was the wrong way round because I didn't know that one thing! If I'd known I would have asked different questions.'

'It isn't her fault,' Fanny soothed, joining them. 'And, anyway, Johnny love, it was a nice surprise, coming out of the blue like that. I didn't see anything about it in the Press beforehand, so we had a little scoop. It will be in the papers tomorrow that he announced it out of the blue on the Fabian show, and that is always good publicity for us, isn't it?'

Sulkily Johnny agreed. 'But I don't like being caught out like that; it makes me panic. You know how I hate to improvise.'

Fanny patted his cheek. 'Lovely, you were wonderful, wasn't he, Megan? Rose to it magnificently; not a hair out of place and asked all the right things, gave all the right reactions. Couldn't fault you, honestly.'

Johnny purred. 'Really? You aren't just saying

that?'

'Really,' said Fanny, and Johnny went happily off to have a drink before he left. Fanny looked at Megan and winked.

'I'm sorry to fall down on that one,' Megan said flatly.

'Not to worry, love. I gather Devlin Hurst can be a difficult guy. He may have held the bombshell back deliberately. It had more impact that way. Johnny looked so taken aback! It was obvious he really didn't know.'

'Has he left?' asked Megan, and Fanny looked blank.

'Who?'

'Devlin Hurst.'

'I think he has—walked off without a word. He's a surly devil at times, isn't he?'

Megan laughed humourlessly. 'Yes, you could say that. Excuse me, Fanny . . . I have to rush . . .'

She reached the car park just in time to see Dev drive away, and slowed, biting her lip. What had she chased down here for, anyway? It was all over. They had said their goodbyes and it would be foolish to see him again. It wasn't her business if he chose to return to the Amazon. What had she been intending to say to him, if she had caught up with him?

She walked over to her own car and got behind the wheel, but sat there for several minutes to pull herself together before she tried to drive. Her mind was shot to pieces—she didn't want to be a danger to other drivers.

She had only been home for half an hour when

the doorbell went. For some reason she leapt to the conclusion that it was Dev and ran to answer it, her loose white lounging robe flying around her, but to her disbelief she found herself facing his sister, Emma Stansfield.

'Is he here?' Emma burst out, and Megan dumbly shook her head. Emma gave her a hostile survey from her tousled hair down over the white robe. 'I don't believe you,' she said, and pushed past Megan calling her brother's name. 'Dev! Dev!'

Megan followed her, closing the front door. Emma looked into the kitchen and then into the sitting-room before heading purposefully towards the bedroom.

'Where do you think you're going?' Megan tried to stop her and was pushed aside.

'I saw that stupid programme you work for! I know he's talking about going back there tomorrow and he can't. It could kill him.' Emma hurled the words over her shoulder as she pulled the bedroom door open. 'Dev! I've got to talk to . . .' Her voice trailed away.

'He isn't here,' Megan repeated flatly.

'Then where is he?' Emma's hands curled into fists at her sides, as if she wanted to hit somebody. Me, most likely! thought Megan. Emma had made no secret of the fact that she disliked her.

'You've tried his flat?'

'Of course I have!' snapped Emma, scowling. 'Do you think I'm stupid?'

Megan felt like answering that, and Emma read as much in her eyes. She stared back, her curved red mouth furious, then let out a groan.

'Oh, maybe I am! Did you know he was going back tomorrow?'

Megan shook her head.

'Can't you talk him out of it?' his sister demanded, glaring.

Megan shook her head again.

'He's supposed to be going to marry you! Haven't you got any influence over him?' Emma used a sneering voice, ran her scornful eyes over Megan again.

'None,' Megan said. 'And we aren't getting married now. It's all over, you'll be relieved to hear!'

Emma looked taken aback, her pale eyes fixed on Megan's face. 'He came to his senses, did he? Well, that's something, I suppose.' She walked back to the front door and Megan escorted her without saying anything, but instead of leaving Emma suddenly stopped and burst out, 'What happened, anyway? Why did he break off the engagement? I saw him a few days ago, and he didn't mention it.'

'Perhaps he didn't want to talk about it!' Megan said coolly, and his sister shook her head.

'He talked about you! He said he was going into the country for the weekend with you; but he didn't breathe a word about the marriage being off.'

Megan winced at that, realising that Dev had been refusing to believe she was serious about not marrying him.

Emma Stansfield watched her intently, her face tight with suspicion. 'Did he catch you with someone else?' she abruptly accused.

'No, he did not!' Megan muttered, flushing darkly.

'Then why do you look so guilty?' Emma ran a shaking hand through her immaculately styled hair. 'My God, it's happened again!'

'What has?' Megan was bewildered.

Emma's eyes were angrily contemptuous; they were worried, too. 'Poor Dev, no wonder he's decided to go back to South America right away. It almost broke him into little pieces the last time—when Gianna ran out on him! He took years to get over it and he was scared stiff of getting involved with anyone else in case it happened again.' She saw Megan frowning and snapped at her, 'Don't tell me you didn't know all about it, because I remember it being mentioned on that stupid programme. Johnny Fabian asked Dev about Gianna and Dev changed the subject.'

Megan remembered that, too. She had seen the veiled look on Dev's face, the coldness in his eyes as he talked about something else. Johnny hadn't been surprised; he was used to famous people changing the subject if he ventured on to delicate ground. He rarely pursued the matter; that was not the name of the game on the Fabian show. It was far too cosy, too warm and light-hearted. Their viewers did not want to see Johnny going for the jugular. They wanted to watch with a smile, and Johnny was far too shrewd not to give them what they wanted.

'Gianna was so beautiful, that was the trouble,' said Emma. 'Too many other men were chasing her, and the one who got her was ten times richer than Dev. It was his money that she wanted, and Dev knew it. Why else do you think he ever settled for you? Because you weren't pretty and he didn't need to be afraid of losing you to someone else.'

Megan held the door open, her mouth a stiff white line. 'Would you go now, please? You've insulted me enough, don't you think?'

'I couldn't do that! Why, I've barely scratched the surface. If I told you what I think of you I'd be here all day.'

'Just go!'

'If Dev dies out there, I swear I'll come back here and kill you!' Emma hissed, and Megan lost her head.

'If he dies, you'll be welcome to kill me.'

Emma's grey eyes narrowed; for a brief instant she looked so like Dev that Megan did a double-take. 'You sound as if you mean that!'

'I do,' Megan said hoarsely, then felt like biting out her tongue, because she had not meant to blurt out the truth to Emma, who might repeat everything she said to Dev.

'If you feel like that about him, why is the marriage off? Did Dev jilt you? Or was it the other way around?'

Megan closed her eyes for a second, then looked stubbornly at the other woman. 'Look, I'm tired. I've had a bad day. Will you please go away? There's no point in talking about it any more.'

'I wish I understood all this,' Emma said, then stopped talking as someone else loomed up behind her. She looked round to stare. It was Mark

Bond, in evening dress, looking very elegant.
Emma gave Megan a sarcastic look. 'Is he the part
of the puzzle that you neglected to mention?'

Megan had had enough. She turned and walked
into the sitting-room and a moment later heard the
front door close. She didn't look round as Mark
joined her, but said wearily, 'I'm sorry, Mark, but I
can't talk now.'

'I saw the show tonight—so Hurst is going back
to the Amazon? Does that mean it's finished, you
and him?'

'Oh, please, Mark!' she groaned, putting her
hands over her face to hide the slow tears escaping
from her lashes.

'Megan! For heaven's sake!' He put his arms
around her tightly and she couldn't break free; she
shut her eyes and leaned on him, sobbing
soundlessly, her whole body shaking.

When she had stopped crying he wiped her wet
face with a clean handkerchief and made her sit
down while he poured her a stiff drink from a
bottle of whisky she had on hand for friends
arriving unexpectedly. She didn't like it, herself,
and tried to refuse it, but he held it to her lips and
insisted she drank some.

Sitting beside her afterwards, he held her hand
tightly, watching her. 'What's this all about,
Megan? Don't you think I'm owed some sort of
explanation?'

She gave him a rueful glance, shaking her head.

'Now, come on, Megan, you aren't the type to
burst into tears over nothing at all!'

She grimaced at him. 'Right, I'm the tough-guy

type.'

He smiled at her with sudden tenderness. 'I wouldn't say that, exactly, but you are very inhibited.'

'Inhibited?' She went pink and he laughed.

'A dirty word, huh? I wasn't talking about sex, although I would, given any encouragement . . .?' He slid a wicked, sideways glance and she shook her head at him. Mark heaved a dramatic sigh. 'Too bad, but anyway, what I meant was that you find it hard to talk about yourself, you're secretive, shy, especially where your feelings are concerned. I've known you for months now, but you're still something of a mystery to me. But I still like you, inhibited or otherwise, so if you do ever need a shoulder to cry on, I've got two!'

She laughed shakily. 'Thanks, Mark.'

'You know I fancy you like mad,' he said ruefully, 'and I'd thought I was getting somewhere with you, only then Hurst came back, and when I realised you'd stood me up for him, and lied to me about it I lost my temper.'

She nodded without answering.

He grimaced. 'Yeah, I remember it well, too! He beat the hell out of me, and I deserved it, after what I'd said to you!'

She couldn't help laughing at his droll tone, but she knew him well enough to realise that Mark hated admitting to her that Dev had won that fight. He was proud of his muscularity and fitness; it must really stick in his throat that Dev had beaten him, and she admired him for talking about it so frankly.

'You had provocation,' she comforted, smiling at him. 'I'm sorry if I hurt you. I like you, too, Mark, but . . . well, I met Dev first, I'm afraid.'

He nodded, frowning. 'Megan, tell me about you and Hurst—that was his sister, Graham Stansfield's wife, wasn't it? What was she doing here? I got the impression the two of you were having a row. Is she at the root of whatever is wrong?' His eyes were gentle. 'Come on, you can trust me, Megan!'

He was right; she needed to talk to someone or she would go mad, so she slowly said, 'You remember the accident I had?'

He looked surprised. 'Yes, of course.'

'There was more to it than I've told you,' she said huskily. 'They had to operate immediately I reached the hospital. I was very badly injured and I didn't really know anything about what was happening to me. When I did start taking notice, they didn't tell me for a long time that the worst of my injuries wasn't something anyone could see.' Taking a deep breath, she muttered,' They had to remove my womb, Mark. I can't have babies.'

Mark made a thick sound of shocked incredulity and, worse, of pity. 'Megan! My God!' He looked down, frowning and very pale. 'I don't know what to say; you poor kid, what rotten luck.'

She nodded. 'I'm getting used to it now, but at first it was almost more than I could bear, and there was something else . . . you see, Dev had asked me to marry him.'

Mark sucked in breath, staring at her. She wished he wouldn't; it was hard enough to talk about all this without feeling his horrified, compassionate eyes on her face.

'Was this before he went to South America, or . . .'

'I crashed my car on the way back from the airport the day he left.' She suddenly remembered the pain of those moments, watching Dev walk away through the barrier after icily ignoring her. Mark had confessed that he had been jealous of her and Dev—but his feelings were mild compared to Dev's jealousy. What had happened to Dev years ago, with Gianna Montesi, had made him the man he was today—or had he already been a violently jealous man? He was naturally passionate, both physically and mentally, she knew that both personally and from watching him work—but had that passion always led to a possessive instinct, a jealousy that resisted logic or persuasion?

Mark was absently massaging her cold hands. 'So I suppose he didn't know about the accident for quite a time?'

'He still doesn't,' she said, and Mark did a double-take.

'Didn't you keep in touch with him?'

'I would have written every day, if it hadn't been for the accident, but once I was told I couldn't have children, I only wrote one letter—ending our engagement.'

'What?' Mark's eyes widened. 'But . . . why?'

'Dev wanted to get married because he wanted children, and I couldn't give him any—what else could I do? I had to set him free to find someone else, someone who would give him children.'

'And he accepted that?' Mark's mouth twisted in contempt. 'I wish I'd known all this last time I saw him, I'd have kicked his teeth down his throat! If he had really loved you, he wouldn't have let you go. The man's a bastard.' Then his brows met and he stared at her, scowling. 'But if the engagement is off, why have you been seeing him since he got back to England? And why did he act as if he owned you the other night? The way he was knocking hell out of me, I could have sworn he was jealous of me and hated my guts.'

Megan sighed. 'Mark, I didn't tell him the truth.'

Mark looked bewildered. 'Then what did you tell him? You must have given him some reason for breaking off the engagement?'

'I told him there was another man,' she said, and Mark stared at her in silence for several minutes, shaking his head.

'Why on earth did you do that? What a stupid lie. The man isn't a child, doesn't he deserve the truth?'

She smiled sadly. 'I knew how much he wanted children. I think that was why he proposed. I couldn't let him go ahead and marry me when I knew it would mean the end of any chance of Dev having his own children.'

'So you lied to him?'

'I had to!'

'Couldn't you have given him the benefit of the doubt? Don't you think you owed it to him to let him do his own deciding?'

'It wouldn't have been fair to him to force him to choose between me and the family he wants so badly. I overheard him talking about it to his sister, you see; I know how he feels about me, about having children.'

'Well. *I* wouldn't thank you for refusing to let *me* make my own choice,' Mark said flatly, then his eyes narrowed, a startled look coming into them. 'Hang on! Did he think I was the guy who had taken you away from him? Was that why he knocked me all over the place that night?'

Megan bit her lip. 'I'm afraid so.'

Mark let out a long whistle. 'Well, I don't feel too comfortable about that, Megan. It looks to me as if you've been using me, and I'm not very happy about it.' He stared hard at her, frowning. 'I'm beginning to think I really didn't know you at all. You can be pretty devious, Megan. I'm sorry if that sounds harsh, but I don't approve of the way you've treated Hurst, or, come to that, the way you've manipulated me. I've been set up to hoodwink Hurst, haven't I? I think I ought to go along and see the guy and tell him the truth.'

CHAPTER TEN

'NO, MARK! You can't!' Agitated, Megan grabbed his arm, her fingers biting into it as she stared pleadingly at him. 'Promise me you won't!'

He took some persuading, but reluctantly in the end he did promise to keep her secret. He tried to talk her into coming out for a late supper somewhere, but Megan shook her head.

'I'm very tired, Mark. Can I take a rain-check?'

He surveyed her pale, smudged face and grimaced. 'You look like death.'

She managed a smile. 'Thanks, that makes me feel a lot better!' and Mark looked guilty at once.

'Meggy! I . . .'

'I was teasing,' she said quickly wishing he would go, because she really was barely managing to stay on her feet, and as soon as he had gone she was going to collapse. Perhaps he read it in her face, because he began to walk to the front door almost immediately after that, and Megan went with him, hiding her eagerness to see him go.

He gave her a quick kiss. 'Goodnight, take care of yourself.'

'And you,' she said. 'I'm sorry for . . . everything, Mark.'

'Forget it, I don't blame you,' he said, with an odd look on his face. Mark had been chasing her for weeks, busily trying to turn their friendship into something more, but now all that was over. Mark might have asked her out to supper, but he was only being polite. She wondered wryly how he would have reacted if she had accepted.

She wouldn't be seeing him again, she suspected. Mark was backing out. He knew now that she was in love with Dev, and there was really no point to their relationship, but there was more to it than that. He had just discovered that Megan could not have children; she had seen what a shock that had been to him. Mark had never seemed eager to have children—but he was an artist, and obsessed by perfection. She couldn't have a child, which meant that she was not perfect; she was flawed.

Mark was too nice, and too kind, to want her to realise how he felt, but Megan was ultra-sensitive about what had happened to her. Her intuition picked up all the things he was trying to hide. She wasn't surprised; she didn't even blame him. Mark was reacting the way she was sure Dev would react—with compassion, with concern, but still in shocked dismay. Mark didn't need to feel guilty, that was the difference. He knew that she was not in love with him. He could walk away without shame.

Dev was not in that position. If she told him about the accident and all it meant, and then admitted that she still loved him, Dev would be torn apart by the choice he had to make, and Megan couldn't do that to him. Her love meant she had to shield him, even if it meant bitter unhappiness for herself. Mark might say that she should give Dev the chance to choose for himself, but her woman's instinct told her to protect her man at all costs. If love was selfish enough to let a man sacrifice his most cherished dream, how could it call itself love? she thought, getting into bed after Mark had gone.

She couldn't get to sleep, though; tossing and turning, she could only think about Dev, and that he was going away again in the morning. She wished she knew whether or not his sister had found him, and managed to talk him out of it. Emma Stansfield was a very determined woman, but Dev was not a man you could push around or even persuade to change his mind once his mind was made up.

Megan had never liked Emma. The other girl was too arrogant and too spoilt, for one thing, and for another it was hard to like someone who went out of her way to make it clear that she did not like you. Megan often wondered why Emma had taken such an immediate dislike to her. Of course, when she overheard Dev talking to his sister she had found out! Emma simply despised her. She didn't think that a 'plain little nobody' was good enough to marry into the Hurst family. Megan had resented it and disliked Emma even more, but tonight she felt somehow less hostile.

When they'd talked tonight, though, there had been a flash of understanding between them for the first time.

It had come when Emma had threatened to kill her if Dev died out in South America, and

Megan had wearily said that, if Dev died, Emma would be welcome to kill her.

Megan had been beyond trying to hide the unhappiness she felt. Emma had seen it; her face had changed, they had looked at each other for that instant; two women recognising their mutual predicament, the age-old trap of human love.

Megan wished it had come earlier, that possibility of a friendship between herself and Dev's sister. But there was no point in daydreams. Outside fairy-tales, wishes didn't come true.

Leaning over, she picked up the clock from her bedside-table and stared grimly at it. She had been in bed an hour, and was still as far from sleep as ever. Lying down again, she shut her eyes and ordered herself to relax, to stop thinking. It was thinking that was keeping her awake.

When she opened her eyes again it was to see grey light filtering through the curtains. Rolling over, she looked at the time in surprise. Seven o'clock! She must have slept, but it didn't seem to have done her much good. She felt just as terrible as she had last night, especially now that she was conscious and remembered.

Dev was flying back to South America today! She shut her eyes with a stifled groan, then quickly slid out of bed and ran to the bathroom, her stomach heaving. She was going to throw up.

A few minutes later she sat on the rim of the bath, shuddering and still feeling sick, wishing she was dead. In the mirror her face showed green, her tangled hair all over the place.

'What a sight you are!' she told her reflection glumly, and at that moment the front door bell rang in a peremptory fashion.

Her heart turned over. 'Who now?' she asked her face in the mirror. Was it Emma back again, with news of Dev? Or still looking for Dev?

Megan ran back into her bedroom and grabbed up her lacy white négligé, putting it on as she hurried through her flat to the front door.

The bell rang again, louder, just as she pulled the door open. 'Oh, you're not dressed!' Emma Stansfield said with urgency in her tone. 'Look, I just got a call from Dev at last. He's at Heathrow and his plane leaves in an hour. If we hurry we can get there, but you'll have to throw on the first thing you find. There's no time to waste.'

Megan remembered the last time she had rushed to Heathrow to see Dev. Miserably, she began, 'There's no point! He won't listen, and anyway . . .'

'Get dressed, will you?' Emma pushed her forcibly down the corridor, protesting at every step. 'Just run a comb through your hair, forget make-up.' Emma was at her wardrobe, pulling down a turquoise sweater and some jeans. 'Here, these will do. Hurry up.'

'You don't understand,' Megan muttered, opening a drawer to look for underwear. 'Even if we get there, Dev will be in the departure lounge and they won't let us through. This isn't an emergency.'

'Don't keep arguing. If he goes back this early, he'll undo all the work the doctors put in on him.

That isn't guesswork. I have it from the horse's mouth. His specialist rang us to say he was very worried, and to ask us to stop Dev if we could.'

Megan stood still, staring at Emma, her face bloodless. Emma stared back, nodding insistent confirmation. She was pale, too; her eyes were rimmed with pink as if she had been crying, and she had dressed in such a hurry that the buttons on her red striped shirt were half undone. Megan had never seen her look so human and vulnerable, but there was no hesitation in the angry way Emma said to her, 'For God's sake, get on with it!'

Without another word, Megan dressed with shaky hands, washed her face, cleaned her teeth, combed her hair, before Emma rushed her at whirlwind speed out of the flat, into the car parked outside on a yellow line, oblivious of any law-breaking.

'Hold on to your hat,' Emma said, putting her foot down as they drove off.

The car was a sleek sports model with a purring engine. As Megan soon realised, it was capable of incredible speeds.

Her hands gripped the edge of her seat as Emma hurtled along the half-empty roads, but she didn't give vent to the scream of terror locked in her throat. She had doubted if they could get to the airport before the plane left, but then she had had no idea that Dev's sister was a fiendishly daring driver.

Glancing sideways, Emma asked, 'Scared?'

'Petrified,' Megan said. 'But carry on. I don't

mind being killed in a good cause.'

The other woman laughed; her grey eyes bright. 'I love speed, myself. I rarely get a chance to let my baby out for a really good run.'

Megan watched the appalled faces of other drivers as they passed like a flash of light. 'How long do you think it will take us?'

'Fifteen minutes now.' Emma's hair blew in the wind as she gave Megan another quick look. 'I had a call from Mark Bond last night, by the way.'

Stiffening, Megan tried to look indifferent. 'Oh?'

'He told me a surprising story.'

'Mark is a surprising man.' Megan was furious with him.

'Is it true, though?' demanded Emma.

'I don't know what he told you!' Megan was carefully offhand.

'Oh, I think you do!' Emma looked at her again and Megan gave a cry of panic.

'Please! Keep on your eyes on the road if you must go so fast!'

'Don't worry, I know what I'm doing. I used to be a professional driver once.'

Megan gave her an incredulous look. 'Really?' It sounded like fantasy; she had supposed that Emma had married straight from finishing school. She knew Emma had been married for around ten years, and she only looked about thirty, so she must have been very young at the time.

'For a few months!' insisted Emma. 'Until

Graham, my husband, put his foot down. I was
good, though, and that isn't just conceit.' She
roared round a corner, terrifying a lorry driver,
who yelled soundlessly after them. Ignoring
him, Emma said crisply, 'So it is true, is it?'

Megan sighed. 'Mark had no business telling
you . . . he promised!'

'He said he promised not to tell Dev, but he
didn't promise not to tell me!'

'Oh, how could he?'

'He stuck to the letter of the law, that's all,'
said Emma. 'What tough luck for you, though. I
had no idea you had been involved in an
accident.'

Megan was staring at the motorway ahead of
them. 'It happened just up the road from here,
actually. I was on my way back from the airport
the day Dev left and I went into a lorry. Oh, my
fault, not the lorry-driver's. I was thinking of
other things.'

'Dev?'

'Dev.'

They were almost at the airport and Megan
looked at her watch, her stomach full of
butterfiles. Were they too late, anyway, though?
Dev must surely be in the departure lounge and
the security people weren't going to let them
through to talk to him.

'I'm sorry,' Emma Stansfield said abruptly,
and Megan gave her a blank, uncomprehending
look.

'For not being very friendly in the past,' Emma
added in a rough, embarrassed voice. 'I'm very

fond of my brother and I was afraid he was making another ghastly mistake. I didn't care for Gianna much, even before she bolted with her oilman, but she was quite a beauty, and . . . well . . .'

She was pink and Megan laughed shortly. 'And I'm not! No need to beat around the bush, I know I'm just an ordinary girl.'

'Oh, I don't know,' Emma said. 'You do rather grow on people. You have nice eyes and a lovely smile.'

'Thank you.' Megan was touched and surprised.

'And if you love my brother, I could easily start to think you're beautiful!'

Megan's lips quivered and her eyes filled with tears. 'Oh, I love him, but . . .'

'No buts,' Emma said with a touch of her customary arrogance, then turned into the terminal area.

'I'll drop you, then I'll go and park,' she said as she slotted into the traffic queue. 'With any luck Dev won't have gone through into the departure lounge yet. He said on the phone that there might be a short delay because it was misty earlier. It has obviously cleared now, but Dev said there was a backlog of delayed flights to go before his plane could leave.'

'Emma, listen . . . even if I see him, there's nothing to say—don't you understand? I can't have children, and Dev badly wants to start a family. I can't marry him. And if I don't mean to marry him, what am I doing here? I have no right to ask him not to go.'

'Stop talking nonsense,' Emma bluntly said, pulling up outside the main entrance of the terminal. 'You're here to stop Dev chucking his life away! If he goes back to South America and dies out there, all your noble qualms about not being able to give him children will sound pretty hollow to me, and I think they will to you, then! I realise it must have been a terrible blow to you to find out you couldn't have a baby, and you must still be in utter turmoil and not making much real sense inside your head. But Dev's going back because he thinks you don't love him, and you do, so go and tell him, and stop being such a bloody fool.'

Megan stared at her, open-mouthed, and Emma laughed.

'Get going!' she ordered, and Megan found herself obeying. As she stumbled out of the car Emma shot away, and Megan, still arguing with herself, began to run.

She had never thought that she would ever find herself liking Dev's sister, but then she had never really known Emma until now. There had been a wall between them, but their shared love and fear for Dev had broken it down, and Emma had just been making an astonishing amount of sense. Megan had failed to see the obvious—if Dev went back to South America before he was completely cured, and died out there, she would blame herself for the rest of her life.

The terminal was crowded and blaring with messages on the tannoy. Megan caught sight of the digital clock high above her, and groaned.

Dev's flight left in half an hour; he must be boarding the plane by now. She halted in front of a monitor screen to check, and saw with a leap of the heart that most of the listed flights seemed to have the words delayed next to them. Her eyes fixed on Dev's destination. That, too, was showing as delayed. She began to hurry towards the departures barrier to see if the passengers for that flight had gone through, yet. The huge lounge seemed to be so full of people that perhaps many passengers hadn't been allowed to go through yet.

She was so intent that she ran past Dev without even seeing him until she was a little distance away, when her mind suddenly flashed her the image of him sitting among a lot of other patient people, his hand-luggage at his feet, his face pale and set.

Turning, Megan stared without speaking or moving. Dev hadn't seen her yet. He was in a world of his own; his eyes staring straight ahead, his jaw taut. For all those crowds, he looked so alone; her heart moved painfully inside her and she went back to him, feeling as if she was on the end of a string he was slowly reeling in.

He was casually dressed in a combat-style jacket and dark green cotton trousers, a black cotton shirt and lightweight boots. For the first time she could really imagine him on the Amazon; she remembered the lyrical excitement he had breathed when he talked about it and how much he obviously loved it. Yet from his

face now he could have been going to his
execution. He certainly wasn't overjoyed to be
getting back there.

She halted in front of him, and the others on
the seat stared at her, but at first Dev didn't
seem aware of her, then his eyes focused and
darkened, his pale skin grew paler, his mouth
harder.

'What are you doing here?'

'I came to find you.'

He shrugged, unmoved. 'Emma, I suppose? I
shouldn't have rung to let her know I was
leaving. It didn't occur to me that she would tell
you, of all people. I suppose she bullied you into
coming along to talk me out of going? Well, I'm
afraid you've wasted your time.'

Their audience had listened with interest to
Dev, they then all looked at Megan for her
answer. Aware of this, she grew very flushed,
stammering.

'Can we go and talk outside, in private?'

'No, I want to make sure I don't miss my flight
being called,' said Dev flatly.

'We can't talk here!'

'We don't have anything to talk about!'

'Dev!' she pleaded. 'Please!'

'If you've got something to say to me, say it
here and now, or forget it,' he said in an icy
voice.

He was making it as hard as possible, but even
if she had to talk to him with all these witnesses,
she wasn't backing off this time. She took a long,
deep breath. 'Last time you went off to South

America, I tried to see you . . . talk to you . . . do you remember?'

'I remember,' he said without interest.

'You saw me but you walked away, ignoring me.'

The eyes of their audience widened; they all looked at Dev with reproach, but he still seemed unaware of them, or else it was giving him some sort of kick to force Megan to make these very personal revelations in front of a lot of strangers.

Dev didn't bother to answer at all, and after a pause, Megan said, 'So I drove home, but I didn't get there. I crashed my car.'

Dev did look at her, then; startled, frowning. 'Were you badly hurt?'

The rest of her audience seemed as interested; they were staring at her from head to toe, inspecting her for signs of damage.

'Yes,' she said. 'I was in hospital for months. I hadn't been out long when you came back, in fact.'

'You're OK now, though?' There was a shadow of anxiety in his eyes.

'That's what I want to talk to you about! But I can't talk here. I have to tell you something in private, Dev!'

His brows together, he hesitated, and she gave him a pleading look. 'Please, Dev!' He glanced from side to side, saw the interested faces of their audience, and glowered at them before getting to his feet.

He picked up his hand-luggage and slung it by wide straps from his shoulder, then followed

Megan began towards the entrance. They met
Emma coming through the electronic doors and
she grinned broadly, unperturbed by the glare
she got from her brother.

'Thank heaven for that! You found him.'

'I'll talk to you later!' Dev said menacingly. 'If
I have time before I get my plane!'

'Don't be a bigger fool than God made you,
Devlin Hurst,' his sister said. 'My car's in the
short-stay car park when you want me. I'll drive
you both back whenever you're ready.'

'I am going to South America!' he insisted,
and Emma just laughed and vanished.

Outside, Dev and Megan walked to one end of
the pavement to where there was a low wall.
Dev gestured. 'Sit down and tell me whatever
you have to say, but make it quick, because I am
not missing my plane.'

She sat and gripped and edge of the wall with
both hands. The sharp rim of the bricks dug into
her flesh, but she barely noticed that. 'After the
crash I had an operation,' she said without
preamble. She made a face at him. 'I have to say
this and there's no easy way, so I'll just have to
blurt it out or I won't say it at all. I had my womb
removed.'

Dev stood there, staring at her. If he had
seemed pale before, he looked like old grey
parchment now, and Megan put out her hands
and took hold of his cold fingers, wanting to cry.

'Don't look like that! I'm sorry, Dev.'

His fingers tightened around hers until she
almost cried out with the pain. He swore and she

winced. 'You're sorry!' he ground out harshly.

'I knew you would take it like this,' she whispered, watching him sadly. 'That's why I didn't tell you before, I had to lie to you, make an excuse for not marrying you, so that you wouldn't feel you had to . . .'

'Lie to me?' he cried out in a low, hoarse voice. 'You lied . . . this was why you wrote and said you couldn't marry me?' Before she could reply he answered himself in that strange, almost frightening voice, 'Of course—and there wasn't anyone else, no other man?'

She shook her head dumbly.

'What about . . .' be began, and she answered without waiting for him to finish.

'Mark? No, he was just a friend, I lied about that, too, to throw you off the scent.'

He suddenly caught her face between his long, thin fingers and stared down at her fixedly. She wasn't sure how she had expected him to react, but it hadn't been with such bitter anger.

'You lied to me? How could you? I ought to hit you,' he broke out thickly. 'Something this bad happens to you and you don't tell me! Worse, you lie to me? I should have been here, been with you! You went through this hell all on your own? Why did you shut me out? You knew I loved you, for God's sake!'

'I didn't,' she said in a still, flat voice, and Dev's grey eyes flashed.

'How can you say that? I'd asked you to marry me!'

'Yes, that night at the party at your family

home,' she said quietly. 'But I practically had to propose to you first and even then you seemed very reluctant. I could see you weren't very sure, and you didn't tell me you loved me—it was all very half-hearted, and then I overheard you talking to your sister.'

He frowned. 'You shouldn't take any notice of what Emma says—her bark is far worse than her bite. When you get to know her better you'll like her.'

'I think I do already.' Megan gave a faint smile, then sighed. 'But it wasn't what Emma said that really upset me, it was what you said.'

Dev's face was blank. 'What did I say?'

'That you wanted children; you said you needed a family and a home, and I would give you those, even though I was just a plain little nobody.'

'I could never have said that!' He was either acting brilliantly, or he was amazed, but Megan couldn't believe that look of bafflement.

'You did, Dev! Don't lie about it! I heard you say it!'

Dev was looking furious now; his eyes glittering. 'I don't know what you think you heard, I just know I never said anything of the sort. I couldn't have done because I have never thought you were either plain or a little nobody. I'm sick with love for you. Sick with it, Megan.' He said it through clenched teeth, as if it was an insult he was throwing at her, as if he hated her, rather than loved her, and yet her heart sang wildly.

Dev stared into her eyes, breathing as if there was no air, and Megan felt hot colour pouring up her face at the way he watched her.

He looked around, making a desperate noise. 'We can't talk here!'

'Emma said she would wait for us in the . . .'

'Damn Emma, let's take a taxi.'

'But she'll wonder where we are!'

'Let her wonder.' He seized her hand and began to drag her away and Megan went, protesting.

'Emma brought me here, you can't do this, Dev, it isn't fair to her. She'll wait there for hours before she realises we've gone without her.'

'She'll work it out. She isn't stupid, that's half her trouble—too damn clever by half.' He bundled her into a taxi, still talking, and gave the driver his address.

'Oh, your luggage!' Megan suddenly remembered, looking back at the disappearing airport. 'It will be on the plane! Shouldn't you go back and do something to stop it going off to South America?'

'Let it go,' he shrugged, his arm curving around her shoulders. 'It doesn't matter. I'll deal with it later. At the moment, I've got something more important on my mind.' He bent towards her, his eyes fixed on her mouth.

Megan gave the taxi driver a glance and went pink as she caught him watching them in his mirror. 'Dev!' she whispered, and Dev looked that way too, grimacing.

'This is going to be the longest taxi ride of my life!'

'We have to talk, anyway,' she said, her voice very low.

Dev watched her. 'Do we? I thought we'd talked enough, myself.'

'I came this morning because I don't want you to go back to the Amazon until you're really well, Dev, but nothing has changed—I still can't marry you.'

'Why not?'

'You know why not. I told you.'

'You told me you've had to have your womb removed, but I don't see why that means you can't marry me!'

Megan looked desperately at him, her lashes wet with slow tears. 'Of course you do. You're just being kind and sorry for me, but you know you want children, a family . . .'

'We'll adopt.'

'You'll want children of your own, Dev!'

'I want you.' His fingertips caressed her cheek and she shivered, closing her eyes.

'No, Dev.'

'Yes, I do, and when we're alone in my flat I'll show you just how much I want you.'

Her blood ran hotly and she shuddered with desire as she heard that note in his voice. She couldn't bear the thought of losing him; she wanted him with the same hunger and she turned her burning face into his shoulder, whispering, because she dared not say this out loud. They were talking in very low voices, but the taxi driver might still overhear them, and Megan couldn't bear anyone to hear what she was going to say now. 'I'll go to bed with you, I'll live with you until you're tired of me, but I won't marry you, Dev.'

He drew in air audibly, as though she had just punched him in the stomach. 'Darling!' His hand came down on her hair, stroked it lingeringly, his cheek lowered down towards the thick, dark strands he was fondling. 'The most immoral and wonderful thing anyone ever said to me,' he whispered with a smile in his voice.

'I'm serious, Dev, I mean it!' she insisted, trembling.

'I'm glad to hear it, but I want you on a more long-term basis,' he said, his fingers twining in her hair and tugging to make her look up at him.

Megan's face was burning as she met his eyes. 'I hope you realise that I'm not in the habit of making that sort of proposition to men,' she muttered.

'I should hope not!' He dropped a light kiss on her nose. 'But I can see I shall have to marry you to save you from this tendency to make impulsive offers in taxis.'

That made her laugh, as he'd intended, but her eyes sobered quickly. 'Oh, Dev, you haven't really thought this out, you haven't realised what it would mean. How can I deprive you of having your own children? You might come to resent me, you might . . .'

'Get run over in the street tomorrow,' he finished for her. 'Life is full of imponderables. We

just have to deal with the certainties we know,
and one of those is that I love you and don't
want to have to spend the rest of my life without
you. How about you?'

'Oh, I don't know . . .' she wailed. 'I don't
want you to come to hate me one day.'

He watched her ruefully. 'How can I convince
you?' He ran a hand over her hair, then
exclaimed, 'Wait a minute!' and to her disbelief
started to unbutton his shirt.

'Dev, what on earth are you doing?' She shot a
look at the taxi driver's back, but he was busy
watching the crowded road ahead, thank
goodness, and hadn't noticed. Megan caught
hold of Dev's hand and hissed, 'Stop it! Not
here. Wait until we get to your flat.'

He grinned at her. 'This won't wait.' Holding
her hand captive he slid his other hand inside his
shirt and pulled out a plain silver locket on a
matching chain. Megan stared, bewildered.

Dev clicked the locket open and held it out to
her. Inside were a small circular photograph of
her, taken by Dev not long before he first went to
the Amazon, and curled around it the dark
strands of the lock of hair he had cut from her
head the night he proposed.

Megan stared at them in utter silence, then
Dev clicked the locket shut and put it back inside
his shirt.

'I've carried that around for months. You see, I
love you very much, Megan. I've been in love
before; you know all about Gianna. That was a
very bad experience and it made me wary; it

made me a potentially jealous and suspicious man, too. I was jealous when I saw you with Mark Bond that night.'

'I told you the truth, Dev . . .' she began anxiously, and he nodded.

'I believe you, but at the time I didn't want to listen to any explanation because it had all welled up inside me. You can't imagine it, Megan—it's a terrible feeling, as black as hell. I rushed away because I was hurting too much to stay there, and when you came to the airport in the morning I still couldn't bear to talk in case you saw it. I was ashamed of how I felt; jealousy is a sickness. But I still loved you; I still wore my locket and I would have written if you had written to me, but no letter came, and when it did I was too ill to do anything about it, and I knew I'd be coming home, soon, anyway.'

She looked quickly at him, and he made a wry face. 'You don't think for one moment that I ever intended to leave it like that? I was still feeling very low when I first got back, but I was going to come and find you as soon as I felt strong enough, then I saw you at that party and I knew right away that nothing had changed, I still felt the same way, and it wasn't long before I'd convinced myself that you did, too. We hadn't known each other well enough before I left, I thought. You had been attracted, but the feeling you had hadn't had a chance to grow roots. If I stayed around and we saw each other often enough, this time we would make it.'

'You should have said all this before, Dev! I've

been working in the dark for too long. You're much too secretive. How could I guess what you thought and felt when you went out of your way to hide it from me?'

'I'll never hide anything from you again, Megan, if you promise to tell me the honest truth about how you feel, in future!'

She searched his face with desperate eyes, wondering what to say. Dev had somehow manipulated her to this point, in spite of all her firm intentions about saying goodbye to him. She felt herself weakening, her grasp on that common-sense decision slipping. His eyes were brilliant with feeling as they stared back at her, and she gave a long sigh.

'I love you, Dev,' she capitulated. It might be folly, it might be selfish, but she needed him badly and she would do everything in her power to make him happy.

Dev leaned forward in urgent silence and they kissed passionately, their arms around each other, while the fascinated taxi driver watched in his mirror, but by then they were in a world of their own and had forgotten everyone else existed.

OUT OF CONTROL

BY
CHARLOTTE LAMB

WORLDWIDE BOOKS
LONDON • SYDNEY • TORONTO

*First published in Great Britain in 1987
Reprinted in Great Britain in 1993
by Worldwide Books, Eton House,
18-24 Paradise Road, Richmond, Surrey TW9 1SR*

© Charlotte Lamb 1987

ISBN 0 373 58953 0

99-9309

Made and printed in Great Britain

CHAPTER ONE

LIZA would never have invited Bruno down to her cottage if she hadn't worked through her lunch hour the previous Friday.

It was rare for her to have the chance; she was usually booked for lunch. She sent her secretary out to buy her some cottage cheese and an apple, deciding to eat them in the viewing-room while she looked at a video of one of her new models, to assess the girl's performance in her first TV commercial. Liza hadn't had time to see it until now.

The outer office had been empty when she had walked through it—all the girls had been at lunch, except her own secretary, Maddie, who was operating the photocopier, running off profiles of some of their models for a new customer.

Settling in the dark after she had eaten, Liza watched the video a second time with the volume turned right down so that she wasn't distracted by the sound-track and could concentrate on the model's movements and facial expressions.

Two minutes later she heard Joan Temple talking as she came through the swing door with the other typists. 'It's obvious—she's got a man down there—why else is she so secretive about the cottage?'

Liza's head swung round and she froze, listening with a frown. They weren't talking about her, were they?

'She never misses a weekend, no matter how busy we

5

are! I suspect the guy's married, whoever he is, and either can't get a divorce or doesn't want one anyway. Nobody would spot them if they met out there in the wilds of Essex, the cottage is miles from anywhere, she admits that.'

'But what about Bruno Morris?' Daphne said slowly, sounding upset. 'I mean, where does he fit in, if she's involved with another man? I thought it was serious with Bruno, that they'd announce their engagement any day. The Press seem to think so.'

'Oh, the Press!' Joan said cynically. 'What do they know? They're simple-minded—look at the way they nicknamed her The Snow Queen just because she was too smart to get caught with anyone when the Press were around! They may believe that there was never a man in her life until Bruno came into the picture, but you can't kid me. I bet she's been having a secret affair with this guy down in Essex for years.'

'But sooner or later someone would be bound to see them together,' protested Daphne. 'Nobody can have that sort of secret for long these days! The Press would have found out by now, if it was true.'

'I told you, Liza is too smart to get caught!' Joan drawled. 'But you're right—the Press ought to know. Maybe someone will tell them, tip them off!'

Liza's frown deepened and she heard Daphne give a gasp. 'You wouldn't, would you, Joan?' She sounded half horrified, half gleeful and Joan laughed.

'It's a thought, isn't it? No, why should I spoil her fun? Good luck to her, that's what I say. Men have always played the field and got away with it. Why shouldn't we?'

From a distance Liza heard Maddie call them. 'Come and give me a hand with these profiles, I want to post them off today.'

Liza had thought herself hardened to being talked about. Before she had founded a model agency of her own she had been a top model herself; earning a small fortune in a mere two years of intense and highly paid work. She had attracted a lot of Press attention during that time and since; she was still a public figure because her agency had grown rapidly to become one of the best of the kind in the country.

This gossip was different, though; Liza grimaced distastefully. It wasn't pleasant to know that people who worked with you talked about you in that vein when you weren't around to defend yourself.

Was it just Joan, or were other people talking? A frown pleated her finely pencilled brows. Bruno had been rather persistent the other day when he was asking about the cottage. He had wanted to know all about it: what she did there every weekend, why she couldn't spend more weekends in London. Bruno was a city animal; he loved the ambience of a town: bright lights, parties, night-clubs, dancing and dinner in swish restaurants. He wasn't attracted to anything in the countryside except, perhaps, horses and then only on a racecourse. Not that Bruno rode or liked horses much; but he did gamble and Liza suspected he often lost large sums. He could afford it, or course; he was one of the Giffords, his uncle was G. K. Gifford, the head of the merchant bank and the chairman of an international consortium which owned a wide variety of companies. Bruno was a jet-setting playboy, if you believed the gossip columnists.

Liza didn't. She knew Bruno better than that. He might be a light-hearted, rather spoilt young man with more money than was good for him, but he had quite a few qualities which endeared him to Liza. Bruno was kind and good-tempered, and he needed affection. No doubt people like Joan Temple wouldn't believe it, but he had never tried to talk Liza into bed, although they had been seeing each other for three months. Bruno didn't want sex; he wanted to have fun. He didn't want a passionate lover; he wanted a playmate.

When they went out they danced and joked, laughed and chatted, and Liza never felt the slightest tension between them, no sexual magnetism or awareness.

Bruno was like a teddy bear, he even looked like one— big and bulky with thick, curly, golden-brown hair and round brown eyes which shone when he laughed.

It was easy to be fond of Bruno and hard to take him seriously as a lover, but the Press only saw the image. They created myths of childish simplicity and one of them was that Bruno was a jet-setting playboy. He certainly flew around the world a lot in jets. He certainly loved to play, and he was undoubtedly more a boy than a man, but the label the Press pinned on him was light years from the reality.

Liza sighed, staring out of the window at the glass and concrete of the skyscraper opposite, without seeing anything of it.

She couldn't let Bruno read maliciously angled gossip in the papers. He would hate that, and his family, the Giffords, wouldn't be too pleased either. Liza had never met any of them, but the bank were her landlords; they owned this whole building, all thirty storeys of it, and she did not want to offend them any more than she wanted to embarrass or upset Bruno.

The solution was obvious, but she wished she could think of some other way out of the dilemma. The cottage was her sanctuary, her refuge, her private world, and she had never invited anyone from her other world down there. She liked to keep London and her public life well away. Having Bruno there might wreck the whole atmosphere for her for ever.

No, I'm being absurd, she told herself impatiently. I'll ask him down for the weekend and he'll come because he has been so curious about the place, but, once he has been there and seen the windy, echoing solitudes of the marshes, the birds, the melancholy lavender and navy blue of the sky after the sun has set, the whisper of the tidal ebb and flow between the reeds and the cosy shabbiness of the furniture, Bruno will politely thank me for his visit, go back to London and never suggest coming again.

She was right about Bruno's reaction to the invitation. 'I'd love to come! I've been dying to know what's so special about the place.'

'You'll probably find it boring,' Liza told him frankly.

'If you go back there every weekend it must have something!'

'Oh, it does—but I'm just not sure you'll enjoy the peace and quiet as much as I do. After all, you rarely visit your family's place in Somerset, do you?'

'Hartwell? Oh, but that's different,' Bruno said, making a horrible face. 'It's big and draughty and smells of damp, and whenever I'm there I have to talk to some pretty boring people. My uncle's involved in local committees of one sort or another; local politics, you know, dinner parties and tea parties, farmers come to shoot rabbits over the land, and my uncle drags me round the farms. When he isn't in London at the bank, he's in Somerset playing at farming and he'd like me to follow in his footsteps, but that's not my scene at all.'

'Well, you won't have to bother about local politics or dinner parties,' agreed Liza with amusement. 'We'll sail, though—I hope you're a good sailor. Can you handle a small dinghy, or haven't you sailed before?'

'Done a bit,' Bruno agreed airily. 'I won't let myself get bonked by the boom, don't worry, and you won't have to fish me out of the river. Very often, anyway.'

Liza laughed involuntarily. 'I can always tie you to the mast!'

'So that I can go down with the ship when you sink her? No thanks, think again.'

Liza felt more at ease with Bruno than she had ever done with a member of the opposite sex. Most men felt they had to make a pass at her; their macho self-respect demanded it. They always had to prove something; show they could 'pull a bird' who looked like her and had probably dated some very rich and powerful men. Too many men believed everything they read in the newspapers; they would have been incredulous if she had tried to tell them how quiet and hard-working and unglamorous her life had always been. Bruno didn't find that hard to believe because he, too, carried a label and a public image which didn't fit the man behind it.

Liza sometimes suspected that if she and Bruno hadn't met in a very odd way he would never have asked her out. He would have taken one look at her elegant façade—the smooth blonde hair pulled back off her face into a tight chignon, the classy, expensive clothes, the cool, English, go-to-hell remoteness of her features—and he would have run very fast in the opposite direction. But she hadn't looked like that when they had met; she had been soaking wet and windblown because she hadn't been able to get a taxi on a raw March day when rain poured down from the black cloud centred right over that part of London. By the time she had walked to the office her chignon had been ripped apart and her hair blown everywhere, her thin raincoat was sodden and her silk stockings splashed with mud from passing cars. She had run towards the entrance of the office block with her head lowered against the wind and Bruno had come running from the other direction. They had collided right outside the doors. Liza was the lighter of the two of them; it was she who went flying and fell full-length into the gutter. Bruno was too solid; he merely rocked and swayed a moment before he hurried to help her to her feet.

'I'm sorry,' he'd said. 'Come up to my office and I'll show you where you can wash and do something about your hair.'

'Thank you, I work here too, and I can do without your help,' Liza had snapped and marched away with a dignity somewhat marred by having to limp because the heel of one shoe had come off.

'Oh, come on, it was an accident, I'm very sorry,' Bruno said, pursuing her into the lift.

That was when Liza first caught sight of her appearance in the mirror on the wall in the lift. She stared and began to laugh, and Bruno joined in. He had followed her out of the lift, and into her life, that casually, and he was still here.

'Are we driving down?' Bruno asked her when they had dinner two days before the weekend. 'My car or yours?'

'Mine,' Liza said firmly. 'I know the way, you don't. Once we're off the main road it's easy to get lost along the winding marsh lanes, and it isn't easy to explain the route, even with a map.'

'I'm looking forward to it more and more,' Bruno said, grinning. But next morning, when Liza opened her paper at breakfast time, she found an old photo of herself splashed across an inside page and next to it a large picture of Bruno. The headline said it all. 'Romance for Jet-set Banker Playboy and Blonde Model', it ran, rather confusingly, since it had no punctuation and might lead some people to believe that Bruno was a blonde model! But Liza was in no mood to find that amusing. She read hurriedly, her face angry. There was nothing much in the story except cheap innuendo, but it did imply that she and Bruno were on the verge of getting married, and that was embarrassing to read. She wished she hadn't invited Bruno to the cottage for the weekend. What if he read this garbage and started wondering if she was trying to nudge him into proposing?

Or, even worse, trying to compromise him by having him at the isolated cottage alone with her?

She had lost her appetite. She drank a little strong, black coffee and left for the office. It didn't improve her temper to find the whole of her staff looking curious and fascinated, or to be met by grins every time she looked round.

She decided to ring Bruno and cancel the plans for the weekend, but as she was considering how to explain the change of plan the phone rang.

'Liza?' Bruno said miserably. 'Liza, I'm sorry, I can't come this weekend.'

'I see,' she said, and she did see—very clearly. Bruno had read the morning paper; he had been appalled by the innuendo and he was backing out as fast as he could. She couldn't blame him and she wasn't hurt, but she felt depressed about the whole thing.

'I've just had a phone call from my mother,' Bruno told her. 'I've been summoned down to Hartwell to talk to my uncle. Have you seen the paper today, that ghastly rag with the rubbish about us in it?' Liza made inaudible noises and cleared her throat to say she had. 'I thought you must have done,' Bruno said gloomily. 'Sick-making, isn't it? What loathsome brutes they are, they need shooting. Sorry about it, Liza, but don't brood over it. Lies, all of it, so that's what I'll tell Uncle.' He paused and groaned. 'God knows how he'll take it. He can be a cynical swine at times.'

'Can he?' Liza sounded doubtful, which she was, because she knew next to nothing about his uncle, the manipulating, string-pulling all-powerful G. K. Gifford who lived in the fabulous Hartwell, a country house in the dreaming depths of Somerset. Bruno had told her more about the house than about any member of his family. Hartwell was within view of Glastonbury Tor, he said, but Liza had once visited Somerset and driven all over Salisbury Plain and the surrounding countryside. She knew that you could see the dark, pointing finger of Glastonbury Tor for miles and miles in all directions, so Bruno's vague placing of the house didn't help much to fix it in one locality.

'God, yes,' Bruno groaned. 'He's worse than my mother, much worse. She runs straight to him if there's any trouble, and he always fixes it for her. They're very close, more like twins than anything else, so Uncle's always on her side.'

'What does the G stand for?'

'The G?' Bruno repeated in a bewildered way. 'What G?'

'G. K. Gifford,' she prompted, and he laughed flatly.

'Oh, that—George, would you believe? I think that's why my mother insisted on calling me Bruno—my father hated the name, but she always gets her own way, twists all her men round her little finger, my Mama. Her parents gave all their children such boring, old-fashioned names, so she was determined I shouldn't have a name like George.'

'What's her name, then?'

'Phillipa!'

'What's wrong with that? I rather like it.'

'Well, she hated it. She made everyone call her Pippa, and that suits her much better.'

'Pippa—yes, pretty. Is she?' Liza had always been careful not to ask Bruno questions about his family; she hated people probing into her background and from Bruno's reluctance to talk about his she guessed that he felt the same.

'She's not bad,' he said uneasily and she smiled, glad he couldn't see her. 'Anyway,' he said hurriedly, 'I'm very sorry I won't be coming for the weekend—you will ask me again some time, won't you?'

'The invitation stands,' Liza said wryly, sure that he wouldn't want to come now, and half relieved because it meant that the cottage would not be invaded. Sometimes she felt as thought it was a time capsule, outside ordinary time and place; a small circle of peace for her alone. She was afraid of what the arrival of someone else would do to that shining silence.

'Maybe one day you'd like to see Hartwell,' Bruno said vaguely and she laughed silently, sure that his family would never extend an invitation to her. Didn't he know *why* he was being summoned down to face his terrifying uncle and his mother? Bruno was about to be told to drop her; she wasn't suitable. Liza could imagine everything they would say. 'A girl like that? Who is she, anyway? What sort of family does she come from? Has she any money, influence, power?' Bruno's family had all three and they would want his wife to come from the right circles, have the proper credentials for a future Gifford.

'I wish I didn't have to go,' Bruno suddenly blurted out. 'If you knew my uncle . . .'

'He can't eat you!'

'He can try!'

'Oh, poor Bruno,' she said gently. 'Stand up to him, you're a big boy now.' Twenty-three, to be precise, and a broad-shouldered, solid-fleshed young man who could play an aggressive game of rugger and had boxed at university, which made it all the more bewildering that he should be so nervous of facing a middle-aged man who spent most of his time hunched at a desk.

'I must go,' Bruno said with a sigh. 'I wish you could come with me, Liza. I feel I can do anything when you're there.'

Then, horrified by his own admission, he muttered goodbye and rang off before she could answer. Liza frowned, replacing the phone. Bruno wasn't getting *too* fond of her, was he? She was very fond of him and he made a good playmate, but it would never be a serious love affair on her side. She hoped it wasn't developing into one on his side, because she would only have to be frank with him and she would hate to hurt Bruno.

Everyone in the office had read the stupid gossip in the paper, but nobody mentioned it to her directly; they didn't dare with Liza looking at them with frozen eyes and a remotely haughty expression. That was easy for her to assume; she had learnt how to look like that when she was modelling. It wasn't so easy when other newspapers rang up and wanted interviews, wanted a comment, a quote to put in among the acres of sheer invention they called a news story.

Liza was afraid to refuse to speak to them, in case that gave them *carte blanche* to invent what they chose. She had to tell them it wasn't true and she did with curt insistence, but they brushed her denials aside and fired impertinent questions at her without seeming at all aware of their own rudeness.

'Are you in love with Bruno?' one even asked her.

'I just told you . . .'

'How long have you known him?'

'What has that to do with . . .?'

'What do his family think?'

'I have no idea.' Liza's voice was brusque.

'You haven't met them?' asked the reporter eagerly.

'No,' she said without expression, deciding to hang up.

'They won't meet you? How do you feel about being cold-shouldered by the Giffords?'

'I didn't say that!' Liza was beginning to panic.

'Have they tried to stop you and Bruno meeting?'

'This is ridiculous, listen to me . . .'

'We've tried to get in touch with Bruno at his London flat in Hyde Park Gate, but he isn't answering his phone. Can you tell us where he is?'

'Down at Hartwell,' Liza said coldly, and with faint malice because that would transfer the baying hounds to the Gifford family's end of this muddle. Let G. K. Gifford face their persistence and their shameless curiosity!

She put down the phone without saying goodbye, in the end, because every time she tried to get away the reporter thought of a new question. Liza had a strong suspicion that the girl on the switchboard in the outer office was listening to every call and retailing what was said to the rest of the girls, because as the day wore on the excitement in the office seemed to mount with every call.

Even the models who came in for interviews seemed to know more about it than Liza did. Tawny Holt asked outright, big-eyed with coy interest.

'Are we going to hear wedding bells soon?'

Freezing, Liza said, 'Are we?' without commenting, and Tawny batted her long, false lashes, giggling.

'He's so rich too, but sexy with it! My boyfriend plays squash with him, you know; he says Bruno is all muscle.'

'Your boyfriend?' Liza stared and Tawny gave a naughty grin, one hand twining a bright red-gold curl and pulling it to her mouth to nibble it.

'Don't tell anyone, it's a deadly secret. I'm dating Jeremy Bell, but all hell would break loose if his wife found out.'

'The Earl?' Liza was amazed as she remembered the lovely face of the Countess, a famous model herself some ten years ago. 'But, Tawny, she's pregnant, isn't she? I read somewhere that this is her third try—she lost the other two.'

'That's why she has to stay in bed the whole nine months!' Tawny said indifferently. 'And no sex! How do you think poor old Jerry feels? She can't go to parties or the races or dancing—I mean, nine months of utter boredom, poor darling. He couldn't stand it—could anyone?'

Liza eyed her coldly. 'His wife doesn't seem to have much choice, does she?'

'Oh, well, it's different for women,' Tawny said, tossing her vivid head and looking impatient.

'Sometimes I feel like giving you a good slap,' Liza said to herself and Tawny looked amazed.

'Why? What did I do?'

'Oh, get out!' Liza said.

'What about that perfume ad? No news yet?'

'None,' Liza said, although she had heard that Tawny was the front runner among the girls being considered for the job. She was too annoyed with Tawny to tell her. Let her eat her heart out over it for a little while longer. The only thing that did have any real impact on Tawny was success. She wanted fame and money, she wanted to get to the top and she might well do it because she had a thick skin. She didn't care what she had to do to get up there and, of course, she was lovely. Liza looked at her coldly, admitting that much. Tawny was beautiful in a gypsyish way, but she was not someone Liza liked, or approved of, especially today.

'I hope it never happens to you, Tawny,' she said as the other girl swayed to the door, and Tawny looked back blankly.

'What?'

'What you're doing to Jeremy's wife,' Liza said. 'It's indecent. It's mean. One day you may realise that, if it happens to you in turn.'

Tawny wasn't shaken. 'Oh, come off it!' she said tartly. 'She's done OK for herself—little Cathy Black from Hoxton, going to school without socks when she's seven according to the gossip columns and a Countess with a stately home and a private plane when she's twenty-three? Don't ask me to cry for her, because I wasn't born with easy tear-ducts. I'm from Hoxton too, or near enough. I know where she comes from and I know where she landed up— and so do you, don't you, Liza? You're not from a silk-lined drawer, either. We both had to fight our way up and we know it's a jungle out there, and if you want to survive you have to fight tooth and nail.'

'I didn't,' Liza said flatly. 'And I didn't marry to get where I am. I worked and I used my head, not my body.'

'How moral, darling.' Tawny said viciously, showing her teeth and looking ugly. 'Haven't you forgotten Bruno? Don't tell me it's purely platonic, because I wouldn't believe you if you swore it on a stack of Bibles.

He's not middle-aged, like poor old Jerry, and you may really fancy him—I can see how you would, he's got a good body, and he isn't bad-looking at all, but he's also a Gifford and has a bank full of the green stuff, and that's what it's all about in the end, isn't it?'

'Oh, get out!' Liza said, feeling sick. 'And take your mind to the cleaners.'

'I love you, too, honey,' Tawny said, laughing angrily and slamming the door on her way out.

That was the last straw for Liza; she sat behind her desk staring at nothing, shaking with rage, then she looked at the clock and saw that it was nearly three o'clock. She had had enough; she had to get away. She wouldn't bother to dictate a batch of letters for Maddie to do on Monday before she got back. She would just go now, drive down to the cottage and forget all this madness.

She kept her packed suitcase in her car boot, she was ready to leave and she was the boss, after all. Why stick to a routine she had worked out herself?

Maddie looked up in surprise as Liza put her head round the door. 'Sorry, did you buzz for me? I didn't hear you, something must be wrong with the console.'

'I didn't buzz, I just came to say I'm off. See you on Monday, usual time, have the coffee ready.' Liza used a light tone but Maddie wasn't deceived; she stared, frowning in concern.

'Are you OK?' They had worked together for nearly five years, ever since Liza had started the agency. They had built it up together, and Maddie could run it all on her own if she had to, Liza knew that. Maddie was more or less the same age, but she had never been pretty. Liza sensed that that bothered Maddie; she would have liked to be beautiful and she envied the models who came in and out all day. She was kind-hearted and calm and unflappable, tall and bony with short brown hair and dark, rather melancholy eyes. Liza liked her face; it was full of gentle warmth. Maddie hated it, herself; she looked at it in mirrors and wished it didn't belong to her because it was plain, and not all the tips Liza had given her could make much difference to its broad, raw-boned lines. Maddie was an incurable romantic; a dreamer. She would have loved to meet Prince Charming; instead she looked after her invalid mother when she wasn't working. Liza wished she could think of some way of convincing Maddie how much more lovable she was than someone like Tawny with her vivacious looks and her mean, selfish little heart and mind.

'I'm just fed up,' Liza said with a wry smile. 'I want to get out of here and I can't wait.'

Maddie looked worried. 'Are they going to stop Bruno seeing you?'

'Not you, too,' Liza said with a groan. 'I don't want to talk about it, Maddie. Why do you think I have to get out of here?'

'I understand,' Maddie said with deep sympathy, but she didn't, of course, she had no idea. Maddie's eyes were wearing rose-coloured spectacles; she saw Liza and Bruno as star-crossed lovers, not friends and playmates. Liza envied her suddenly; it must be nice to have a loving heart and a peaceful mind like Maddie.

'Have a nice weekend,' Liza said.

'You, too,' said Maddie kindly.

It took Liza nearly an hour to get out of London's snarling traffic and closely packed streets—the suburbs went on for ever—but eventually she emerged on to the wide, dual carriageway which ran across the flat Essex miles into the countryside surrounding the Thames estuary. At that time on a Friday, even in June, there wasn't too much traffic heading in that direction and Liza was able to cover quite a distance in the next half-hour. But when she turned off into the maze of winding little lanes which criss-crossed the marsh she found herself forced to slow to a crawl, because a river mist had drifted inland, thick and wet and white, coiling around trees and houses like damp cotton wool, making it impossible to see far ahead. It was lucky that Liza knew her way so well; she was almost feeling the way now, like one of the blind, recognising landmarks and twists of the road without seeing anything on either side.

A pub sign flashed out of the mist at last and she gave a sigh of relief, recognising the local pub, the Green Man. The sign was new, a vivid painting of a dancing, capering figure dressed from head to foot in green leaves. There was a faintly sinister element in the painting, and the local regulars at the pub didn't like it as much as the old sign, which had been a faded, weatherbeaten picture of Robin Hood, but the landlord was pleased with his new sign and ignored complaints.

Liza carefully inched her way down a tiny lane leading off at right angles, hearing the slap of the tide against the wooden jetty at the far end of the lane. Her cottage was a stone's throw away; she had got here safely and was very pleased with herself for her navigation under such difficult circumstances, but she congratulated herself a minute too soon.

She was grinning cheerfully when her car ran smack into the back of another car. She hadn't seen the tail-lights or heard another engine. She had had no warning of any kind.

It was lucky that her car was only crawling along the kerb at about five miles an hour, and even luckier that

Liza had her seat-belt on—it might have been much worse. As it was, she was thrown forwards with a violent jolt into the steering wheel and had all the air knocked out of her lungs for a minute. She was too shocked to hear the crumpling of the car bonnet or the splintering of the glass in her windscreen. When she was conscious of anything again it was very quiet and still. She sat up, her heart beating like a sledge-hammer and her breathing thick and painful, and peered into the waves of white mist.

Through it she heard the sound of striding and then a face lunged at her through the mist; an angry face, dark and ruthless, without an ounce of sympathy for the pain Liza was in or a trace of kindness for her to appeal to. A face Liza disliked intensely on sight. It was obviously mutual.

'What the hell were you doing, driving like a damned maniac in this weather?' he snarled, his hard mouth curling upwards as if he might bite at any minute. Liza eyed him coldly. His face was wolfish, she decided; he had thick black eyebrows above fierce, blue eyes and moody features. She couldn't imagine him being the life and soul of a party, even in a good mood, if he ever had any.

'I was almost at a standstill!' she hurled back. 'It was you who was the cause of the accident—you weren't showing any lights.'

'You mean you didn't see them!' he said, but she saw a flicker in his eyes, a passing uncertainty—had his lights failed without him noticing? Too late to check now; she only had to lean forward to see the battered rear of his car, the smashed glass of his lights.

That was when she saw that he was driving an estate car; a very muddy estate car which looked as if it was at least ten years old. That was a relief; if she was found responsible for the accident, at least he couldn't claim much on a vehicle in that state.

'Look, I'm sorry,' she began, turning to him and taking in more about him this time. He was wearing a shabby old fawn mackintosh which was open and under which she saw a well worn tweed jacket, and olive-green sweater, rough cord trousers in more or less the same shade and muddy green wellies.

'And how could you drive in those boots?' Liza attacked, pointing. 'Your feet would slip on the controls!'

'I wasn't driving. I was debating whether to go into the Green Man or set off for home!'

'Don't you mean go *back* into the Green Man?' she asked. 'Had you been drinking?'

'No, I had not,' he said with a bite, yanking open her door and gripping her arm. 'I think you'd better get out of there. We'll walk back to the pub and ring the police.'

'My cottage is nearer,' Liza said with cold dignity. 'We can ring from there.'

'Cottage?' He looked around him, his black brows lifting.

'Behind you—you can see the gate, it's only a few yards.'

'Well, out you get, then,' he said and Liza felt herself being pulled out of her seat. Her head went round and she gave a silly little moan, swaying.

'Don't do that,' she said and found herself talking into his sweater. She was leaning on his chest, her body slack and cold. What on earth am I doing here? she thought stupidly.

'What are you doing?' he asked a second later and Liza tried to stand upright, but only slithered down his body until she was seized and propped up against her car. He leaned forward and spoke slowly and clearly, an inch away from her face.

'Where is your key?'

Liza tried to reach into her car for the keys dangling from her dashboard, but the movement made her dizzy again. A moment later she was over his shoulder, seeing the ground from a strange angle; it was swinging to and fro and Liza felt seasick so she moaned weakly, shutting her eyes, and that was better. Not much better, but a little.

He must have found her door key on the key-ring in the dashboard, because he opened the front door of the cottage and a moment later the hall light came on and then the sitting-room light. Then Liza was lying on the comfortable sofa, and the stranger took of his fawn mackintosh and covered her with it. She heard him switch on the electric fire on the hearth; the bars slowly glowed orange and she sighed as the heat reached her. She was shivering, but the appalling coldness was passing.

'Where's the phone? I think you should see a doctor as well as the police,' he said, then walked away, probably having caught sight of the phone in the corner.

Liza struggled up. 'No, please, I don't need a doctor. It was just the shock. I wasn't injured. A cup of tea and I'll be fine.'

He came back and stared down at her, looming darkly, with those thick brows together above his vivid blue eyes.

'A cup of tea? What you need is a stiff drink,' he said. 'And so do I—have you got anything or shall I walk back to the Green Man?'

'There's some brandy in a cupboard in the kitchen, but I don't like it, I won't have any.'

'If I have some, so do you,' he said tersely.

Liza stared, baffled by the irony of his mouth.

'When the police do a breath test I'm not going to be the only one with brandy in my veins,' he told her and she laughed.

'Look, no need to report the accident—I'm sure we can reach an amicable settlement. I'll pay for the repairs to your car, how's that?'

He considered her shrewdly, his eyes narrowed and thoughtful. 'How do I know you'll pay when the bill arrives?'

'Estimate it and I'll give you a cheque at once.'

'And if the cheque bounces?'

'It won't,' she said coolly, and he ran assessing eyes over her from head to foot. Liza's clothes were elegant and expensive; even a small farmer could see that.

'Poor little rich girl?' he mocked. 'Well, well. And Daddy will pay, I suppose?'

Liza's mouth tightened, but she didn't snap back. She had no wish to talk to the police about the accident because it had suddenly occurred to her that a local reporter might get to hear about it. Liza was news at the moment because of Bruno and the Giffords; any of the London papers would pay well for a news item about her, and if by some mischance a gossip column heard about her Essex cottage they might also hear about her weekend visits and start to wonder who she met down there.

Liza had had enough of newspaper publicity. She would much rather pay the no doubt exorbitant bill for repairing the estate car. It would be cheaper at the price.

'OK, it's a deal,' the stranger said and walked out. She heard him opening cupboards in the kitchen, then he came back with two glasses of brandy.

'I shouldn't drink this on an empty stomach,' Liza said.

'Nor should I,' he grimaced, swallowing the brandy. 'When we feel better we'll make a meal and some coffee.'

'We?' Liza repeated, frowning. 'Shouldn't you be on your way home? Your wife will be worrying about you.'

'I haven't got a wife.' he said, eyeing her through his lashes with amusement.

'Well, somebody . . .' protested Liza.

'You're forgetting something!'

'What?' she asked warily, tensed to meet whatever was coming.

'My car,' he said coolly. 'It's a write-off. I won't drive five yards in it tonight in this mist. And don't suggest I stay at the Green Man, because they don't have a spare room. There's a fishing competition being held locally and all their rooms are occupied by contestants wanting to be up at the crack of dawn.'

'You could phone for a taxi,' Liza began, but he shook his head.

'It would never find us in this mist. I don't know how you managed to find your way here, or do you use radar?' His eyes mocked her. 'Have you got ears like a bat, or X-ray vision?'

'But how are you going to get home?' Liza asked slowly, sitting up and watching him with growing apprehension. She didn't know the man, and they were quite alone here. The Green Man was only just up the lane, at the top of the hill, a mere five or six minutes' walk away, but that was too far for safety. They wouldn't hear her scream from there and she couldn't run fast enough to get there before he caught up with her, even if she tried to make a dash for it.

'Well, I've no intention of walking it,' he said with

irony, watching her face as if he could read every passing expression on it. 'I don't want to walk into the river, and that mist is getting thicker, if anything.'

Liza looked at the window; the curtains hadn't been drawn across it and she saw the mist pressing against the glass like a pale, smoky cat, soft and sinewy. He was right; the mist was thicker and it stifled and smothered every sound outside as if they were alone here at the end of the earth.

Her nerves leapt like flames in a wind as she faced the obvious. He meant to stay here with her tonight.

CHAPTER TWO

'YOU can't stay *here* tonight!' Liza said in dismay.

'What else do you suggest?' he enquired, his hard mouth twisting as she stared at him.

'Well, surely—the pub!'

'I told you, they're full up.'

'But, if you were stranded——!'

'I'm willing to sleep on a sofa, but when I was there earlier they told me that they even had a couple of people sleeping on the floor in sleeping-bags. No, there's no room there.' He gave her a wry smile. 'Don't worry, I won't be any trouble to you. That sofa looks comfortable, I'll sleep on that, and the mist will probably lift in a few hours. As soon as it does I'll ring for a taxi and get a garage to come and pick up my car.'

Liza bit her lip uncertainly; she could hardly refuse to let him stay the night in the circumstances—he couldn't sleep outside in his car, could he?

He watched her uneasy face. 'Do you live here alone?' It was obvious that the cottage was empty; she looked at him, hesitating, wondering whether to invent a brother or a boyfriend who might arrive at any minte.

Before she could decide what to say, he began to laugh. 'I see you do! There's no need to be scared, if that's what's bothering you.'

'I'm not bothered,' Liza said shortly. 'Not by you!'

His brows lifted. 'No?'

She didn't like the smile he was wearing. 'No!' she

insisted, determined not to admit that he affected her in any way at all. She couldn't understand the edgy awareness she was beginning to feel. Was it because he wanted to stay here all night? She lowered her lashes and looked at him through them secretly, frowning. He was much taller and stronger than she was; would she be able to handle him if he made a pass?

'We haven't introduced ourselves,' he said casually. 'My name's Zachary—what's yours?'

'Liza Thurston,' she replied automatically and then stiffened, wishing she had given him an invented name. He might have read that newspaper story, he might talk about spending the night at her cottage—she met his narrowed blue eyes, searching them for some hint of recognition or surprise, but saw nothing. I'm getting paranoid, she told herself angrily. For heaven's sake, try to be rational, she thought, and forced a smile at him.

'Well, Mr Zachary, if you don't mind sleeping on my sofa tonight, you're welcome to it. Now, I'll see what sort of meal I can throw together—I keep a few basic items in stock. It won't be anything special, I'm afraid. It will probably be out of a tin.'

He watched her take off her coat and hang it up in the hall cupboard. 'I'm not fussy,' he murmured. 'Anything will do, I'm so hungry I could eat a horse. Fresh air and exercise always make me hungry.'

'Me, too,' she agreed, walking into the kitchen as he shed his coat and tweed jacket.

'It's Keir, by the way,' he said and she looked round, bewildered.

'What?'

'My name—Keir.'

'You just said it was Zachary!' she said sharply,

frowning in suspicion. Had he forgotten what he had told her?

He laughed. 'It is, but Keir is my first name. It's absurd for you to keep calling me Mr Zachary if we're to spend the night together.'

She stiffened, her face hot. 'We're not going to do anything of the kind!'

'Under the same roof, I meant, of course, sorry,' he corrected, but his eyes held teasing mockery and she was sure he had phrased it deliberately. He was having a little fun at her expense, and Liza wasn't amused. It was nerve-racking enough to have him stranded here, without that sort of provocation!

She opened the larder door and looked at the assorted tins and packets on the shelves of the little store-room, her teeth tight. 'What would you like?' she asked icily.

That was the moment when she really began to feel uneasy, because Keir Zachary squeezed past her to study the contents of the room, and she felt his long, lean body touching hers intimately. It was over in a second, she was out in the kitchen, shaking a little and dark-eyed as she wondered if she should ring the police right now. Maybe it hadn't been wise to let him see that she wouldn't want the police to come here. After all, what did she know about him, other than the sort of clothes he wore, the sort of car he drove and whatever information she could glean from his face? He could be a perfectly respectable farmer—but on the other hand he could be a sex maniac. How was she to know?

'Are you a good cook?' he asked, and she jumped, looking round defiantly, ready to hit back if he attacked her.

'What?'

His eyes opened wide at the aggression in the question.
'Sorry, did I hit on a sore point? It doesn't matter if you're
not, because I am! I spent a year at the North Pole when I
was just out of university, and one of my jobs was cooking
for the whole team.'

'Team?' Liza's nerves had steadied and her colour had
come back.

'I was out there with the British Expedition. I was
supposed to be doing research into human reaction to the
pressure of loneliness and danger, but it was mainly fun.
It was one of those special years; I learnt a lot about
myself and I suppose about other people, too.' He was
gathering up tins of soup, tomatoes, a packet of
spaghetti. 'Show me where everything is,' he said,
emerging into the kitchen with his arms full. 'Saucepans,
plates, cutlery?'

'Are you a doctor?' Liza said uncertainly, trying to
work out a little more about him, while she opened
cupboards and showed him where she kept everything.

'No, I'd studied psychology at university, though,' he
told her, dumping the tins and packets on the kitchen
table, and surveying the room with narrow eyes. 'You're
very tidy, everything in its place, I see.' His tone
approved and she lifted her sleek blonde head, her eyes
flashing.

'Thank you,' she said tartly. 'I'm so glad.'

He stood watching her, his smile ironic. 'And what do
you do, Liza?' He let his eyes wander down over her,
from her immaculate features and the slender lines of her
body in a Bond Street dress down to her long, shapely legs
and the hand-made Italian shoes she wore. 'One thing's
certain, you aren't short of money! Do you earn it or . . .'

'I earn it!' Liza interrupted sharply, afraid of what he

might have been going to suggest. From the way he had looked her over she suspected that he might have thought she was kept by a wealthy father or boyfriend. Hadn't he sneered some such comment earlier? 'I run an agency in London,' she added.

'What sort of agency?'

She didn't want to tell him, she didn't want him to find out too much about her, which made it very difficult because at the same time she wanted to probe his background as much as she could because she found him a little overpowering. He was a formidable man; whatever he did for a living she was certain he was accustomed to authority. Even in his shabby, well worn cords and that olive-green sweater he had a distinct air of assurance. He had taken off the muddy wellies and was just wearing socks, she suddenly realised. That ought to make him more approachable, but it didn't because he was too tall, too tough-looking. If he wasn't a farmer, he could be a thug, Liza thought grimly. Look at those shoulders, that height!

She talked rapidly to change the subject. 'What can I do to help with the cooking? I do know my way around this kitchen, after all, and I usually cook for myself. Sorry if I gave the impression that I couldn't cook. Shall I open the tin of soup? Are we starting with that while whatever else you planned is cooking?'

'I cook my whole meal in one pan,' he said. 'It saves on washing up.'

It sounded simply disgusting and Liza glanced at the tins and packets, her brows rising. 'Really?'

He laughed. 'Wait and see. You'll like it!'

She did; much to her own surprise. She wasn't sure what to call it, but it tasted great: something like a hearty minestrone stew, thick with spaghetti strands, rich with tomato and beef. She had never tasted anything like it, but it was certainly filling and delicious. She congratulated him.

'I'm glad you enjoyed it,' he said, smiling, and for the first time Liza saw a flash of charm in his hard face. An involuntary answering smile lit her own features, and she offered to do the washing up alone.

He didn't argue. 'OK, and I'll make us some coffee.'

There wasn't much washing up to do, owing to his economical way of cooking, and by the time Liza had restored the kitchen to its normal tidiness he had made coffee and laid a tray which he carried into the sitting-room.

She joined him and found him stretched out on the sofa, his hands linked behind his head and his slim body relaxed. The room was much warmer now, he had taken off his olive-green sweater and was yawning.

'Sorry,' he said, sitting up as she appeared. 'Fresh air and good food, I'm afraid—I'm half asleep already. I'm used to early nights.'

Liza looked at her watch and was taken aback to find that it was nearly nine o'clock.

'I'll find you a pillow and some blankets,' she said, turning, but he caught her wrist, his hand clamping it in an iron grip.

'After you've had your coffee!'

Liza glanced down at her trapped wrist, then up at his insistent face. 'You're hurting!' she said tersely and he released her.

'Sorry.' He turned and began to pour her coffee. 'Sit down by the fire,' he ordered, as though this was his house and he was her host, and she slowly obeyed, bristling a little at the commanding tone.

She was not going to sit on the sofa, however, or anywhere near him, so she chose a chair on the other side of the fire, taking her cup of coffee with her and nursing it on her lap as some sort of barrier against him. If he tried anything, she could always chuck the boiling hot coffee at him!

'You know, I'm sure I've seen you somewhere before,' he said thoughtfully, staring, and her nerves prickled. 'What sort of agency did you say you ran?'

'A modelling agency,' she reluctantly admitted, because she could see that he was the persistent type. He wouldn't forget to ask again if she changed the subject this time.

'Modelling?' He studied her. 'Were you a model?'

She nodded, and sipped a little coffee.

'That's probably it,' he decided. 'I must have seen you in a magazine or something—did you do that sort of work?'

Liza nodded again. 'And you?' she said. 'What exactly do you do? You said you studied psychology—are you a practising psychologist?'

'In a way,' he said blandly. 'Modern psychology isn't a matter of listening to patients lying on a couch and fantasising about their sex lives, you know. It's more a question of group psychology; why women buy one brand of perfume and not another, for instance—that's my job.'

'You mean market research?'

'Something like that, yes.'

Liza looked at him with interest. 'We employed a firm of market researchers last year, trying to find out which was the perfect model to sell a new kind of soap.'

'What was the result? A blonde?'

'A child,' Liza said drily and he laughed. She stared at him. 'I got the impression you were a farmer!' she said half accusingly, because he still looked more like a farmer than anything else.

'Interesting you should say that,' he murmured. 'My family do have a farm, and I spend a lot of time there.'

'Is it near here?'

He got up and came over with the coffee-pot. 'Have some more coffee.'

Liza held up her cup and he filled it, bending over her. She glanced up and saw his eyes fixed on her face; then she felt that stare focusing on her mouth, and her body tensed. It wasn't a casual look, Keir Zachary was staring intently; Liza's face began to burn and then his gaze lifted until their eyes met. He straightened and turned away, went back to the sofa and sat down, but the room was no longer warm and cosy, it was full of tension and Liza's nervous anxiety was back.

She wasn't the type to be highly strung or imagine things, but he was a total stranger to her and they were in this cottage alone, too far from the nearest building to be heard if she started yelling for help. Her fears had been allayed while he was cooking that meal, because a man as calmly capable as that was hardly the type to turn nasty suddenly or make a violent pass at her, but just now there had been something in those hard blue eyes which made her uneasy and disturbed. He was much bigger than her, and those were real muscles under his thin shirt; he looked like a tough customer even when he was relaxed and smiling.

'Well,' she said, drinking a little of the coffee and then putting the cup down. 'I think I'll get you the bed linen, then I'll head for bed myself.'

This time he didn't try to stop her; he leaned back, sipping coffee, watching her with his lids half drawn over his blue eyes. The gaze was drowsy, lazy, without any visible threat, yet Liza felt the back of her neck prickle as she slid out of the room and went up to find blankets and a pillow. She went to her bedroom and switched on the electric fire in there; that would warm the room a little before she came up to get undressed.

She went back downstairs with an armful of blankets and found Keir Zachary on his feet by the electric fire, his hands in his pockets and his lean body lounging casually. Liza began to make his bed up and he turned to watch her. A curious shiver ran down her spine under that gaze; she wished she knew what he was thinking.

'I hope you'll be able to sleep on it,' she said with a brief glance at him as she turned back towards the door.

'I'm sure I shall,' he murmured, moving faster than she had expected.

Her nerves leapt again and she looked up at him, her green eyes wide and dark-pupilled. 'Well, goodnight,' she said huskily, but he didn't answer. His hand reached out before she could move away and she felt his fingers moving in her hair. He was watching her through those half-closed eyes and Liza swallowed uneasily.

'What do you think you're doing?' She put up a hand to push him away, but too late. Her long pale hair fell and tumbled around her face, down her back, over her shoulders.

'I wondered what it looked like when it wasn't dragged off your face so ruthlessly,' he said softly.

'I think you'd better go!' Liza flared, her face running with angry colour as she grabbed the heavy weight of hair and tried to gather it back into a chignon. 'I should have rung the police, shouldn't I? I think I'll do that now. I'm not going to let you think you can maul me about . . .'

'Don't over-react!' he drawled, his face derisive. 'And don't put your hair up again—it suits you better like that. It makes you look less severe.'

'Severe!' The word startled her; she didn't like having it applied to herself. 'Don't be ridiculous!' She turned bright, furious green eyes up to him, catlike and spitting with rage. 'You're just trying to distract me, but it won't work! Don't ever dare to touch me again!'

'Didn't your mother tell you it isn't wise to dare a man to do anything?' he murmured, standing much too close and she took a step backward in sudden alarm because the way he was watching her had made alarm bells ring in her head.

'Goodnight,' she said, trying to edge round him to the door.

'You're very beautiful,' he whispered in a soft, intimate voice and she shivered in panic.

'You can stop right there!' she muttered, sliding a hurried glance around for a weapon in case he turned violent. 'Lay a finger on me and . . .'

'Goodnight, Liza,' he said, suddenly sitting down on the arm of the sofa, his hands linked behind his head as he yawned.

For a few seconds she didn't move, she just stood there dazedly, staring at him, and then she turned and hurtled out of the room and heard him laugh.

'Goodnight,' he called after her, but she didn't answer because she was too furious. Had he been having a peculiar kind of fun at her expense? He had been teasing her, had he? She didn't think it was so very funny. For a minute or two she had been really scared, disturbed, anxious—if he *had* been making a heavy pass, what could she have done to stop him, all alone here, with no other dwelling within earshot? He was far too powerful for her to be able to deal with. Her heart was beating slowly, heavily, now, as though it beat in every far corner of her body, the pulse running strongly. When their faces were so close she could see every pore in his skin, the line of the bones which built the structure of his face, the streaking of blue and grey in his irises and the mysterious, hypnotic glow of those shiny black pupils. If you looked into those eyes for long enough you would slide into a trance, Liza thought, then angrily shook herself. What on earth was the matter with her?

In her bedroom she stripped and put on her nightie and dressing-gown, but only when she had locked her door. She did not want him walking in on her. She washed in the little vanity unit in her bedroom, although normally she would have had a bath before bed; it relaxed her and made it easier to sleep.

She was about to go to bed when she heard the knocking. Tensing, she listened incredulously—who on earth could that be? She had had this cottage for years without having a single visitor, not even a tradesman, because she bought what she wanted from the local shops or brought it down from London with her in the car. She had no milk or bread delivered, and the heating was all electric.

Yet tonight she was apparently going to have *two* visitors! Or was it the police? she thought, moving towards her bedroom door at the idea. Had they seen the two crashed cars outside and come in to investigate?

She heard movements in the hall—Keir Zachary was going to open the door! Liza shot out on to the landing and hissed down the stairs. 'No, wait! I'll answer it! Go back into the sitting-room!'

He turned and looked up at her, his black brows rising. He was still in his shirt and the cord trousers; he hadn't undressed to sleep on the sofa, but Liza still didn't want whoever was at the door to see him until she knew who the caller was!

'Go back!' she insisted, coming down the stairs and trying to ignore the wandering speculation of his eyes. Luckily, her dressing-gown was long and covered her from neck to foot; a deep pansy-blue, it was hand-made in brushed wool, soft and warm on such cold, misty nights.

There was another loud knock and Keir Zachary sauntered back towards the sitting-room, shrugging. Liza opened the front door and a man almost fell into the hallway. He must have been leaning on the door. Liza looked blankly at him; she had never seen him before in her life, but he wasn't wearing police uniform, in fact his clothes were shabby and disreputable. One look and she had a strong suspicion that he was a tramp; he needed a shave, he smelt of drink and it wouldn't have hurt him to have a wash, either.

'What do you want?' she asked sharply, stepping into his path as he tried to move further into the house.

'Miss Thurston? Liza Thurston?' He gave her what he obviously believed to be a placating smile. 'I'm from the *Argus*, the local paper. I'm sure you know it . . .'

'A reporter?' Liza's tone betrayed disgust and he looked uneasily at her.

'Well, yes, but I don't just work on the *Argus*, I'm a stringer for several Fleet Street newspapers and one of them just rang me up and asked me to get over here and talk to you.'

'Well, I don't want to talk to you,' Liza informed him icily, holding the door open in a pointed way. 'Goodnight.' With the door wide open, freezing air drifted in and she shivered, clutching the throat of her dressing-gown together. 'Please hurry up and go—that fog is thicker, if anything. I can't imagine how on earth you got here in it!'

'I was at the Green Man,' he said, making no attempt to leave. 'I'm covering the fishing contest they're holding and I decided to stay the night.'

'Have you got a room?' Liza's eyes widened as it occurred to her that he might let Keir Zachary share it. Then she started thinking a little more coolly and realised that at all costs he must not even know that Keir was in the house with her!

'Well, not exactly,' he said, grimacing. He was a short, bulky man with a round, balding head and a red neck. His sharp little eyes had already made a tour of the hallway and Liza and she was glad she hadn't been alone in the cottage when he arrived. He made her far more nervous than Keir Zachary had done.

'I'm Bob Tanner,' he told her. 'Call me Bob, Liza.'

'Call me Miss Thurston, Mr Tanner,' she said with hauteur, but he just laughed, as though he thought she was being funny!

'Why did you ask if I had a room?' he asked eagerly, looking up the stairs. 'You haven't got one free, have you? The Green Man is full; packed up to the rafters, in fact. I've been told I can sleep in an armchair in the bar, but if you had a room I could use, I'd be glad to pay.'

'I don't have any free rooms, I'm not a hotel,' Liza said

impatiently. 'Look, Mr Tanner, will you please go? I am not talking to a newspaper. Tell them I said "no comment".'

'You here alone?' he asked in a tone which made her face stiffen, and she was so angry that she got hold of his arm and pushed him forcibly towards the door.

'Get out!'

'I just want to ask a few questions!' he said, resisting her efforts to evict him. He was short but he was heavy, and Liza could not budge him. 'Is is true that the Gifford family have objections to Bruno marrying you? What are you and Bruno going to do if they refuse their consent? Are you going to marry in spite of them? Where is he, by the way? At Hartwell? Is he going to join you here?'

'I'm not telling you anything, so please go away!' Liza fumed, pushing as hard as she could without managing to shift him, and he leered down at her, catching one of her hands.

'Just give me a few quotes, and I'll go, I promise, Liza! And I don't blame Bruno, by the way—you're a real knock-out, aren't you? I go for blondes myself, always have.'

Liza was so furious that for a second she was almost blind with rage and distaste, which was why she did not hear or see the arrival of Keir Zachary at first. One minute she was staring in helpless fury at Bob Tanner's grinning, unshaven face, the next he was whirled away as Keir picked him up by his coat collar and the seat of his trousers and threw him out of the door.

Liza had pulled herself together enough by then to hear the crash as Bob Tanner hit the path. She didn't have time to see what he had done to himself, because Keir snarled after him, 'And don't come back, or next time I'll break your neck!' before slamming the front door.

'You may have killed him!' Liza gasped.

'Good,' Keir said through his teeth, his face dark red.
'I hate scum of that sort. I kept quiet because I could see
you didn't want him to know I was here, but when he
started making a pass at you that was more than flesh
and blood could stand . . . the miserable little toad!'

Liza couldn't deny the aptness of the description, but
she was still angry with Keir for interfering. 'Don't you
realise what you've done?' she asked him fiercely,
glaring. 'You've given him exactly what he came here to
get—a story! And much better than a couple of weak
quotes! He's going to scurry to the nearest phone and tell
the world that I've got a man staying with me down
here!'

He stared at her, his brows together, and in the silence
they both heard Bob Tanner pick himself up and hurry
away. His running footsteps sounded very loud in the
damp river mist shrouding the house.

'You can explain to your boyfriend . . .' Keir began
and Liza looked at him scathingly, interrupting.

'That I didn't even know you, but you stayed the
night?'

'That we crashed into each other and I couldn't get
home!' he re-phrased drily.

'And that's what I tell Fleet Street? You think they'll
believe that lame story?'

'The cars are outside for all the world to see!' He
considered her with a cool smile. 'I think you're making a
mountain out of a molehill.'

'That's what reporters always do!' she snapped.

He shrugged. 'I apologise if I've embarrassed you, but
that guy was asking for a good punch on the nose. If I

hadn't intervened he might have done more than tell you he fancied you. I got the impression he was leading up to a little demonstration!'

Liza shuddered. She had had the same impression and the thought of that odious little man touching her made her feel sick.

'Did I hear him mention the name Gifford?' Keir asked, staring hard at her. 'He didn't mean the merchant bank people, did he?'

Liza was too weary and distraught to think of an evasive reply. She just sighed and nodded.

'I'm going back to bed,' she said, turning towards the stairs, but Keir caught her arm and detained her.

'Is your boyfriend one of the Giffords? Are you engaged to him?'

Liza turned on him, heavy-eyed and fed up. 'Look, I've had enough questions from that reporter! I'm not answering any of yours, either. It's none of your business.'

'Are you in love with him?' he threw at her, as if he hadn't heard a word she had said.

Liza shook herself free and ran up the stairs, aware of him standing in the hall, watching her, but when she was safely out of reach she paused to look back at him, half apologetically.

'Thank you for coming to my rescue,' she said with faint reluctance. 'I realise you meant well!'

'Thank you,' he said with wry impatience. 'Next time I'll let the guy do what he likes with you, shall I?'

'Don't be angry,' Liza said, suddenly smiling down at him. 'I'm sorry, it's just that you don't understand—you don't realise what's going on!'

'So tell me, maybe I could help?' He put a foot on the

bottom stair and Liza's body stiffened.

'Don't come up here!'

He leaned on the banister, his lean body relaxed and yet held in a controlled tension she could feel, as though he was willing himself to stay calm, but was coiled for action all the same.

'Are you afraid of me?' he enquired, the blue eyes holding hers, and she suddenly found it hard to breathe, although she couldn't think why she should be having trouble dragging air into her lungs, just because a total stranger looked at her.

'Afraid of you? Why should I be?' she retorted, wishing she didn't sound so husky.

'You tell me!'

'Do *you* think I should be?' Liza asked, wishing she knew what he was thinking. 'You know yourself better than I do—should I be afraid of you?'

He smiled slowly, a cynical, amused, half-teasing smile. 'I think maybe you should, Liza,' he said, and she turned and almost ran into her bedroom and bolted the door.

CHAPTER THREE

LIZA slept so heavily that when she woke up it was a wrenching shock; her nerves jangled as she felt herself coming back to life, and for a few seconds she was too disorientated to know where she was or remember everything that had happened last night. She lay there, eyes closed, hearing noises she could identify, but which for some reason filled her with alarm. Shouts, the slamming of a door, knocking.

Then she sat up, trembling—what was going on downstairs? It was daylight; a cool, clear daylight. It was morning, but Liza could have slept on for hours if she hadn't been forced to wake up. She slid her legs out of bed and stood up, staggering, as if she was drunk, and in a way she was—drunk with sleep, almost drowning in it.

She had been so tired when she'd finally got to bed— not merely with the long journey she had made from London, or the alarums and excursions when she arrived—all the tension of running into Keir Zachary's car and arguing, the reporter, everything that had happened—but with the exhaustion of the previous two days, Bruno and the Press. Emotional hassle could be as tiring as physical exhaustion. She had needed to sleep to process everything that had happened to her over the past few days.

And now she had woken up to what sounded horribly like more problems! It sounded, in fact, as if the house was under siege, and Liza grabbed up her dressing-gown and splashed her face with cold water to make sure she was awake, then groped for the door, yawning convulsively.

The hall was empty and as Liza made her way down the stairs the banging and shouting outside the house faded away. From the kitchen floated a delicious smell, though.

Coffee, Liza thought, following her nose. She pushed open the door and was surprised to find the kitchen shadowy; Keir Zachary had pulled down the blinds, something she almost never did, although they were very pretty—white cotton printed with apple blossom and red apples and green leaves, very sharp and bright. The colours matched the green and white of the kitchen units. The whole room was gay and cheerful, especially in the mornings, when the sun flooded in, so why on earth had he pulled down the blinds?

'Why haven't you gone?' she demanded as he turned to look at her. He was surprisingly well groomed for a man who had spent the night on a sofa; his dark hair was brushed and neat, his skin smooth and shaven, his clothes were not the ones he had worn last night, and Liza stared in stupefaction and growing suspicion. 'Where did you get those clothes from?' she asked furiously.

'My suitcase,' he said.

'Suitcase? What suitcase?'

'It was in the back of the estate car.'

Liza thought about that, frowning at him. 'Why did you have a suitcase in the back of the car?'

'Because I've been spending a few days with some friends in Essex, and I was on my way back home when you ran into me!' he said, pouring coffee. 'Sugar? No, I remember, you don't take it.' He handed her a cup and she absent-mindedly inhaled with a sigh of pleasure.

'So that's why you were able to shave, too,' she thought aloud, and he nodded. Then Liza remembered the noise outside the house, and asked, 'What on earth was all that shouting and banging?'

'I was up an hour ago,' said Keir in a casual, conversational tone. 'I had my first cup of coffee, then I went out to my car and got my case and changed, and had a wash and shaved. I meant to be on my way long before you woke up, so I rang the local garage and they promised to come and get my car and tow it away. They arrived ten minutes ago and they brought a hire car for me. They handed me the keys and drove off and I was just leaving myself when that reporter came back.'

'Oh, no!' Liza groaned and he grimaced.

'Oh, yes, and he brought a friend.'

'A friend?' she asked, apprehensively.

'A photographer.'

Liza went white, then red. 'They . . . they didn't get a . . .?'

'Picture of me? No,' he said grimly. 'They almost did, but my antennae are too good. I opened the front door and they dived out a car at once, but I spotted them immediately, saw the camera, and got back indoors. They pounded up the path and started yelling and knocking.' He sipped his coffee and lounged on one of Liza's tall, kitchen stools, green leather with shiny chrome legs. She had thought of them as very functional, but Keir Zachary's lean body draped on them gave them a distinctly glamorous air; the kitchen took on the look of a night-club.

'Damn!' Liza said, biting her lip.

'You're very mild this morning. I expected something a little more explosive,' he drawled and she ignored him, going over to the window to let the blinds up.

'Why on earth did you pull these down?' she asked, reaching for the cord, and Keir Zachary's body hit her at that instant, dragging her away and clamping her so powerfully that she couldn't breath. Her eyes opened wide in shock.

'What do you think you're doing?' she managed hoarsely, her skin now icy cold, now feverish, as she felt his hard body so close, touching hers from neck to thigh.

'Don't touch the blinds! Are you stupid?' he asked in a deep, impatient roar, and she jumped again, afraid and bewildered.

'Why shouldn't I? What are you talking about?'

'Why do you think I pulled them down? Those men out there have already prowled round the house, looking in the windows—luckily I'd anticipated them and they didn't see a thing.'

'They can't do that,' Liza said blankly. 'That's trespassing. They can't walk through my garden and look in my windows!'

'They're the Press—they think they can do what they like!'

'I'll call the police!'

'Do that,' Keir said drily as though he didn't believe she would, and Liza bristled because the only reason why she hadn't called the police yesterday to report the crash was because she did not want the Press alerted as to her presence at the cottage. Since the Press now knew she was there, it no longer mattered if she called the police.

'I will, don't worry,' she said furiously, trying to break away from the hard grasp of his hands on her back. 'Let go of me!' she insisted and Keir looked down into her face, a funny, crooked smile curling his mouth.

'I like you better like this,' he murmured, and his voice was deep and warm and sexy, and Liza felt her skin break out in goose-bumps as though in fear, which was crazy, because why should a man's voice make her scared? But she *was* scared, she looked back at him nervously, her pupils huge and her throat pulsing violently.

'I'm going to ring the police. Let go,' she said in a stilted little voice she tried to make normal.

'With your hair down and your face flushed, just out of bed,' he continued softly, one hand slowly moving up her back, stroking and pressing along her spine.

'Stop that,' she said, her voice rising.

'Why are you shaking?' asked Keir, watching her, and his hand reached the back of her neck and pushed into the cloudy blonde hair lying heavily on the nape. She shivered as his fingertips caressed her neck.

'Rage,' Liza said through her teeth. 'I'm shaking with rage! Will you get your hands off me? We may be marooned together in this house for a little while, but that doesn't give you any rights. Get away from me and stay away, or I swear I'll maim you, Mr Zachary! And don't think I don't know how, because when I started modelling I soon discovered I needed some lessons in self-defence and I could do you some nasty injuries, believe me, without needing any weapon but my own two hands.'

He looked at her with incredulity and then mocking amusement. 'Amazon!' But his hands dropped and Liza darted away again, her knees weak and her legs only just bearing her weight. She didn't know why she felt so light-headed; she hardly knew Keir Zachary and he certainly wasn't the first man to make a pass at her. She had fought off far too many other men without ever getting this funny, swimming sensation which was dangerously close to fainting, so why should Keir Zachary do this to her? She knew nothing about him, she didn't know if she like him much; in fact, she was beginning to dislike him intensely. He was taking advantage of being alone here with her; he seemed to think it funny to scare the living daylights out of her. He was *not* a nice man.

'You're not what I'd have expected,' he said thoughtfully, staring at her with narrowed eyes. 'Aren't models usually rather more ... experienced?' The hesitation made the question insulting. What he really meant was: don't models usually go to bed with any man who shows an interest? Liza glared back at him, her teeth together.

When she could speak, she said icily, 'We come in all shapes and sizes, we aren't identical! I don't sleep around, Mr Zachary, so keep your hands to yourself in future.'

He didn't believe her, she could see that; his cynical amusement made her even angrier, but there was no point in insisting that she was telling the truth. Let him think what he liked. If he tried to touch her again she would hit him so hard he wouldn't need another warning!

'I'm going to ring the police and ask them to come and send those men on their way!' she told him, turning.

'They won't,' he drawled indifferently. 'They never do. There's no law against sitting in a car on the public road, you see. If they commit a crime, the police can act, but the Press are far too sharp to get caught doing anything illegal. The police will just talk to them and go away and the reporter and his chum will sit out there until the crack of doom.'

'We'll see about that,' Liza said determined to make somebody do something. The police were polite, but not exactly breathing fire and brimstone. They said more or less what Keir Zachary had said—unless the journalists broke the law they had every right to park their car on the public highway and sit in it.

'Unless they're in a no-parking zone?' the policeman suggested helpfully, and Liza grimly said they weren't, but would he send someone along to talk to the men, anyway? That might scare them off. He said he would ask one of his cars to drop by on their usual round, but they were very busy.

'I didn't realise this was such a criminal area,' Liza said, but the sarcasm was water off a duck's back.

'We get our share,' the policeman said and hung up. Liza put the receiver down and began to walk away. The phone rang and she went and picked it up, but a voice began to gabble questions at her and she slammed the receiver down again, then took it off the hook and left it on the hall table.

'How are you going to get away?' she asked Keir Zachary, who was cooking in the kitchen. He had found a tin of ham and one of tomatoes, and he was making one of his extraordinary meals. Liza wished she wasn't hungry, but she was; emotion made her hungry. She stood there looking at his hard profile and hating him. If he hadn't been there in his car in the mist she wouldn't have run into him and he wouldn't be here, cluttering up her life.

'They'll get tired of waiting,' he said, with an optimism she could not share. 'But we may run out of food in the meantime.'

'If you stop using every tin in my larder, we *may* manage,' Liza said bitterly.

'There's some flour and a packet of yeast—you could make some bread for tea,' he said cheerfully and she wailed in fury.

'You aren't going to be here for tea! You're leaving here soon, even if I have to put a paper bag over your head and make you run for it.'

'It won't come to that,' he said. 'Lay the table, this is nearly ready.'

'What do you call that concoction?' Liza asked as she obeyed him.

'Ham and tomatoes,' he mocked, sliding her a sideways grin, but she was not in a mood to be friendly to him. He was the cause of all this hassle; why hadn't he left before that photographer arrived?

'I normally eat just a grapefruit for breakfast,' she said gloomily as she sat down with a plate of food in front of her.

If it hadn't been for the mist and the accident, she would have gone out last night to the village shop and bought supplies—fresh bread, fruit, salad, eggs. It wasn't far in a car, just five minutes away, but she wouldn't care to walk it in a thick river mist; it would be easy to miss a turning or walk off the road into the low-lying fields or even into the river.

'You're in no danger of putting on weight,' Keir assured her and she bristled at the way he was eyeing her.

'Keep your eyes on your breakfast!'

He laughed. 'Can't I even look?'

'No,' Liza said with a bite, her eyes serious, and he stopped smiling, his face tightening. She heard him draw an angry breath, staring at her, his eyes blindingly bright and icy.

'You're beginning to annoy me, Miss Thurston! Stop picking me up on every word. Have you got some sort of hang-up about men? You seem very touchy—mustn't touch, mustn't look! What's your problem, Miss Thurston?'

'You, at the moment, Mr Zachary,' she told him coldly, 'I wouldn't have to tell you not to touch if you kept your hands to yourself, and as for looking, it all depends on the way you do it, doesn't it? Some stares can be an insult.'

He didn't like that; a dark flush crept up into his face and his eyes narrowed dangerously on her, threat in them. He expected every woman he made a pass at to swoon into his arms, no doubt. He wasn't used to getting a red light—but he was getting one from her, whether he liked it or not. Liza lifted her chin and glared back at him.

'Afraid your boyfriend will be jealous?' he asked and the sneer made her angrier.

'Leave Bruno out of this!'

'Bruno!' he repeated, his mouth twisting. 'What sort of name is that for a man? It's a name for a teddy bear!'

'I like it!' she snapped.

'Are you in love with him?' he asked curtly, watching her closely.

She didn't answer, beginning to eat, and he waited a minute before he concentrated on his breakfast too. It was good; Liza had to admit that. She wasn't sure how he did it with such unpromising materials, but she ate every scrap on the plate and enjoyed every mouthful, even though she was in a very bad temper by then.

'If there was any justice, you'd have indigestion for hours,' Keir told her as he got up from the table. 'I probably will! Eating when you're furious is a mistake.'

'When are you leaving?' Liza merely asked, although she knew she ought to tell him how good the meal had been. She should, but she couldn't because Keir Zachary made her feel aggressive. The sideways glance of those blue eyes made her blood run faster and hotter and did something drastic to her peace of mind. The only way she could handle the way he made her feel was to lose her temper. Ever since she'd met him in the mist her temperature had been rising and she had to have some safety valve.

'As soon as I can, don't worry!' he snapped back, dumping the dishes into the sink and running hot water on them.

'Leave that, I'll do it,' Liza said.

'I can walk out now, if you don't mind the vultures getting a shot of me leaving the house,' he said nastily, and she felt like hitting him because he knew very well that she did not want a photo of him appearing in the papers.

'Maybe they've gone,' she said optimistically and went into the sitting-room to peer out through the curtains, taking care not to be seen herself.

The car was still there, but she couldn't see anyone in it. Perhaps the two men had gone off to the pub to check on the fishing contest? It was far too early for the bar to be open, but perhaps they were eating breakfast?

'They've gone. Hurry!' she told Keir, who joined her and studied the empty car thoughtfully without seeming in much haste.

'Will you be OK on your own?' he asked, without moving.

'Yes, don't just stand there—get moving!'

'I'll have to collect my case,' he said, wandering away, as if he had all the time in the world.

'They may be back any minute,' she pointed out, then remembered something. 'We didn't exchange addresses

—when your car has been fixed, send the bill to me. I've got a card in my wallet. Hold on, I'll get it for you from my bag.' He might not feel any sense of urgency, but she did. She ran all the way, and was breathless when she got back from her bedroom.

It was the agency business card, not her private address; he studied it when she handed it to him and his brows curved upwards in that dry, sardonic way of his.

'The Gifford Building? You must make a fortune to be able to afford offices in that.'

'We're successful,' she admitted with quiet pride, because when she set up the agency nobody had believed in her ability to run a company. She had been risking her own money; no bank would lend her any then, although now she could walk in anywhere and be sure of a warm reception and a loan. When you had money it was easy; it was when you didn't that problems started.

'You must be,' Keir drawled. 'And if you're dating one of the Giffords you're moving in the big league, too. They built that block a few years ago, didn't they? One of the new monsters on London's skyline; all that glass and concrete—there was quite an outcry, I remember. Do you like it?'

'I do, as it happens, but this is no time for discussion on architecture,' Liza said furiously. 'Are you going or not?'

He put the card into the top pocket of his jacket and walked down the hall towards the front door. Liza followed close on his heels and was taken aback when he swung suddenly and dropped his suitcase, caught hold of her shoulders in a tight grip, bent his head and kissed her.

She was too surprised to evade that kiss; her mouth had already parted in a gasp of surprise at his swoop. His lips hit hers fiercely, but the first bruising impact softened a few seconds later; his hand closed on her waist and drew her up against him, her body helplessly yielding because her mind hadn't started working yet, she was too shaken. Her hands closed on his shirt, her eyes shut, her mouth taken and coaxed, warmly caressed.

The pleasure was unexpected, a sensual sweetness that made her weak. A tremor ran through her from head to foot and then she dragged herself out of the physical trance, pushing him away.

He had his eyes shut, too; as she looked up at his face his lids slowly lifted and she saw the brilliance of his eyes—the excitement in them made her shudder with shock. Was that how she looked? She was feverish, angry, dismayed. What had happened to her? What had he done to her?

Blindly she reached for the door, opened it, muttering something thickly. 'Please go,' was what she tried to say, but she didn't know if he would understand the incoherent noise which she had made.

Whether he did or not, he walked past her without a word and she stared after him as he reached the hire car parked outside, unlocked it, got behind the wheel and drove off without looking at her once. She closed the door and leaned on it. If she hadn't, she might have fallen down. Her legs were like water. Her body was trembling violently. She was in shock.

It was a very long time since a kiss had had any real effect on her. Years, she thought, closing her eyes and trying not to remember. She had been badly hurt and she had been too young to cope with it. She had come out of it scarred, and determined it would never happen again. You couldn't get hurt if you didn't run any risks, and so she picked her men carefully from then on; she didn't go out with a man if she didn't like him, enjoy his company, of course, but at the same time she froze off anyone who might get to her, anyone she might fall for. If she had met Keir Zachary at a party or on a blind date she would have avoided him instinctively.

She had known last night, even in the mist, even when he was in a black rage, that he was dangerous to her. Right from the first moment there had been that prickle of electricity, a heightening of awareness, not only of him but of everything around her. She had come alive and Keir Zachary had been responsible, but now she felt sick and she was terrified. She remembered how it had felt before and she knew she could not bear to go through that again. It had been wonderful at first, falling in love *was* wonderful—the air sparkled, your feet hardly seemed to touch the ground, you felt like laughing and singing, as if you were crazy, out of your mind!

But however high you floated, you always had to come down, and the descent broke you.

Keir Zachary hadn't given her his address, she realised. Maybe he didn't intend to send her that bill, or maybe he didn't want her to know where to find him— with any luck she might never see him again. If she did, she would have to make it clear she was otherwise occupied; there was no place in her life for him. He was too dangerous.

The police drove up half an hour later. One of them knocked at her door and asked if she had had any more bother from the reporter. 'His car's there but he seems to have vanished,' admitted Liza, looking past the broad, uniformed shoulders, across the road.

'At the river,' the constable nodded.

'At the fishing competition?'

'He'll be back when the pub opens,' said the policeman, grinning. 'If you get any more hassle, give us another ring and we'll stop on our next drive around and give him a few words.'

'Oh, thank you,' Liza breathed, opening her green eyes wide and smiling very gratefully. 'You are kind. It was scary having them hanging about, banging on my door and shouting.'

'Don't you worry,' the constable said, admiring her tight-fitting white jeans and the casual white and black shirt she wore with them. 'We'll sort it out for you.'

Liza thanked him again and he left, waving as he drove away. He was a very big powerful young man and she thought he would throw a scare into the reporter, which would mean she need not leave and drive back to London, as she had decided to. All the same, her tranquil life and the cottage had been wrecked for the weekend. She felt as if she had been invaded—trampled underfoot.

As she passed the telephone, still off the hook, she heard the high-pitched signal it was making and sighed, replacing it on the stand, then dialled the local garage and asked them to come and tow her car away for repairs.

'Have you got a car I can hire?' she added and the garage manager said he had and he would bring it along while his mechanic drove the break-down truck, then he asked for directions. Liza told him the address, then remarked, 'But you've been here once this morning, already, haven't you? Didn't you pick up the other car?'

'What other car?'

'The one I crashed into!'

'We haven't had any other repair jobs today—the break-down truck hasn't been out for a couple of days, in fact,' he said, sounding irritable.

'Oh, it must have been some other garage then,' Liza said and the man asked, 'Which one? Around here?'

She had no answer to that because she couldn't think

of another garage for a mile or so, and that one didn't deal with repairs, it merely sold petrol.

The men picked up her car and delivered the hire car, and the manager told Liza that her own vehicle shouldn't take too long to repair as he had no other jobs on at present. When he had left, she went out shopping and stocked up with fresh supplies: bread, eggs, orange juice, milk, salad and cheese. On her return to the cottage she had to run from the car to the cottage because the reporter was back with his photographer. Liza dropped her carton of eggs and heard them smash. She was so angry that she turned round and pelted the gentleman of the Press with a large, red tomato which hit his forehead and burst, running down his face. The photographer took running shots of her, but she was an experienced hand with cameras and managed not to be full face every time he snapped. She got her door unlocked and ran in and the reporter put his foot in the door, talking fast.

Liza grabbed an umbrella from the tall, chinese jar behind the door and brought the spike of it down on his foot.

He gave a yelp and jumped back and she slammed the door and then stood there, breathing hard and laughing. She was still angry, but it had been fun. She wondered what sort of pictures would surface in the papers and didn't care.

The phone was ringing. Warily, she picked it up. 'Hello?'

'Liza?' It wasn't anyone from Fleet Street, it was Bruno, sounding stiff and on edge.

'Bruno?' she asked, wondering if he had had a rough ride from his family. He probably had; he sounded upset. Poor Bruno, she thought, grimacing, perhaps he had been ordered to stop seeing her—was he ringing to tell her that?

'Who is he?' Bruno asked, the words shooting out of him like bullets, and she stiffened.

'What? Who?'

'The guy down there with you!' Bruno's voice was raw and she frowned, a pang of compassion shooting through her. He was jealous, he had been hurt. Liza wasn't in love with Bruno, but she was fond of him and she had been there—she knew how he was feeling. Love was a killer, it tracked you invisibly and pounced from high places when you weren't expecting it, like a tiger in the jungle, and like a savage animal it tore you limb from limb and you were helpless to save yourself. She should have warned him off long ago. She shouldn't have gone on seeing him, kidded herself that he was just a friend, it was platonic, he wouldn't get hurt any more than she would.

'It's a long story,' she said, trying not to sound guilty or defensive, although that was how she felt because she should never have encouraged him to think they might be anything but friends.

'Is he your lover?'

'No! Of course not, Bruno, and how did you hear about it, anyway? It only happened last night.'

'What did?' He sounded bewildered.

'The crash.'

'Crash?' His voice changed. 'What crash? Liza, are you hurt? What happened? I opened the papers this morning and there was a gossip item about you and some man staying at your cottage—a mystery man, they called him, the bastards, and there was some stuff about us, about you and me.' Bruno's voice deepened, roughened. Yes, he had been hurt, she recognised, sighing. 'So what's all this about a crash, and what's it got to do with this guy at your cottage?'

'He isn't, not any more.' Liza explained and Bruno listened, breathing audibly. She didn't know if he was believing her or not because she couldn't see his face, but when she paused for breath he spoke, sounding less distraught.

'Is he still there?' Bruno sounded suspicious even now and Liza sighed.

'No, he left early this morning. The garage came and towed his car away. I hope the bill isn't going to be too enormous, as I'm going to have to pay it.'

'Was it your fault? Can't you say it was all due to this fog?'

'Mist, river mist—and no, Bruno, I can't say that because it wasn't really true. I wasn't looking where I was going, I had too much on my mind.'

'Yes,' he said with a groan, then asked, 'This guy . . . does he live near there?'

'I'm not sure. He looked like a farmer; muddy boots, shabby old clothes—but then he said he was a psychologist.'

'A psychologist! Sounds to me as if he was fantasising.' Bruno sounded worried. 'You know, you should never have let him stay the night. You took an awful risk. He could be a dangerous lunatic.'

'Well, he wasn't and he's gone now, so everything's OK.'

'No, it isn't,' Bruno gloomily told her. 'My mother read the gossip in the paper.'

'Oh, dear,' Liza said weakly, an inadequate response to news that had clearly disturbed Bruno.

'She can be very unreasonable!' he said. 'Now I know

what happened, I can tell her about the mist and the crash, but . . .'

His voice trailed away hopelessly, and Liza could tell that he didn't think his mother would believe a single word of her story. 'Look, Liza, I've had an idea,' he said suddenly. 'If you and my mother could meet, she'd see what you're really like, and she'd stop believing everything she reads in the papers. What are you doing on Sunday afternoon?'

'I'll still be down here. Why?'

'Could you come back to London earlier than usual? On Sunday morning, for instance?'

'I suppose I could—why?'

'On Sunday afternoon we're going to watch a polo match at Windsor. Could you come?'

'Polo?' Liza was intrigued; she had never seen a game of polo. It could be fun, but if she turned up his family were going to believe it was serious between her and Bruno, and what was worse, Bruno would think so too and she did not want that. She did not want Bruno getting any more deeply involved with her; she had to start withdrawing from him, keeping her distance.

'I'm sorry, Bruno, I don't think that's a good idea,' she said. 'I've got to go, Bruno, sorry. I'll see you when I get back to town.'

She said goodbye and ignored his hurried, 'Liza, please come tomorrow, just for an hour.'

'Goodbye, see you,' were her only words before she hung up, then felt mean as she stood there in the silence. She wished she had never let Bruno take her to dinner in the first place; she wished she had never let him into her life, even as a friend, because this was a stupid mess she had got herself into, and it wasn't going to be easy or painless getting herself out.

She put away her purchases in the kitchen and made herself a salad lunch which she ate with the blinds down, because the photographer was hanging around and she did not want to look up and find herself being snapped with a forkful of lettuce half-way to her mouth. She could stay indoors and ignore their noisy comings and goings; from her cottage to the pub and then to the river to check on the latest state of affairs among the anglers and then back to check on her and see if they could persuade her to open the door. She could turn a deaf ear to what they were up to, but the quiet and peace of the cottage was totally shattered. She was irritable and fed up and she couldn't stand any more of it, so in the end she packed her case again, and as soon as the coast was clear she got into her hired car and drove back up to London.

At least nobody would know where she was now. They would all think she was at the cottage, so she might be able to get a few hours peace, which was what she did, from Saturday afternoon until Sunday lunchtime, when Bruno arrived at her flat, flushed and agitated, because he had driven down to Essex to see her, only to find her gone and the cottage empty.

Liza opened the door because she recognised his voice. 'Bruno, what on earth are you doing here?' she asked, letting him walk past while she stared hurriedly around the hallway. 'How did you know I was back?'

That was when he told her that he had been to the cottage, and Liza looked horrified. 'You didn't run into the local press? They didn't get a picture of you at the cottage?'

'No, I met a policeman,' Bruno said. 'Nice chap, he told me he'd seen you driving off and you hadn't been back. I thought he was going to turn nasty at first, because when he saw me hanging around the cottage, banging on the door and peering in the windows, he came over as if he was going to hit me or arrest me or something, but then he apparently recognised me, because he stopped looking ferocious and asked if I was Bruno Gifford and I explained that that wasn't my name, but I was who he thought I was, and then he told me about seeing you leave and I guessed you must have come back to London.' He was breathless and she took him into the kitchen and gave him a chair while she made some coffee.

'Are you OK?' Bruno asked anxiously, looking at her like a worried little boy, and she ruffled his hair and smiled at him although she should have begun her new policy of freezing him off. How could she, though, when he looked so helpless and unsure of himself?

'I'm fine. How about you? Any bruises?'

He seemed baffled. 'Bruises? Why on earth . . .'

'From your family? Did your uncle read you the riot act?'

'He was in one of his dry moods,' Bruno said. 'More in sorrow than in anger, you know the tone. He said it was a pity to get myself into the gossip columns and he asked me if I planned to marry you. He wasn't quite as tough as I'd expected, but my mother was pretty upset. She'd got a crazy idea of you from the newpapers. I told her she just didn't know you and she shouldn't jump to conclusions until she'd met you, but . . .'

The phone rang and Liza handed him his coffee and said, 'Excuse me, I'd better answer that.' He didn't have to finish what he had been saying about his mother, anyway, because she had a shrewd idea that his mother would not want to meet her and did not want to change her ideas about her.

She picked up the phone and said 'Yes?' coldly, hoping

to scare off the Press, if it was them, but the deep, intimate voice at the other end made her pulses leap in shocked surprise.

'Hello, Liza. I rang the cottage, but got no reply so I thought I'd try your London number.'

How had he got it? She had given him her office card with the office telephone number and address, she hadn't told him her London address, and it wasn't in the directory—so how had he got it?

'What do you want?' she asked and he laughed.

'Not very friendly, are you? I've had the estimate on my car—the damage isn't as much as I'd expected. Two hundred pounds, though, I'm afraid. Shall I tell them to go ahead?'

'Of course,' she said offhandedly.

'Right, and I'll send you the bill when it comes.'

'Yes.' She wanted to him to get off the phone, because hearing his voice made her feel hot and cold at once and she was afraid. No, that was an understatement; she was terrified—not of him exactly, but of how he made her feel. If he ever touched her again she had a sinking suspicion that she would go crazy, she wouldn't be able to think straight or stop him. He could make her feelings explode and send her out of control, and she was appalled by how she felt.

She didn't even know him; he was a stranger, a man she'd only spent a few hours with, yet he had somehow managed to pierce her defences, get to her—and she had been so sure she was safe, locked up behind high, icy walls. She hadn't been. He had reminded her of how she had felt once before, when she was young, and hadn't learnt to keep a tight hold on her emotions. She had blazed then, gone up like dry straw when a match is dropped into it. It had been a wild, fierce conflagration for a little while and then she had been left dead and blackened and destroyed, so she had learnt to fear fire and dread emotion.

'What are you doing later on?' he asked softly, a smile in his voice. 'Can I see you?'

Liza was shaking and feverish; she was mentally running, too, getting away from him.

'No, I have a date,' she said. 'I'm going to watch a game of polo.'

Then she hung up and Bruno was standing there watching her, frowning. 'Who was that?' he asked and she shook her head.

'Nobody important,' she said, which was a mistake because her evasiveness made Bruno even more suspicious.

'Did you mean it? Are you coming to watch the polo and meet my mother?' he asked, still frowning, and she sighed and nodded, because it would distract him from asking about Keir Zachary. All she wanted to do was forget she had ever met him.

CHAPTER FOUR

'WHAT'S the time? Only ten past twelve?' Bruno looked surprised. 'I thought it was later. I'm starving—have you had lunch yet?'

Liza shook her head. 'I was going to have a sandwich.'

'Why don't we eat in Windsor? I know a great pub,' Bruno said. 'They do the best roast beef and Yorkshire pudding for miles—out of this world! You'll love it, and I'm ready to eat a horse! I've been driving since early this morning—all the way to Essex and then back again. It seems a century since I had my egg and bacon at breakfast.'

'OK,' said Liza, because she didn't want to argue with him. She was going to have to make a break with Bruno; that was obvious. She had thought of him as a good friend, a playmate, someone to have fun with, but not a man you might ever love, and that wasn't fair to Bruno. He was a man, he wasn't a little boy, and he had feelings, just like anyone else. She had got them into an invidious position; people believed something was going on between them and it wasn't, but she was beginning to realise that Bruno didn't see their relationship in quite the same light as herself. She might have thought of them as just good friends; but what had Bruno thought?

'You'll be nice to my mother, won't you?' Bruno said a little helplessly as he drove along beside the winding river towards Windsor. 'She's really very soft-hearted, but she worries about me. She's got the wrong impression of you, but once she knows you everything will be fine.'

'I'll be very nice,' promised Liza, smiling at him. She had changed before they left; when he'd arrived at her flat she had been wearing casual jeans and a top, which wasn't suitable to wear on a polo ground, not if she wanted to impress the Giffords. She had picked out a cool, summery linen dress, classily styled by a top designer; very simple, very chic. The gentle green of the material flattered her, brightened her eyes; she wore a hat with it, white with a green edging to the brim, and that emphasised her eyes too. In the soft shadow of the hat her eyes took on a vivid glimmer.

'Will your uncle be there?' she asked and Bruno looked surprised.

'He's playing—didn't I say?'

'Playing?' Liza's voice rose in disbelief and Bruno laughed.

'Oh, he's good, very good. He plays like a demon, surely you must have read about his polo? He's one of the best players in the country, and he has a whole stableful of polo ponies. He breeds them.'

'Isn't he a bit old for a rough game like that?'

'I expect he'll give up if he has any more accidents,' admitted Bruno. 'He says his broken bones don't heal as quickly as they did when he was young, but if you're as fit as G. K. you can go on playing polo well into middle age. After all, it's the horse that does all the running about!'

He turned into the forecourt of a large country hotel. There were plenty of other cars parked there and when they entered the bar of the restuarant they saw that the place was packed. They had a drink while they read the menu and chose what they wanted. Bruno had the roast beef; Liza chose salmon hollandaise with a salad. The food was delicious and the restaurant delightful. They sat by an open window looking out into a beautifully maintained garden; the sunny afternoon was full of perfume from roses and carnations and old-fashioned pinks, the gillyflowers of Shakespeare, with their frilly pink petals and clove scent, heady and aromatic. Birds flew and called, the air was warm on Liza's cheek, she relaxed and felt much happier. Bruno was laughing and cheerful; not a trace of sexual awareness in his eyes. She could almost believe that the events of the last few days had never happened and they were the same easy friends they had always been.

'I told you you would love this place, didn't I?' he congratulated himself and she laughed.

'You did and you were right, I do love it.' She hoped it was a good omen; she hoped she was going to like his mother and his demon uncle, too.

'Do you remember your father?' she asked, because she knew Bruno had been very small when his father died.

'Vaguely,' he said. 'In flashes, you know how it is—I have a few clear pictures and a lot of fuzzy ones. My mother married against her family's advice and they never cared much for my father. We didn't see much of them until after he died. In fact, that's my first real memory of G. K. He came to the funeral and he looked terribly grim all in black. He's over six foot and looked taller to me. I was terrified, I didn't understand what was happening and I was miserable. Funny what you remember and what you forget. I don't remember my father dying, but I remember the day he was buried and the day we drove to Hartwell to stay for good. My father had lost all his money; our own house had been sold to pay debts, so we went back to my mother's old home to live. She was never quite the same. I remember her as being very different when my father was alive.'

He had never talked so freely about his family and Liza listened thoughtfully, curious about them all.

'She was happier, I suppose,' she said and Bruno looked at her in surprise, as if he had forgotten she was there. He wasn't the introspective type; he didn't spend too much time worrying about life or brooding over the past. Bruno lived in the present and liked to be happy.

'I suppose so,' he agreed. 'She must have been wild about him, because it certainly isn't in character for her to cut herself off from her family. He had no money, my father, you know. He was no business man; he was charming and good-looking, but he didn't like offices and working for a living. I don't blame him. I probably take after him—I look like him, my mother says. I think that worries her.' Bruno grinned, but his eyes were a little sad. 'She'd rather I took after her side of the family; she'd like me to be like her father or her brother, I suppose, only interested in money!'

'Yet she picked your father, who was nothing like them?' Liza said gently and Bruno looked at her, eyes widening.

'Yes, that's true. Odd, isn't it? Funny business, love.'

'Very funny,' Liza said wryly, but she hadn't found it so. There had been nothing remotely amusing in what happened to her.

'Have you ever been in love like that?' Bruno asked, and in a sense it was a relief to hear him ask that question, because he wouldn't ask it if he thought she was in love with him. Would he?

She looked secretly at him through her lashes, wondering—would he, though? Bruno was a queer mixture of confidence and uncertainty. He seemed so outgoing and assured, yet she knew how easily you could shake that happy confidence of his, it was more than possible that he might hope she cared about him yet not be sure, not ready to risk rejection by being too open.

'Once,' she confessed deliberately and it was the first time she had ever told him, ever told anyone since it happened. 'When I was seventeen,' she said. 'Eight years ago now, a long, long time, but I'm still not ready to have another shot at it. The first time was hell and I'm the cautious type. Once burnt, I definitely fear the fire!'

'Eight years ago?' Bruno queried with a frown. 'You must be over it by now, Liza . . . It isn't someone I know, is it?'

She laughed. 'Good heavens, no! I haven't seen him myself since . . . no, that was another place, another life.'

'Were your parents alive?'

Liza wished she hadn't started talking; hadn't opened this Pandora's box and let out the spectre of her past. There was a lot about her that Bruno did not know and she didn't want to talk about any of it.

'Hadn't we better be moving?' she asked, looking at her watch, and Bruno exclaimed ruefully,

'Oh, God, you're right! They're probably in the middle of the first chukka by now.'

'First what?'

Bruno signalled to the waiter, who brought the bill. As he wrote a cheque Bruno said, 'Haven't you ever been to a game of polo? It isn't very complicated, I'll give you a brief outline of the rules as we go. There aren't many, and I often think they make them up as they go along! Once they're in the mêlée you can't see who hit what, anyway.'

'It's just hockey on horseback, isn't it?' Liza asked as they got back into the car, and Bruno winced.

'Please! Don't say that to my uncle or he may hit you with his mallet.'

'It's already beginning to sound like a dangerous

game,' Liza muttered as they parked and walked along the grass verge towards the polo field near Windsor Great Park. There were crowds of people milling around, but Bruno whisked her through; he was obviously well known there, for officials smiled and nodded. Liza was very nervous. She hadn't been looking forward to meeting Bruno's mother, but she couldn't back out of it now at the eleventh hour, so she let Bruno put an arm around her and lead her forward.

'Mother, this is Liza. Liza, my mother.' He was very formal and very nervous; the back of his neck was dark red and Liza could feel the rigidity of the arm around her waist.

Bruno's nervousness made Liza more nervous too, but she managed a quavering little smile and held out her hand to the woman turning to look at her. Philippa Morris was still beautiful; no question about that. She had blue eyes and dark hair and a long-nosed, faintly haughty face. She looked like a rather beautiful horse, thought Liza, feeling the long, cool fingers touch hers in a well-bred handshake. It was over in a second; the less contact Philippa Morris had with her the better, obviously!

'So you're Liza,' the other woman drawled. 'You look even more lovely in person.'

Liza smiled. 'Thank you.'

'My mother saw your picture in the paper,' Bruno explained and then clearly wished he hadn't reminded his mother about the gossip item.'

'Oh, that nonsense!' Liza said and felt the other woman's quick, narrowed glance.

'Absolute rubbish,' Bruno hurriedly agreed, laughing, then he looked at the field. 'G. K. has got the ball!'

Heads swivelled to watch the field and Liza looked

blankly at the blur of galloping figures, hearing a strange
whirr as a player hit the ball and sent it flying. At first she
couldn't make anything of what was happening, or see
any individual faces; things happened too fast, men bent
and whirled in their saddles, striking at the ball, the long,
twangy handles making an arc as they bent. She saw
polished boots, white breeches, sweating horses and
heard the crowd watching the game shouting, laughing,
yelling encouragement or praise.

'Which one is your uncle?' she whispered to Bruno,
who muttered out of the corner of his mouth.

'On the grey.'

Liza studied the horses; two of them were white, was
that what Bruno meant by grey? But which one was G.
K. Gifford? It shouldn't be hard to guess since there were
only eight men playing altogether, but she was sure none
of them looked old enough. Bruno's uncle was middle-
aged and presumably had grey hair; none of these men
looked much above thirty-five.

Her eye floated from one to the other and froze
suddenly on features she recognised with a blinding
shock.

It couldn't be! All the colour flowed from her face as
her eyes widened until they stretched the skin around
them painfully; her pupils dilated, glowing brilliantly,
black and shiny, and she stared hard as the tall man on
the white horse wheeled and began to gallop after the ball
he had just struck. The others wrenched their mounts
round and followed, jostling him, and Bruno made a
crowing, cheering gurgle.

'G. K. Gifford? She slid a look at Bruno. 'Is that your
uncle? Is that him, the man who just hit the ball?'

'That's him!' Bruno said, exultant, grinning. 'He's a

damn good player—ruthless as hell and faster than lightning!'

'Yes,' Liza said.

'Never misses a trick,' Bruno cheerfully added.

He could say that again, Liza thought with bitter irony. If she had ever seen a photograph of him in the newspapers, she would have recognised him, of course. Bruno had often told her that his uncle hated having his photograph taken, especially by the Press. He loathed personal publicity, would never be interviewed or answer questions by any of the journalists who hung around official functions at which he appeared.

He preferred privacy, Bruno said, and of course he would—it made it easier for him to play his vicious little games, to lie and cheat!

Her throat closed up and she had to bite down on her inner lip not to scream out. She mustn't let it show; Bruno and his mother couldn't know, if he had told them it would show in their faces and there was no awareness there at all.

She kept her eyes fixed on the flying figures, watching his supple body bending and striking. He had lied to her about everything right from the start; made a fool of her, without caring what he did to her, and she hated him, her hands screwed up into fists as she imagined hitting him. If she got hold of one of those twangy cane-handled mallets she would . . .

Bruno looked round, smiling. 'Enjoying it?' Then he did a double-take, staring, and she had to hurriedly change her expression.

'I would if I knew what was happening!' she said, flashing a smile at him.

'Oh, still confused? I thought you were furious about something. You were scowling!'

'Was I? Trying to concentrate, I suppose,' she said lightly, and Bruno gave her a running commentary on the game after that, making it hard for her to think. G. K. Gifford had changed horses; he was riding a big, glossy black now and Liza watched, wishing he would get thrown and trampled by some of those curvetting, skirmishing horses. At the very least she would like to see his crisp white clothes muddy!

The field moved further their way and Liza could see him closer; he was sweating heavily, she saw the damp patch down his side, on his shoulders, and his skin carried a sheen of perspiration, on his face, his neck. The thick black hair glistened with sweat, too. He would have a shower after the game, of course; she stared and suddenly her mind conjured up the image of his naked body under the cool water, the muscled chest and brown skin, black curly hair growing down the centre of his body, above his thighs.

She shut her eyes, shuddering in angry disbelief and recoil—what was she thinking? She was icy cold, yet she felt the trickle of sweat between her breasts and her throat was hot and raw.

She hardly knew what happened after that, but the minutes stretched past endlessly while she wished she could walk away, leave this place, be alone to brood. She couldn't face him; the very thought of meeting his eyes made her shiver.

Then she frowned, pulling herself up—why should she feel ashamed and guilty? Why should *she* want to avoid *him*?

He was the liar and the cheat, not her! She wasn't running away from a confrontation! She'd look him right in the eye and hate him openly. She wanted him to know what she thought of him; not that he would care, of course. He would probably be amused, no doubt he had thought it very clever to lie to her. He'd had his fun and she couldn't do a thing about it.

'Shall we go and have some tea?'

Liza started as Bruno turned to smile at her. She hadn't even realised that the game was over, the players leaving the field to enthusiastic applause, taking off their hard hats and laughing as they chatted to each other. Liza's eye followed G. K. Gifford bitterly.

'He had a good game,' Bruno said to his mother, and Liza listened to them talking about him casually, quite unaware of the explosive feeling Liza was hiding.

'At least he didn't break anything today,' Pippa Morris said, grimacing. 'One day he'll break his neck.'

Oh, please, let me be there! Liza thought, following them slowly through the drifting crowds on their way out of the field. Mrs Morris wasn't heading that way at all, though. She was making for a green marquee. A lot of other people were streaming into it, too, but there were free tables left when Bruno, his mother and Liza arrived.

Under the sloping canvas there was a mingled smell of trampled grass and flowers; tubs of geraniums and hydrangeas, pungent and fragrant, blue and red in white tubs.

Voices rose all around them; people laughed and chattered. Tea arrived; pots of Indian or China tea, cucumber sandwiches, scones and jam, cream, iced fancies or strawberry tarts.

'Where do your family live, Liza?' Pippa Morris asked, offering her a sandwich.

'Liza's parents are dead,' Bruno hurriedly said, his voice heavy with sympathy, and Liza felt herself flushing guiltily because she had never told him that her parents were dead, she had only let him assume it and hadn't corrected his mistake. It was a white lie, a lie of omission; but it was a lie none the less and she ought to say so. She didn't, though, she took a sandwich and ate it in one bite because it was so tiny. Bruno's mother took several and ate them daintily, nibbling.

Liza drank her tea and Mrs Morris asked, 'So you live alone?' and, 'Why did you stop modelling?' and, 'I'm told your agency is very successful.'

Liza answered quietly, accepted a strawberry tart, refused a scone, and watched Bruno's mother with reflective eyes. Mrs Morris was hostile at first, very antagonistic, eyeing her with cold dislike and suspicion, but slowly the ice thawed and she became curious. Perhaps Liza wasn't what she had been told to expect?

By her brother? What had he said about her to his sister? Did Pippa Morris know what he had done? Liza's backbone stiffened at the very idea of that conversation, a flare of red invading her cheeks.

'You built the agency all by yourself? Gracious, how very enterprising of you! Weren't you nervous of losing all your hard-earned money?'

'Terrified,' Liza said lightly, laughing. 'But never venture, never gain!'

Mrs Morris stared, eyes round. 'I suppose you're right, but I think I'd have been more cautious. Why do you think you've been so successful so soon? Because you've been a model yourself?'

'And know my market,' Liza agreed. 'I have high standards for my girls and it soon gets about—clients realise they won't get amateurs and they come back when they're satisfied.'

'Who manages the business for you?'

'I do,' Liza said drily.

'You must be very clever. I don't think I could run a

business.' Mrs Morris watched a newcomer walking to a nearby table and exclaimed, 'Oh, there's Lavender—I must just run and ask her how her daughter is. She's bedbound, you know, poor girl. Keeps miscarrying, so with this one the doctor advised total bed rest until the birth.'

Liza frowned, staring after Mrs Morris. That must be the Countess of Salop's mother. Liza liked the look of her; a small, plump woman in a flowered hat and a flowing pink dress. She had a kind face; her daughter would need that loving kindness. I wonder if she knows about her husband and Tawny? Liza thought grimly. How can he do it?

'Well, what do you think of her?' asked Bruno eagerly.

Liza looked blankly at him for a second, then realised what he meant and smiled back. 'She's not as alarming as I'd expected!'

'It was a bit hairy at first, but you've impressed her,' Bruno nodded. 'She probably envies you—she's never had a job in her life. I think she missed out on a lot, getting married so young and then running Hartwell for G. K.' He grinned at her. 'What about him? What did you think of him?'

Liza took a deep breath—if she told him the truth Bruno would look appalled and she was half tempted to do just that, but before she could open her mouth a voice drawled behind her.

'She seems to be lost for words.'

Bruno looked up and laughed. 'Oh, you changed quickly! Lucky you arrived when you did, before Liza got a chance to commit herself!'

'Isn't it?' the cool voice murmured and Liza felt him walking round her chair, she looked up—a long way up. His blue eyes were bright with mockery. She had been right—he thought it was funny. He was amused and pleased with himself. Damn him, Liza thought angrily. He had come down to check up on her in person; that was why he had been parked right outside her cottage so that she ran into the back of his car in the mist. He had been spying, and she wished she had made a complete write-off of his estate car. She would never have let him into her cottage if she had known his true identity.

'Liza, this is my uncle,' Bruno said. 'G. K., this is Liza.'

Liza considered the extended hand without warmth; for a second she almost didn't take it but at the last instant her nerve failed because she did not want to have any sort of scene. If she told Bruno that his uncle had been the man at her cottage the other night there would undoubtedly be a scene, so she held out her fingers and let his hand grip them, but pulled them away almost at once.

'How do you do, Mr Gifford?'

'Call me Keir,' he said, eyes teasing.

'That's what the K stands for?' she said bitingly.

'That's right. Didn't Bruno tell you?'

'I didn't ask,' she lied, implying that she hadn't been interested enough, but she had asked Bruno once and couldn't remember what he had said. If he had told her, the name hadn't rung any bells, but then why would it? She hadn't been expecting to find his uncle parked outside her cottage in that mist, and a frown pleated her brows as she remembered the way he had looked, the shabby old car he had been driving.

Her eyes ran over him now with angry irony. He looked very different. He had changed out of his polo gear and was elegantly casual in a smoothly tailored summer suit, a silk shirt, a silk tie. He wore them with panache but Liza had liked him better in the old cord trousers and sweater, in his tweed jacket, driving that broken-down old estate car.

'Sit down and have some tea,' Bruno urged and Keir Gifford dropped into a chair, his lean body very relaxed. Bruno tried to signal the waitress, but she had stopped to gossip and ignored him.

'I'll get some fresh tea,' Bruno said, getting up and darting over to get her attention.

Liza was looking down at the trampled grass; it looked mournful and ill-treated and she knew how it felt!

'You're very quiet,' Keir said, and she lifted her head then to eye him with glacial dislike.

'Are you surprised? Don't you *dare* even to talk to me!'

He still looked amused, as though the fury in her voice hadn't had any effect on him, and she broke out again, in a low, shaky whisper, because she didn't want to attract any attention from the tables around them.

'I ought to slap your face! What did you think you were doing? What a charade—the old clothes, the broken-down old car? All the lies you told me! The stuff about being a trained psychologist!'

'I am! That wasn't a lie. I took a degree in psychology.' He had linked his hands behind his gleaming black head and was watching her with narrowed blue eyes, a smile lurking in them, as if she was giving him a lot of entertainment, and Liza bristled from head to toe.

'Oh, I see, that's how bankers train these days? Forget the economics and the business course, the modern way is to study psychology! I suppose the idea is to find out how to talk people into handing their money over!'

'Something like that, but I read economics, too.'

'Did you take a degree in detective work? I'm surprised you didn't put on a false beard—after all, I might have recognised you if I'd seen a photograph in the papers!' She took a deep breath, then suddenly caught

Bruno's eye and stopped, dragging a false smile on to her face. He gave her a thumbs up and grinned encouragingly, apparently under the impression that she and his uncle were getting on like a house on fire. There were flames, all right, but Bruno couldn't be more wrong, otherwise. Keir turned his head to follow the direction of her gaze and Bruno gave him a smile, too, then dived away towards the table where his mother was talking to her friend.

The waitress came over and Keir ordered some more tea and sandwiches. There were plenty of cakes left. Liza sat demurely in silence until the waitress had vanished again; her face ached from the strain of having to smile when she wanted to scream.

'You look very cool and elegant in that dress—I suppose I should say chic, that's the word, isn't it?' Keir said softly and she flashed him a hostile glance through her lashes.

'Funny what a difference clothes make,' she bit out. 'You looked like a scarecrow in the shabby old coat and cords—where on earth did you get them? And the car?'

'You don't think I dress like this when I'm out fishing or shooting?' he asked lazily, watching the waitress laying out the fresh pot of tea, the milk jug, the plate of tiny, bite-sized sandwiches. The woman smiled and Keir smiled back, charm glimmering in those blue eyes. Liza watched bitterly; she had seen that smile, he had turned it on her, and you couldn't trust it. He was a very deceptive man.

When the waitress had gone, he considered Liza again, the glint lingering in his eyes. 'I've had the estate car on my farm for years. It's very handy when I'm driving across country and taking fishing-rods and guns and dogs. Nobody drives a Rolls in muddy boots, you know.'

Liza was not to be coaxed into submission. She snarled at him, 'You lied to me!'

'I'm guilty of a little omission!'

'You lied, Mr *Keir Zachary*!'

'They're both my names—I was given the names George Keir Zachary Gifford, to be precise. As I said, I just omitted a few things. I do have a family farm, for instance.'

'Hartwell!'

'Exactly,' he said, watching Bruno talking to his mother now.

'A country house!'

'With a few farms attached to it!'

'Don't smile,' Liza said furiously. 'It isn't funny, I'm not in the least amused. You deliberately set out to deceive me and I call that lying, whatever you may have told yourself.'

He looked penitent, but his blue eyes were blindingly bright and mocking. 'I'm sorry,' he said in dulcet tones and she screwed her hands up into fists, hissing at him, because she did not want anyone else to overhear.

'You're nothing of the kind! You had a lot of fun at my expense and you're still amusing yourself, but I can't imagine why you were prowling around my cottage, anyway. Surely you weren't that scared about me? I'd have expected you to hire a private detective to check me out, not come all that way yourself! What were you planning to do? You must have had some scheme at the back of your mind. What was it?'

He leaned back on his chair, tilting it, his body totally languid and his eyes half-shut in sleepy amusement. 'I had been visiting friends, just as I told you. As I was staying just outside Maldon it suddenly occurred to me to take a little detour on the way home to Somerset. I drove

over to your village to take a look around, see if I could
pick up some gossip locally. I'd had a report on you,
but . . .'

'You've had me investigated?' Her voice rose and
several people at other tables looked round, eyes startled.

'What else did you expect?' Keir asked in sudden
harshness, his blue eyes surprisingly cold. 'Bruno is my
sister's son and could inherit an enormous fortune one
day—of course we have to protect him, investigate any
stranger he starts to see frequently. Don't be unrealistic,
Liza—money has to protect itself.'

She stared at him numbly, appalled by the new note in
his voice, the ice in his stare. This was the real G. K.
Gifford, the ruthless player of an international game, the
one who meant to win and would ride over anyone who
got in his way. He had pulled the wool over her eyes at
her cottage; charmed and deluded her into thinking he
was someone very different, someone she liked, someone
to whom she was very attracted and above all someone
she might be able to trust in a tight corner. He was none
of those things. He was her enemy, and she must never
lose sight of that fact again.

CHAPTER FIVE

BRUNO came back two minutes later, and as she saw him coming Liza said coolly, 'Well, I must be going, it's getting late.'

'But, Liza, I thought we'd all have dinner,' Bruno said, hearing her, and looking from her to his uncle with dismay.

'That would have been nice, but I must get back,' Liza said, getting to her feet.

'Don't run away,' Keir drawled and Liza picked up the hidden meaning even if Bruno didn't. She could have kicked him, and her green eyes burned secretly behind lowered lashes.

'I can get a taxi, you don't have to tear yourself away,' she told Bruno, not bothering to answer Keir. But of course Bruno insisted on driving her back.

'I must say goodbye to your mother,' Liza said and turned to walk away. Keir said softly, 'See you,' and she answered in a remote tone, 'Goodbye.'

His sister seemed distinctly surprised and unashamedly relieved. She shook hands again and said, 'You're still dining with your uncle, aren't you, Bruno?' in a voice which promised trouble if he did not turn up obediently. Bruno gloomily replied that he would be there.

There were far fewer people in the marquee now; most guests had eaten their tea and left, and many tables were empty. The waitresses were no longer running about like scalded cats, they stood gossiping, watching the ladies in the flowery hats, some famous faces half-hidden by those wide brims, the flash of diamonds and rubies on those fingers as a woman reached for a sandwich, or a cup of tea. Liza felt very out of place, despite her own carefully chosen dress. She could mimic the style, but she knew this was a world to which she did not belong—this was Keir Gifford's world, of money and class, and she was strictly a working girl from nowhere. She had money, but she had earned it herself, and she didn't belong among these girls in pretty, summery dresses with their high, drawling voices and restless eyes. He was right about that. She might resent the idea that he had had her investigated, she might be angry with the arrogance that saw her as a threat and an interloper, but she knew in her heart of hearts that she was uneasy with these people, she did not belong here.

Before they left, she glanced back towards the table where Keir sat and felt an odd little jerk of shock as she saw that he was no longer alone—a tall, slender brunette had taken the chair in which Liza had been sitting. She was wearing a designer dress; Liza recognised the style immediately and priced it with a grimace. An expensive lady! With good taste, thought—Liza wished she could always wear that label; she had one dress made by the guy, but he cost the earth.

The brunette had a hand on Keir's sleeve, her long, coral-tipped nails trailing down his arm as she smiled into his eyes, her face animated. She was beautiful and very sure of herself, and Liza had a feeling she had seen her before, although she couldn't remember where.

'Good lord,' Bruno said, following her eyes. 'There's Louise, talking to G. K., I didn't even know she was back in England!'

'Who?' Liza asked casually and he put a hand under he elbow to guide her out of the marquee, talking as they picked their way through the crowds still drifting towards the exit.

'Louise Bresham, her father's one of our board of directors—well, she isn't Bresham any more, I forget her husband's name. She and my uncle were an item a couple of years ago, all the columns were predicting an engagement, but then she met a South American cattleman and married him out of the blue and went to live in the Argentine. From the way she was looking at G. K. just now she still has a soft spot for him, wouldn't you say? I wonder if she's tired of her marriage? She was always restless. Mind like a grasshopper; kept changing boyfriends and jobs, not that she ever needed to work, she was born with the proverbial silver spoon in her mouth, but of course everyone does get a job when they leave school, they can't just sit about waiting for marriage these days.'

'How old is your uncle?' Liza asked, wondering if she had seen pictures of Louise Bresham in the newspapers at some time in the past. If she had and if Keir Gifford had been in the same photograph, he hadn't impinged upon her memory.

'G. K.'s a good bit younger than my mother,' Bruno said, and she laughed shortly.

'I was beginning to suspect as much!'

'He's thirty-seven, I think—or is it thirty-eight now? He's probably not too keen to tell. It will be funny if Louise does get a divorce and marries him—she came pretty close last time, my mother says. Mind you, G. K. has had several near misses—I can remember several girls who looked like becoming Mrs Gifford for a while, but I think he gets cold feet at the last moment. I suppose you can't blame him; he has a busy social life and women do flock when he's around. Must seem a pity to give all that up to settle down with just one woman.'

Liza settled down in the passenger seat of his car without answering, but all the way back to her flat she kept remembering the way the brunette's hand had strayed possessively along Keir's arm without him doing anything to stop her. Had they been lovers?

What's it to me if they have? she thought aggressively, her green eyes fixed on the road as Bruno drove fast, weaving in and out of traffic. Normally she would have turned a little pale, asked him to slow down, for heaven's sake, was he trying to get killed? Today she hardly noticed; her mind was too busy elsewhere.

He had lied to her so cunningly, so convincingly. Damn him, she thought. Keir Gifford was a bastard; hadn't Bruno more or less warned about that a long time ago? Whenever he mentioned his uncle he added a rider to that effect—G. K. was ruthless, he said. G. K. was a demon polo player, merciless and hard-hitting at play and at work. G. K. had women flocking around him and he wasn't ready to give up his busy love-life for just one woman.

'Sure you won't have dinner?' Bruno asked, pulling up outside her flat, and she shook her head, smiling back. He sighed. 'I wish you'd had more time to talk to my mother. I know you and she would get on once you knew each other.'

'I'm sure we would,' Liza said, forbearing to point out that his mother had got away from her unwanted company as soon as she decently could. Pippa Morris didn't care to know her, thank you very much. She was prejudiced; she had been from the very start, no doubt. She had a simple mind and liked stereotypes; she thought that Liza was an ex-model, a *blonde* ex-model, as Fleet Street loved to say, and Mrs Morris would fight tooth and nail to stop her beloved only son marrying her. Liza could, of course, explain that she had no intention of marrying Bruno, that they were just good friends, platonic friends, but unfortunately Bruno was not being as co-operative in giving that impression as she had hoped. His mother probably wouldn't believe her.

'You did like her, then?' Bruno asked, his face lighting up.

Liza leaned over and kissed him lightly. 'Of course. You're a darling, Bruno, it's been a nice day—see you soon.'

She got out of the car and waved as he drove away. He was looking cheerful. Liza wished she felt as happy as he obviously did, but the events of the day had depressed her. If she had had any inkling of Keir Zachary's real identity, she would never have let Bruno take her to that polo ground, but it was too late to grieve over spilt milk. In a way, it was lucky she had gone—at least she now knew exactly what sort of man Keir was and she would take great care to steer clear of him in future.

She walked into the marble-floored lobby of the Gifford building at the usual time next morning, producing her security card as she passed the uniformed man on the door.

'Miss Thurston?' he asked as if he had never seen her before, and when she looked at his face she realised that he was a stranger. The usual man was standing just behind him looking worried and uneasy.

'Yes,' Liza said, puzzled but polite, imagining that this was some new check to make sure that the security cards were being properly used.

'Will you come with me, please?' The man had hard, direct, searching eyes. He looked like a policeman, which was probably what he was—she knew that most of the security people in the building had been in the police force earlier in their lives.

'Why?' she asked, but instead of answering her the security man gripped her arm in firm fingers and urged her towards a lift.

'It won't take a few mintues, miss. Please come this way.'

Other arrivals turned to stare curiously as Liza was politely hustled across the echoing lobby, and she felt herself flushing in embarrassment. It was stupid, she had done nothing, but she felt guilty and nervous, even frightened, as if she might have committed some crime without knowing about it, and had now been found out.

'Now, look here——' she broke out, pulling herself together as she realised what she was thinking. 'What's this all about, anyway? I haven't got time for some sort of random security check, I'm in a hurry, today is a busy day for me.'

'I'm sorry, miss, but I'm just following orders!' the man said, not releasing her arm as the lift doors closed on them. Liza felt even more nervous as she saw that they were alone; nobody had liked to join them in the lift, although people had been flocking around the lobby. No doubt they had imagined that Liza was being arrested and they weren't sure whether she was armed and dangerous. Did they think she was a terroist? A criminal? Whatever they had thought, they had stayed clear of the lift and stared at her until the doors shut and hid their astonished, wide-eyed faces.

'Where are we going?' Liza asked tensely, her colour high.

The security man didn't answer; the lift was shooting upwards like a bullet from a gun, the floor lights flashing as she watched: tenth floor, fifteenth floor, twentieth floor. Where on earth were they going?

The lift stopped and she was urged out into a deeply carpeted corridor, hushed and reverential, like a cathedral. Liza seemed to have left her stomach behind in the lift; she was hollow and taut with shock. She knew where she was now and she knew who had given the order to grab her and rush her up here.

The security man pushed her into a large office and a woman of late middle years got up from behind a desk, smiling.

'Miss Thurston? Go straight in, he's expecting you.'

Liza walked across the room, head up, back straight, her teeth clamped together and her face burning with rage. How dared he? How dared he?

She heard his voice as she opened the door. He was talking on the phone, his tone brusque. 'Yes, maybe, but that's no excuse!'

His sleek black head lifted as he heard Lisa come in, and he watched her coolly from behind the wide, leather-topped desk at which he sat. She hesitated and he gestured to a chair without speaking.

As she walked across the room she was angrily conscious of his wandering eyes; they were busy talking in the eau-de-Nil two-piece she wore; a tight, lapelled jacket and finely pleated skirt, in silk creêpe which clung to her warm skin, outlining her body. He didn't miss an inch of her; his eyes sliding down her long, smooth legs to her narrow feet in the fragile, white high heels.

'Of course the board didn't lie,' he said curtly, into the phone. 'They simply left out a vital fact or two, and we should have expected that. In their place, I'd have done the same. You shouldn't have got caught out.'

Liza reluctantly sat down, crossing her legs, her throat hot under the permanent, fixed appraisal. She would love to slap his face, but the atmosphere of this long, spacious room weighted heavily on her. It was richly austere; warm, golden panelling, a bowl of white roses, deep chairs with oxblood leather upholstery and a panoramic view of London's skyline. The desk was neatly stacked with files, one of which was open under his elbow; a bank of telephones ranged along one side and on the other stood a console.

He looked different again this morning—not the shabby relaxed man she had met in Essex, nor the powerful sportsman on the polo field. This, finally, was the real man—the G. K. Gifford she had imagined, the man the financial press talked about with such awe and envy, the man who had dreamt up the very building in which they sat, whose companies were far-flung and various, whose private fortune, she had once read in a gossip column, was impossible to calculate.

Here he was, in his own persona at last; remote, powerful, authoritative, icily assured in that expensive tailoring, the dark, pin-striped city suit with a tight-fitting waistcoat and a blue and white striped shirt, the dark blue silk tie with the tiny silver emblem on it. A club tie, no doubt; she couldn't quite work out what the emblem was supposed to be—it seemed to be some sort of bird in flight.

The clothes in this case were a form of armour; formal and distancing, proclaiming his authority and keeping you in your place. His face was closely shaven, his hair glossy, his blue eyes half veiled by drooping lids, but they were still flicking over her, almost absently, as if he didn't realise he was staring.

'I want this tidied up, and *soon*,' he said in a voice which left no room for discussion. 'Too much time has been wasted, don't waste any more. I'll expect to hear from you before the end of the week.'

He put the phone down and laid his hands flat on the desk, smiling at her,

'Sorry about that. It was an important call.'

'Oh, I understand about business calls,' Liza said bitingly, without smiling back. 'I have important business waiting for me in my own office.' Her voice hardened, lifted angrily. 'So why was I dragged up here? No explanations, just some goon grabbing my arm and hauling me into the lift while everyone in the lobby stared and probably thought I was being arrested. I got that impression myself! What do you want, Mr Gifford?'

He leaned back, his long fingers tapping on the desk in an impatient rhythm. 'I apologise if you were embarrassed or alarmed . . .'

'Thank you,' she said with icy dismissal, and rose to her feet.

'Sit down!'

The voice was like the crack of a whip and she sank back into her chair automatically, then flushed and gave him a furious look.

'I have better things to do with my time than . . .'

'I'm sending Bruno to the States,' he interrupted tersely.

Liza's mouth froze, parted but silent.

He got up and walked to the enormous window, stared out with his back to her.

'For two years,' he said.

Liza got her breath back and laughed angrily. 'Because of me? You're sending him to the States for two years to get him away from me? I suppose I ought to be flattered that you think me such a threat, but it's ludicrous, crazy.' She thought about it, watching his long, smooth back in the expensive suit. Oh, yes, it was armour—and this was war, a conflict he had every intention of winning.

'I didn't say I thought you were a threat!' He still didn't turn round. He put one hand flat on the glass, his fingers spread wide, his lean body taut and there was a faint reflection of his face on the window as he shifted.

'Oh, of course not!' she snapped. 'Your decision has nothing whatever to do with me, does it? So why are you telling me about it?'

He was silent for a moment, leaning forward to stare downwards, and Liza had to look away, shuddering, because she got vertigo if she ever looked down from a great height. It made her feel as if the street was rushing up to meet her or she was falling helplessly down through empty air towards the toy cars and the antlike people far below.

'You know I'm sending him away because of you,' Keir said harshly, and she bit down on her lip, both angry and strangely excited.

She had made quite an impact of his exclusive, protected world. She had him running scared, scrambling to whisk Bruno out of her proximity before it was too late. It was a backhanded compliment, but she couldn't help a twinge of triumph. She had never seen herself as a *femme fatale* before; it was an intriguing role.

'I'm tempted to marry Bruno just to teach you a lesson,' she told Keir and he turned then, his blue eyes dark with emotion.

'I wouldn't let that happen!'

'You couldn't stop us—Bruno's over twenty-one, he isn't a child.'

'You aren't in love with him!' Keir took a step and she suddenly began to tremble as it dawned on her that she had misread what was being said, misunderstood what was happening.

She scrambled out of her chair and headed for the door, feeling frightened, although she couldn't quite put into words what was alarming her. Keir crossed the room much faster, with long-legged strides, and caught her before she was half-way across the carpet.

'You aren't seeing Bruno again,' he told her as his hand fell on her shoulder and whirled her to face him.

She slapped his arm down, hoarsely muttering, 'Don't touch me!'

'Not yet,' Keir said and her ears buzzed with hypertension. What was going on? What did he really mean?

'You can't stop me seeing Bruno,' she said and he laughed without bothering to answer, because he could and they both knew it. Liza had a drowning feeling; her head was whirling.

'Have you told Bruno?'

'Last night,' he said curtly.

'That you're sending him to the States and . . .'

'That you're not for him,' Keir said, and although he wasn't touching her she felt his stare like burn marks on her skin. He watched her, waiting, not smiling, almost grave and she tried not to believe he meant this, but knew he did.

'You have no right to decide whether Bruno and I could be happy!' She was arguing about it, although she had never had any intention of marrying Bruno, it hadn't crossed her mind, she had always known that Bruno wasn't someone she could love like that. She wasn't going to tell Keir that, though.

'He's leaving at the end of the week and I want your promise that you won't see him.'

'I'm not promising you anything!'

He gripped her wrist and twisted her arm behind her back. Pulling her close to him, his face lowered just inches from hers, those blue eyes staring fiercely at her.

'You will,' he said softly, so softly she had to watch his mouth to read the words. 'You'll promise me here and now.'

'Get your hands off me,' she muttered, writhing in his grasp, but that only made her more aware of the firm muscle and flesh clamped against her body. She could hear him breathing, her eyes were on a level with his mouth and she could see a tiny muscle jerking beside his lips. Keir was angry, tense.

'Bruno didn't dine with us last night, although he'd promised to,' he said. 'Did he stay with you last night? Until the early hours?'

She shook her head.

'Don't lie to me,' Keir said furiously, his skin dark red now. 'I'd begun to think I was wrong about you—you just didn't seem the sort of gold-digger my sister said you were.' His blue eyes were hard and remorseless, lashing her with contempt, making her wince. 'I thought I was being very clever, meeting you without telling you who I was, getting to know you when you didn't have a chance to put on an act, but you still managed to fool me, didn't you?' He glared at her. 'I rang Bruno at midnight. There was no answer, was there? He wasn't in his flat and he didn't answer his phone until after two in the morning—so what the hell were you two doing until then?' He laughed harshly. 'That was a rhetorical question! I don't need to be told!'

Liza frowned, completely taken aback. Where on earth had Bruno gone after he dropped her back at her flat? She had taken it for granted that he was going to have dinner with his mother. Mrs Morris had reminded him that that was what he had promised to do, and Bruno hadn't breathed a word of going anywhere else.

'What did Bruno say when you rang him?' she asked slowly.

'You want to make your story fit his, is that it?' Keir said cynically. 'Oh, no, we aren't playing games. I want the truth, Liza.' He moved his hand, gripping her fiercely by that tethered wrist, while his other hand caught her chin and pushed it backwards so that she had to stare up at him or shut her eyes.

'Tell me, damn you!' he said, his face hard and cold.

Her mouth was dry with fear. If she had ever wondered just how menacing Keir Gifford could be, she knew now. He was an adversary to be wary of, but she was trapped. She couldn't avoid this intolerable physical intimacy, and although she fought not to let it show she was icy and her stomach had butterflies.

The only way she could fight back was to attack; wasn't that the best defence?

'Who the hell do you think you are?' she snapped, and was relieved to find her voice steady, amazingly, almost normal. 'Don't you manhandle me, Mr Gifford! What are you going to do if I don't tell you what you want to know? Beat me up?'

'No,' he said, staring down at her, his blue eyes glittering, compelling, making her face burn hotter. 'I don't know what the hell I *am* going to do about you, Liza! All I do know is that I don't want Bruno anywhere near you!'

She took a long fierce breath, staring angrily. 'Do you realise how insulting you are? You may not think I'm good enough to marry into your family, but . . .'

'Has Bruno proposed to you?'

'If he had, that wouldn't be your business!'

'I won't have it,' Keir grated and she stared incredulously.

'*You* won't have it? You can't do anything to stop it— we're both over twenty-one and . . .'

She never finished that sentence. His mouth came down, crushing and barbaric, as if he wanted to hurt her, hated her—and yet at the same time with a wild sensuality that made her give at the knees. She put her hands on his shoulders to push him away, but her mouth clung and she shuddered in excited pleasure which was bitterly familiar. She had felt like this before! Her body had betrayed her, given in to this sweet delirium which made it so easy to forget everything else.

She broke free of it, shoving him away at the same time. 'Don't you . . .' Her voice broke and then she forced the rest of the words out, '*Ever* touch me again!'

Keir stared at her; his blue eyes seeming blind, dazed. 'Liza', he said hoarsely, reaching for her and a note in his voice made her head spin. This was no game, no pretence—he wanted her and she hated her own weakness as she felt her senses jangle in response. She wanted him, but she couldn't lose control of herself again. Last time she had been hurt so badly. This time she had far more to lose; she knew the world now. She knew what could happen—she was no longer a romantic, wide-eyed adolescent; she was a hard-headed business woman who had fought her way to the top and meant to stay there. No man was muscling his way into her life again, or wrecking it for her. She was free, independent and safe, and she meant to stay that way.

Keir Gifford was a hardened campaigner; a lifetime bachelor who had had a lot of women in his life and always got away before they nailed him. He might want her, but he wasn't telling her that she was the love of his life. He wasn't offering her his heart—just his body, and she had never descended to one of those loveless affairs. aShe was fraid to risk loving, but she wouldn't risk an affair without it, either.

'No,' she said, and balling her hand into a fist, hit him in the stomach before he had any idea what she meant to do.

Keir instinctively doubled up at the blow, giving a winded gasp, and Liza pushed him violently before he could recover.

He crashed backwards and hit the desk, and while Liza had him off balance she ran—unashamedly ran. The door slammed behind her and she felt heads lift, eyes stare, but nobody stopped her as she pelted for the lift.

CHAPTER SIX

LIZA rang Bruno from her office, but there was no reply, either at his flat or in his own office. She persevered and finally got hold of his secretary, who sounded flustered and busy.

'I'm sorry, I'm afraid Mr Morris isn't here, he isn't at work today. He has been transferred to New York and is busy making all his arrangements.'

Liza hadn't identified herself other than to say that she was one of the Gifford clients, in case Keir had given Bruno's secretary instructions not to pass on any information to her.

Casually, she murmured, 'He's at his mother's, is he?' and the woman admitted it.

'I'm afraid I must go, so much to do, such short notice. Sorry.' The secretary rang off and Liza slowly hung up, biting her lower lip. She didn't quite dare risk ringing Mrs Morris's number, and if Bruno had been ordered not to see her by his uncle he might well be too worried to disobey. She didn't want to cause any more trouble for Bruno. How would he feel about a transfer to New York? Would he feel exiled or be delighted? She wasn't sure. Bruno liked America and had often visited it, but would he want to live there for two years?

The console on her desk buzzed and she jumped, completely taken by surprise. It was half a minute before she groped for the switch and said, 'Yes, Maddie?'

'Nicky Wallis is here,' Maddie said, her voice cool and expressionless. Liza could imagine the face that went with that tone. Maddie did not like Nicky Wallis and had a hard time hiding the fact. He was a very successful photographer and a very good-looking man; the agency couldn't afford to offend him because he had marvellous contacts, a great reputation and a book full of highly paid jobs. The agency models were always ready to work for him because he paid them well, but Nicky Wallis was a dedicated philanderer and more than one of their girls had got badly hurt from falling for him. Maddie icily disapproved of him and had often said that she wished Liza would strike him off their list and refuse the work he offered their girls.

Wryly, Liza said, 'Send him in, Maddie.'

There was an irritated click and then Liza's door opened. She swung in her chair, her hands on her desk, smiling politely.

'Hello, Nicky. What are you bringing us today?'

He came sauntering over, lithe as a mountain cat in striped black and yellow cotton jeans with a sleeveless black vest top. He was forty if he was a day, but he dressed like a teenager; even his footwear was adolescent, striking black and yellow sports trainers on which he bounced lightly to curl up on the side of her desk, his knees bent upward and his arms clasping them, his chin tucked over them and his dark eyes gazing soulfully at Liza across the desk.

'You look cool and sexy as usual!'

'I wonder if your mother was frightened by Peter Pan before you were born?' Liza grinned as she spoke, but it wasn't entirely a joke.

Nicky liked the idea; his face gleamed. 'I may quote you.'

Liza leaned back to avoid the hand sneaking over the desk towards hers.

'Coffee?'

'Black, no sugar.' Nicky put his hands up, thumbs together, framing her, peering through the square he had made at her.

'Coffee, Maddie—black,' Liza said crisply and her secretary's voice glumly promised to make some.

'You know, you were crazy to retire so soon—you could have been working all these years, they would have been your prime,' Nicky said.

'It was no job for an adult.'

'And playing desk jockey—is that an adult job?' Briefly, Nicky's dark eyes were contemptuous.

'It beats standing about in ridiculous poses for hours on end, anyway.'

Maddie came in with the coffee, eyeing Nicky Wallis coldly. 'Are you going to drink it sitting there like a monkey on a stick?' she enquired and he took the cup and blew her a kiss.

'Nasty old witch,' he said as Maddie closed the door, and Liza looked down at her own coffee, frowning. She was very fond of Maddie. She didn't say anything, though, because Maddie knew better than to snap at a client. Right or wrong, Nicky Wallis brought the agency jobs they needed, and Maddie ought to guard her tongue.

'I could use you for this job, actually,' Nick thought aloud, one eye on Liza.

'What job?' Liza asked, as he had intended, aware of what he was up to—he always insisted on playing one of these delaying games each time he asked them for a model. He enjoyed the sense of power he got from being able to bring them work, partly because he was the sort of man who loved playing games and partly because he had a personal reason for needling Liza.

Nicky had been one of the first photographers Liza

ever worked with. She had been very young and green, and he had made a pass at her. It had got him nowhere; Liza was already immunised, and the last thing she wanted was to have a man touch her. Funnily enough, her success in modelling sprang from her icy distaste about men—she hardly remembered anything of those first months in the job. She had been one of the walking wounded; so numb with despair and cauterised by pain that she just went through the motions without really knowing what happened around her. She had obeyed like an automaton; photographers had loved it. Her body was graceful and supple, they could move her like a bendy doll and she would stay where they'd put her. Yet her green eyes had been remote and distant; as if a fine gauze curtain fell over them. Her face had been haunted and haunting; fragile bones and drifting nets of golden hair, a tremulous, hurt mouth, a pale and translucent skin.

Nicky had been very excited by her, he couldn't keep his hands to himself. Liza had permitted the touching if she felt that it was professionally necessary, but when he started enjoying himself she slapped his hands away and said that if he touched her like that again she was leaving and she wouldn't be back.

Nicky had looked astounded, incredulous, visibly unsure whether or not this was a bluff, torn between bowing to her ultimatum or telling her to go then, see if he cared!

In the end he had held up his hands, ostentatiously, stepping back. 'OK, sweetheart! If it *bothers* you!'

'It annoys me!' Liza had snapped. 'I pick my own men, thanks!'

Nicky had resented her ever since, but he was good at hiding his feelings behind a beaming smile, and his

innate sense of professional common sense had made
sure that not only did he go on using Liza as a model but,
when she started her agency, Nicky immediately became
one of their clients. Liza was aware that he could have
tried to freeze her out; influencing potential customers
into going elsewhere, spreading malicious gossip, running down her models. There were a hundred and one
ways of wrecking a business as vulnerable as a model
agency, but Nicky hadn't taken any of them and Liza
had learnt to respect his professional standards.

She didn't like him any better, and she didn't kid
herself that he had changed. Given a chance, he would
make a pass, but she never gave him any encouragement.

Now, he told her about the offer he was bringing the
agency, stressing the fact that she was only getting it
through him.

'Interested?'

'Very,' she said, because the job was a long-term one,
not a one-off session for a magazine or fashion house, but
an advertising campaign for a new range of cosmetics.

'They're not using TV at first, that may come later, but
it's an expensive medium. For the moment, it will be
newspaper and magazines, plus small posters for
hoardings.' Nicky outlined the campaign plan, his chin
on his knees, and Liza got up and wandered around the
office, listening intently. He hadn't yet mentioned
money, but she sensed it was going to be a high-paying
project and she was excited. She forgot to keep out of
Nicky's reach and suddenly found his arm snaking out to
capture her.

'Let go,' she said wearily, throwing back her head and
looking at him with cool distaste. 'Don't you ever give
up?'

'Not me, babe,' he said, bending his head to kiss her,

and Liza put her hand on his shoulder to thrust him away.

The door opened behind them and Nicky raised his head again, staring. 'I didn't hear a knock,' he snapped.

Liza freed herself to look round and was stunned to see Bruno in the doorway, rather flushed and frowning.

'I've been trying to ring you!' she said in a husky voice as he began backing out, mumbling something incoherent. 'No, don't go, Bruno, I have to talk to you.' She glanced at Nicky. 'Could we go on with our discussion some other time?'

He was furious, but he turned a wolfish grin on her. 'With discussions like that, any time, darling,' he murmured deliberately as he sprang down from the desk, catlike and graceful, dancing out of the office. As he passed Bruno Liza felt the back of her neck turn cold. Bruno wanted to hit him, she saw his fists curl angrily and so did Nicky, but it didn't alarm him, he just leered at Bruno and vanished. He knew that she had been seeing Bruno, he must have read the gossip columns— was that why he had just made another pass? Had he been trying his luck again because he hoped she might be more ready to respond?

'Who's that?' Bruno asked, coming over to face her as the door shut behind Nicky. 'Arrogant bastard, why was he sneering at me like that?'

'He's Nicky Wallis,' Liza said absently, already forgetting Nicky as she looked at Bruno and wondered if he was angry with her because he was being sent off to the States to part them.

'Who?' Bruno certainly looked grim enough; his lower lip was pouting as if he was about to cry.

'He's a famous photographer.'

'Oh, one of those!' Bruno glowered at her. 'He was

kissing you—are you dating him?'

'No, I've spent the past seven years trying to keep his tentacles off me,' Liza said drily. 'He never stops trying, that's all.' She smiled at Bruno coaxingly. 'Are you OK? You look fraught.'

'I'm not sure whether I'm on my head or my heels,' he said. 'G. K. said he'd tell you himself. Did he? You know he's sending me to New York?'

She nodded, watching him. 'How do you feel about it?'

'It's damned good promotion,' Bruno said, but he sounded uncertain, which in her experience of him meant that he was nervous and far from happy. 'I hope I can handle it. He's putting me on probation—a three month's trial, and if I can't cope he'll move me elsewhere.'

'You'll cope,' Liza said firmly.

'Think so?' Bruno looked eagerly, hopefully at her. He needed a constant injection of reassurance, and she couldn't help worrying about how he would manage in America, away from his friends and family. Bruno was a soft-centred creature, he had no shell to protect him, unlike a guy like Nicky Wallis, who was as tough as leather and thick-skinned into the bargain.

'I'm sure of it,' she stressed.

Bruno sighed. 'I'm going to miss you,' he murmured naïvely and she laughed.

'I mean it,' he insisted, then his face changed and he watched her with curiosity. 'Did my uncle ring you or come here in person? I was taken aback when he said he would deal with you himself. He wasn't objectionable, was he?' He had turned red. 'I mean, he didn't insult you? My mother seems to think that you . . . that we . . . well, she's been nagging G. K. and he always tries to keep her happy. He told me not to see you again, but of course

I'm not letting him dictate to me! I had to come and say goodbye and explain.' He looked down, his eyes shifty, the back of his neck brick-red. 'I wouldn't want you to think . . . that is, the way G. K. was talking, I started to wonder if you thought the same as him! If you were expecting me to ask you to . . .' He broke off, gulping like an agitated bullfrog. 'But I didn't think . . . that is, it wasn't that serious, was it? I mean . . .'

'I know what you mean,' Liza said solemnly. 'And it wasn't serious, Bruno; it was fun and I loved every minute of it, but that was all it was—just fun.'

He gave a heavy sigh of relief, grinning at her. 'Well, that's what I thought, but G. K. had me almost convinced—it's like being hypnotised by a snake that means to eat you. My blood ran cold, but I couldn't get the words out.'

'About last night?' Liza wondered if he had been with someone else last night, especially when she saw the guilty uneasiness in his flushed face.

'He mentioned that?'

'I told him you weren't here.' She held his eyes. 'What did *you* tell him?'

'Well, I couldn't, he'd have stepped on my neck! You wouldn't believe how nasty he can get.'

'I would.'

Bruno shifted restlessly. 'If I tell you, you wouldn't tell him? He'd kill me, Liza.'

'I won't tell a soul.' But she was dying with curiosity— what could Bruno have been doing that made him so frightened of his uncle finding out?

'It just happened, Liza, honestly! I went back to my flat to change after I'd dropped you off and on the way I ran into a guy who was at school with me. Last I heard, he was working in Africa, managing a tea plantation. Two years since I'd seen him, so we went to have a drink—we had a lot of catching up to do, and one thing led to another and . . .' His voice trailed away and he gave her a sheepish look. 'Well, we ended up in this club in Soho.'

'Gambling?' Liza guessed wryly. Keir Gifford wouldn't like that! Bruno was quite right.

'Not exactly,' Bruno said, very pink around the ears. 'It . . . was a strip club, actually.'

She stared and started to laugh. 'Oh, Bruno!'

'G. K. wouldn't have been amused,' Bruno said.

'No, I suppose not,' she conceded.

'He always says it's too risky for people like us to go into that part of London—too many chances of meeting the wrong kind of people, running into blackmail or some sort of trouble.'

Liza could see Keir's point; anyone from the criminal world who recognised one of the Gifford clan out on a spree might be tempted to make something out of it. She frowned, then; wasn't that what he had thought of her? That she was using Bruno, taking advantage of him?

Then she saw the look on Bruno's flushed face and her brows went up.

'There's more?'

Bruno pulled a face. 'Well, it was my friend, not me— he had one too many and there was a fight over this girl and we both got chucked out. Luckily, nobody knew our names and there were no reporters around. I got him into a taxi and saw him back to his hotel and went home, and I was just going to bed when G. K. rang. He came round and I'd sobered up a bit by then; put my head under a tap and drunk a few black coffees, but I looked a bit of a shambles and G. K. was so furious I simply couldn't tell him where I'd really been. I'm sorry, Liza.'

His penitence was only skin deep, she realised, gazing

wryly at him. Bruno was spoilt and selfish and had taken the easy way out yet again. He wasn't going to change; he would always take the easy road, and she hoped G. K. Gifford knew what he was doing sending his nephew off to New York alone. That city was full of temptations for reckless, spoilt young men with too much money. The Giffords might well end up wishing they had let him marry her!

Bruno sighed. 'You know, I'm going to miss you a hell of a lot, Liza. New York's a long way off and it's a very big city. I'll be lonely over there.'

'You'll find a new playmate,' Liza said, grinning at him, unmoved by his soulful look. She knew he would always make sure he enjoyed his life; Bruno was not the serious type.

'Before I go, why don't we . . .' Bruno began then lifted his head to look round, his face startled, as they both heard an angry outburst from the office in which Maddie sat.

'No, you can't go in there!' Maddie was saying fiercely and they heard a struggle right outside the door. The handle turned noisily, a body crashed against the wooden panels.

'What on earth?' Bruno muttered and Liza got up from her desk, but before she could cross the office to ask Maddie what was going on in the outer room, the door was flung open and Maddie fell inwards, still clutching the handle.

Bruno gave a strangled yelp and Liza went pale and then red with fury as she saw G. K. Gifford in the doorway.

'He forced his way in,' Maddie was spluttering as she straightened and began tidying her dress and hair with shaky hands. 'Shall I call security? He wouldn't give a name or wait, and he stopped me using the console to tell you he was here. I think he's crazy. I'd better get security up here right away!'

'That's OK, Maddie,' Liza said tersely, her mouth level and angry. 'I know him.'

'You do?' Maddie seemed incredulous, she gave Keir a stare of intense dislike. 'He's too damn sure of himself, pushing me around like that, giving me orders. Who does he think he is?'

'He knows who he is,' Liza said icily. 'He's G. K. Gifford and he owns this whole building, if you remember, Maddie.'

Her secretary's mouth opened as far as it would go and stayed like it. A thin, high keening issued from her.

'Gifford?' she seemed to be repeating.

'G. K. Gifford,' Liza stressed. 'Remember the face, Maddie. If he ever comes here again warn me before he can get anywhere near the door.'

Maddie nodded violently, backing, staring at Keir, her mouth still wide open in amazement. He stood back to let her leave the office, ostentatiously holding the door open for her in a mimicry of gallantry, his smile dry and sardonic.

'I should close your mouth soon or you may get stuck like that,' he drawled pleasantly, and Maddie's eyes rolled furiously, but he shut the door on her before she could burst out with whatever she had been trying to say.

Bruno had retreated as far away from his uncle as he could. He was not merely behind Liza, he was trying to hide behind the long velvet curtains at her window.

Keir swivelled slowly and surveyed them both with a frozen stare. The fact that he was smiling, too, made his icy rage the more alarming.

'I thought I told you not to see her before you left?' he asked Bruno.

'What are you doing here?' Liza demanded without giving Bruno time to think up a reply to that.

Keir's eyes flicked back to her face and she had a hard time not flinching.

'I was told Bruno had entered the building,' he began and she snapped back.

'Who told you?'

'Security,' he admitted irritably.

'You'd asked them to let you know if he arrived?'

'Yes.'

'Spying on him? My God, how low can you stoop?'

Keir didn't like that. 'I didn't trust him to keep his word,' he said harshly. 'And I was quite right not to, wasn't I? The minute he got the chance he was sneaking up here to see you.'

Bruno made unhappy noises and that attracted Keir's attention to him again. Bruno fell silent, shrinking, as the deadly blue eyes flashed towards him, and Liza felt very sorry for him.

'He just wanted to say goodbye!' she said hurriedly and Keir looked back at her.

'Well, he's had plenty of time to say it, so he can get out.' He swung back to Bruno and his voice cracked like a whip. 'Did you hear what I said? Get out, and in future stay away from her!'

Bruno threw Liza a flustered, uncertain look, shrugged, said, 'See you, Liza, I mean, goodbye, Liza, thanks for . . .' then almost tripped up in his haste to get out of the room.

Liza looked at Keir with bitter dislike as the door closed again. 'Does that make you feel big? Scaring him half to death like that? You bully!'

'Are you in love with him?' Keir asked and she looked up to find those violent blue eyes fixed on her face, searching, probing.

'That has nothing to do with you!' she retorted, dragging her eyes away.

'*Was* he with you last night?' The question was like a steel needle under her skin; she winced at the sharpness of it.

'I'm not going to tell you!' She couldn't betray Bruno's confidence and, anyway, now that she had seen for herself how Keir treated Bruno she could understand exactly why Bruno was afraid to tell his uncle about his little escapade in Soho. Could one blame him? No wonder Bruno was in a state of arrested adolescence! He had never been given a chance to grow up.

'Why don't you let Bruno run his own life for a change?' she asked Keir bitingly. 'Nobody learns anything from being told about other people's mistakes—they only learn from their own, and if Bruno can't be trusted it may be because you've never trusted him. Had you thought of that? You're like a gardener who keeps digging up the bulbs to see how they're growing and then complains because they aren't growing at all!'

Keir stared, his face blank. He obviously wasn't going to listen to her and she gave an angry shrug.

'Oh, what's the point? I'm sorry for Bruno, but it really isn't my business. Now, will you go, Mr Gifford? I have work to do.'

He walked slowly to the door and Liza sat down behind her desk and opened one of the leather-bound files, glancing down at the typed pages although she wasn't able to read a word because all her attention was fixed on Keir Gifford, waiting tensely for him to leave.

He opened the door, then paused and looked back at

her. 'You really think Bruno might respond to a little less supervision? Or are you just making excuses for him?'

'Try it and see,' Liza said with cool indifference without looking up. She flicked a page and pretended to read, but was very aware of him watching her.

'I wish I could work you out,' he said abruptly. 'I can't believe you're serious about Bruno. He's a chump!'

She laughed, looking up, her mouth softening. 'A nice chump, though!'

His face relaxed a little, too. 'OK, a nice one, but a chump, all the same! So why do you keep on dating him, if it isn't for the money?'

'It couldn't be because I'm fond of him?' she asked drily and his blue eyes kept watching her, trying to read her face.

'Is that all it is? But for a long time there hasn't been anyone else in your life—you've just seen Bruno, and you can't tell me that other men haven't shown an interest because I wouldn't believe it. You must have queues of men trying to date you.'

'I like an uncomplicated life,' she said lightly. 'Look, for absolutely the last time—I do not want to marry Bruno, I've no intention of marrying him and never had. But I'm fond of him and he's fun, which is why I went on seeing him. Bruno is my friend—is that so hard to understand, Mr Gifford? Can't men and women ever be friends, with no strings attached?'

'Why no other men, though?' Keir persisted and she sighed.

'I'm not looking for love and marriage, Mr Gifford. I'm too busy trying to run my company, when you're not interrupting me!'

The console buzzed and she flicked the switch and asked, 'Yes, Maddie?'

'Nicky Wallis on the line again,' Maddie's tinny voice said. 'Any message? He says it's urgent, he must talk to you.'

'OK, Maddie, put him on when I buzz.' Liza glanced across the office at Keir, her face coolly polite. 'Now, will you excuse me? This may be an important call and I have a busy schedule today.'

He considered her with his head slightly to one side and his smile crooked. 'You're quite something, Liza,' he said, and then he turned and went and Liza stared at where he had been and felt her heart going like a steam train. It took quite an effort to snap herself out of it and buzz for Maddie to put Nicky Wallis through.

'What can I do for you, Nicky?' she asked unwisely and Nicky chuckled.

'You know the answer to that, darling, but I'll settle for lunch to talk over this new contract. I've been talking to Terry, and the advertising agency definitely wants a new face.'

'Talk to Maddie and she'll give you a date. Sorry, Nicky, but I've got a string of people waiting to see me.' She hung up and Maddie came into the room, eyeing her oddly.

'Ready to start work now? Your appointments have been shot to pieces. Even if you rush each one you'll never get through them all.'

'I'll work through my lunch hour—oh, no, I've got a lunch booked with the editor of that new women's magazine!'

'I've cancelled it,' Maddie said briskly.

'My God, Maddie, why on earth did you do that? She'll be offended and . . .'

'She wasn't offended. I explained there was a sudden crisis and asked her to have lunch at the Savoy next

Wednesday—that was the first free day available in your diary.'

Liza's fraught expression dissolved into a smile. 'The Savoy?'

'I thought we could run to it in the circs,' Maddie said demurely and Liza laughed.

'What would I do without you? Anything else I ought to know?'

'Yes, I've sent down for some cottage cheese, fruit and coffee,' Maddie said, consulting the notebook she carried to check the details. She looked up impishly. 'For your lunch while you go through today's modelling schedule with me, and then dictate a few letters. Oh, and by the way, I slotted Nicky Wallis into a lunch date next Friday—from one till two. I explained that you always left early on a Friday.'

Liza laughed again, then winced—she was still suffering from the after-effects of the last weekend. She wasn't sure she felt like going down to the cottage again for a little while.

'Now, I'll send in your first appointment,' Maddie added. 'Poor girl, she's been waiting for almost two hours.'

Liza groaned. 'This has been one hell of a morning!'

CHAPTER SEVEN

As Liza was about to leave that evening, one of her top models arrived, wearing a very large diamond on her left hand, and all the other girls crowded round her to admire her ring, kiss her, offer their congratulations. Liza opened some champagne from the office fridge.

'I'm afraid I shall be leaving,' Karen told Liza a little while later. 'We're going back to Brazil to his family farm. He doesn't like it here.'

Under her smile Liza was faintly depressed—Karen was at her earning peak and Liza would be very sorry to lose her, but there was more to it than that. She couldn't help envying Karen; she looked so happy and so carefree, so much in love.

They all wished Karen good luck and then she dashed off to celebrate with her family. Liza was about to put the remaining unopened bottle of champagne back into the fridge when she changed her mind and took it home with her, thinking that Bruno might call in before he left and they could toast his new life in America.

The flat seemed very empty, very chilly. She sat curled up on the sofa, her knees bent up and her chin on them, brooding over the strange sadness which seemed to be hovering around her. She couldn't think why she felt so lonely, so blank, and she wished she would stop thinking about Keir Gifford. He kept answering into her head; he was haunting her!

She hadn't eaten and tried to distract herself by considering whether or not to go into the kitchen to find food, but while she was thinking about that her eye fell on the bottle of champagne which she had put down on the table when she arrived.

That was what she needed—something to cheer herself up! She might forget her fury with Keir Gifford and her sudden realisation of how lonely her empty flat could be—she had never felt lonely there before. It was stupid to let the news of Karen's engagement get to her like that! It was hardly the first time one of her girls had got married; in fact, it often happened, since in modelling they rapidly picked up admirers. Marriage did not necessarily follow, but four of her girls had got married since she started the agency, and she couldn't recall feeling this depressed before.

What the hell is the matter with me? she asked herself, uncoiling to pick up the bottle of champagne and carry it to the kitchen to open it. I've got everything I've ever wanted: a fascinating career, a lovely home, a boat, a car. She found a champagne glass, slowly eased the cork out of the bottle in the manner she had noticed waiters using, and poured a bubbly glass. It was warm, but she didn't care.

She raised the glass angrily to the ceiling. 'To hell with Keir Gifford,' she told her empty flat. Her voice had a hollow ring, though; she drained the glass hurriedly to change her mood as soon as possible.

She couldn't remember ever getting drunk, but tonight could be the exception, she thought, deciding to have a warm shower before bed. She would take her champagne with her.

She had begun to feel happier by the time she had finished showering; she sang as she put on a loose white silk nightie and négligé. They were both in Regency style; high-waisted and full skirted. Liza drifted into her bedroom, singing and dancing, holding her skirts with one hand and the champagne in the other. She had the radio playing; why did they always play sad love songs? It was all so phoney; love was just a trap and if you got caught in it you left a bit of yourself behind if you escaped. Why did people write songs about it that made it sound like heaven, when everyone knew it was hell and damnation?

She sat on her bed because her head was a little dizzy and felt she should stop dancing—but the room went on revolving without her. She focused on it, seeing double.

'Stop it!' she said loudly and the room stopped going round.

'This is all Keir Gifford's fault,' Liza brooded. If she ever saw him again she'd tell him what she thought of him, but now that he'd successfully detached Bruno from her dangerous company he would vanish back into his own glittering, exclusive world, she wouldn't set eyes on him again.

Her green eyes fixed on nothing, moodily contemplating that thought. She had been perfectly happy until he had crashed into her life. What had he done to her?

'I hate Keir Gifford,' she almost shouted at the furniture elegantly arranged around her. 'If I knew his phone number I'd ring him and tell him exactly what I think of him!'

That was when the phone rang. She jumped so violently that she almost fell off the bed. Groping for the phone, she whispered, 'Hello?' convinced that it would be Keir, but it wasn't. It was Bruno and he sounded nervous.

'Liza, are you OK?' he asked.

'I'm, fine, fine, fine,' Liza chorused happily, or that was how she wanted to sound—happy! She didn't want

Bruno to know she was in a state of wild misery; it had nothing to do with him, although he had been the innocent cause of it in the beginning.

'You don't sound it,' Bruno said slowly.

'Of course I do,' Liza insisted and drank some more champagne.

Bruno seemed to hear that. 'What are you doing?' he asked and then, more sharply, 'Drinking? Liza, you aren't drinking alone, are you?' He sounded shocked, incredulous, and she thought that was very funny, the idea of shocking Bruno. She began to giggle.

'You should try it, it certainly chases the blues away.'

'I'm coming over to see you,' Bruno announced and Liza said furiously.

'No!'

'Liza, listen . . .'

'Your uncle Mr G. K. Gifford, the eminent business person and louse, does not want you to see me *ever* again, so kindly toe the line or you'll be chucked out of the family, and I wouldn't want you to lose your inheritance over me.' She was pleased with the dignified way in which she said it; it was rather a pity that she hiccupped at the very end. It was even more of a pity that she then could not stop hiccupping. In fact, she hiccupped all the way through Bruno's reply.

'Liza, I'm coming over—we haven't really had a chance to say goodbye.'

Liza tried to explain that they had said goodbye in her office, but she knew she wasn't making much sense between hiccups so she said very loudly, 'Goodbye, Bruno,' and put the phone down.

She went to the kitchen and got some water and tried to drink it from the wrong side of the glass, but it made her choke without stopping the hiccups so she tried standing on her head, a trick someone had once told her about. That simply made her dizzy so she tried to make herself jump by dropping a cup on the floor, but it didn't break, it just bounced, and at that moment she heard a violent shrilling.

Someone was ringing the doorbell. She knew it was Bruno; she wouldn't answer it. He would go away in the end.

He didn't and the bell went on ringing and her head was aching now; bang, bang, bang her head went and she held it in both hands, hiccupping. She felt very ill suddenly, and she had to make Bruno stop ringing the bell so she staggered down the hall and yanked the door open.

'Please stop doing that!' she moaned without looking because she had had to close her eyes in case the whirling of the flat made her sick.

In the same moment somebody kicked the door shut and picked her up bodily. Liza's eyes flew open in shock and the hiccups stopped. She knew it was Keir before she saw him; she felt her whole body respond to the strength of his hands as they seized her.

'No,' she moaned, but he walked into the bedroom with her and sat down on the bed with Liza cradled on his lap.

'Are you crazy?' he asked harshly, those dangerous blue eyes inches away. 'Why have you been drinking?'

'I hate you,' she said with violence, her dazed eyes eating him. He looked so familiar, as if she had known him a thousand years—and yet he looked like a stranger, as if she had never set eyes on him before. There were mysterious hollows in his cheeks, a darkness in his eyes, a threat in the tension of his body.

'How much?' he asked and kissed her, sending fever

running through her veins. His mouth was hot and insistent, it wouldn't take no for an answer and her lips quivered helplessly as he took them.

'And why?' he asked as if the kiss had never happened, looking down at her out of hard blue eyes. 'Because I sent Bruno away? You aren't in love with him, so it has to be the money you wanted. Would you really marry a man for his money, Liza? Do you need money? Or do you just want to be rich?'

She was so offended, so angry, so hurt, that she spat back, 'That's right, I want to be rich. Why not? Why shouldn't I want to be rich? If it's OK for you to want money, why isn't is OK for me?' She had been shocked into a return of sanity; she wasn't drunk any more, but she felt very tired and still faintly ill.

'Is that why you've worked so hard to build up your agency? Are you obsesssed with success and money like everybody else?' He sounded disappointed, as if she had betrayed him, let him down. 'Does it really matter that much to you?'

'None of your business,' she mumbled, finding it hard to think because she was too conscious of his hand below her breast; one thumb was pressing slightly against the full, warm flesh and she couldn't think about anything else. She shut her eyes and at once she imagined her breast naked in his hand, and a strangled groan escaped her and she opened her eyes hurriedly.

'You're not going to be sick, are you?' Keir asked, sounding dismayed.

'Probably,' she threatened, staring at the incisive force of his features and wishing she didn't find them so deeply attractive.

'Bruno said you sounded ill or drunk,' he muttered, frowning blackly.

'Bruno did? When? Did he ask you to come?' She was bewildered by that and angry, too. Why should Bruno have asked him to come round to her flat?

'I was there when he rang you' Keir said. 'He was going to invite you down to Hartwell for his last weekend in this country.'

Liza's eyes opened wide. 'You agreed?'

'It was my idea,' he said, watching her intently.

'But ... why?' Liza was confused; suspicious. 'You wanted to get Bruno away from me, that's why you're sending him to New York. So why suggest he invites me down to Hartwell? What's the catch?'

He didn't answer that, but then she hadn't really expected him to, because Keir Gifford was devious and if he had agreed to let Bruno invite her to his country house he must have had some secret motive for doing so. She didn't know him very well yet, but she knew that much—Keir Gifford always had a very good reason for everything he did, but he certainly wouldn't admit to her why he had been ready to accept her as a guest in his own home.

'Do you often drink alone?' he asked and she looked angrily at him, turning her head to do so and finding his face far too close.

'I've never done it before,' she threw at him, a pulse beating in her throat as she stared at him.

'Why now, then?' His voice was low, husky, worrying, and he shifted his position, making her intensely aware of the intimacy with which he held her on his lap, the warmth of his body reaching hers through the layers of clothes between them. Her head was against his shoulder, she could hear the rapid beating of his heart and her own heart racing that tattoo of deep sound.

'Let go,' she said, trying to get up, but in the little

struggle she fell sideways on to the bed and a second later found herself sprawling on her back with Keir arching over her.

Her ears drummed with immediate fear and excitement. 'Don't!' she gasped, shuddering, her hands against his shoulder, holding him away. She had never in her life been so passionately aware of a man's body or so terrified. She could feel his hands everywhere on her; stroking and caressing, exploring. But Keir wasn't touching her at all. He was leaning over her with his hands pressed into the bed on either side of her head. So why was her body burning and trembling? What was happening to her? Her mind was going.

'Go away,' she told him hoarsely and Keir smiled very slowly, as if he knew what she was imagining, how she felt. Could he read her mind? She shut her eyes because perhaps they were betraying her in a double sense; showing her Keir and making her want him, and at the same time telling Keir what was going on inside her.

'I've got money,' he said coolly, and Liza didn't know what he was talking about. She was thinking about the way his body made her feel, and all Keir talked about was money! 'If that's what you're so desperate to get,' he added. 'How much would it cost me? How much would you take?'

The words were meaningless and she frowned impatiently, wishing he would stop talking nonsense and touch her. Her temperature had climbed until she was on fire and her mouth was as dry as a kiln. Her hands shifted on his shoulders, her palms pressed down, feeling the heat of his skin under that jacket, the shirt beneath that. Her fingers gripped him, but the power of her own emotions frightened her into opening her eyes again and glaring at him.

'What are you talking about?' She didn't really care, she just wanted to distract herself.

'I want you,' he said and her heart began to race like an overheated engine. 'You're beautiful and I've got to have you,' he said thickly, still not touching her, but his blue eyes were restlessly moving over her and *she* could read *his* mind. Those eyes possessed her, ate her.

She couldn't speak; her teeth were chattering because she suddenly remembered this sensation of intense need, of burning fever; she remembered it only too well and what it led to, what followed for her. She couldn't bear that again and looked at Keir with angry, frightened eyes, but before she could say anything she heard what he was saying and her eyes opened wide in shock.

'Why waste your time on Bruno when you can get far more from me?'

Liza stared at his mouth, reading the words on his lips.

'You want a lot of money—OK, I've got a lot and I'm ready to be very generous.'

She couldn't believe he was really saying this to her. The insult was a burn on her skin and she almost cried out, realising now what he had meant when he'd asked her what she would take, how much it would cost him.

'You . . . you're trying to buy me!' she whispered incredulously. That wasn't the look of love in his face; it was only hunger, a physical desire which caricatured love, distorted and derided it.

'That's an ugly way of putting it,' he said, frowning harshly. 'But if that's how you want to see it—I want you any way I can get you.' His mouth twisted cynically and she tensed in a spasm of pain, hating him.

'A little cold-blooded, isn't it?' she muttered, looking at him through her lashes with bitter dislike. She wasn't overheated any more; she was icy cold, she felt sick again, but this time it was a very different sickness—it was distaste and shrinking at the very idea of letting him touch her again.

'Cold-blooded?' He repeated and then laughed softly. 'Is that what you think? I must be slipping. Oh, no, Liza, it won't be in the least cold-blooded.' A second later his mouth was on her throat and she stiffened as she felt his hands slide over her breasts, dragging aside the lapels of her négligé, laying bare the lace and frothy silk of her nightdress. His kiss moved hotly, down, down, between her breasts, pushing aside the fine lace, and his hands wandered intimately, surprising a groan of pleasure out of her before she could stop it.

'Sensuality is never cold-blooded, you see,' Keir said huskily, lifting his head to give her a crooked little smile.

'That's not what I've found,' Liza said bitterly and felt him tense, his blue eyes narrowing.

'What exactly does that mean?'

She pushed him away and wriggled into a sitting position, tidying her négligé with hands that shook a little. She had been more disturbed by the lingering intrusion of his mouth than she cared to remember, but she wasn't going to lose her head for the second time in her life. This time she was not going to get out of control.

'I got taken for a fool by a guy like you when I was just a kid. It knocked me for six. I only knew him a few weeks, but I was head over heels, quite crazy over him. He was a travelling salesman, of all things! Oh, I thought he was so sophisticated, one of the smart set from London, and I was a country girl, I'd never even been to London then. He didn't find it hard to seduce me. I practically threw myself at him.' Her face was darkly flushed and she couldn't meet his eyes; she hated remembering what a fool she had been and she hated even more having to tell him what had happened to her. She was doing it because she wanted to make sure she didn't end up in bed with him. Once he had heard her story she had a strong feeling that he would leave, and even if it didn't scare him off she knew that she would never want to set eyes on him again once he knew. Either way, she would be safe, and that was all that mattered now. She had to escape the threat of falling in love again; she couldn't bear to go through that pain and longing.

He had listened in silence, his face gradually losing all expression until when she looked at him through her lashes she couldn't read his features at all.

'And then?' he asked in a flat, low voice.

She laughed harshly. 'He was married, of course—something he had forgotten to tell me. And had a couple of kids.'

'How did you find that out?'

'His firm told me when I rang to find out his home address,' Liza said in a level tone which partially hid the shock she still felt over that phone call. It was so many years ago, but at that moment the black misery swept back and her eyes stared into space, set and glaring.

'Did you ever see him again?'

She shook her head. 'There was no point by then, not once I knew he was married.'

'That was a bad break, but you should have got over it by now,' Keir said gently, his hand moving as if he meant to touch her, and she pulled away, shivering convulsively.

'I haven't finished!'

Keir froze and sat watching her, his blue eyes intent, like cold blue water behind his half-closed lids. She took a deep breath.

'Two days after he left my home town I'd found out

that he'd left me pregnant.' She had to force the words out. She hadn't ever said them before, to anyone. Why was she telling this man? He wasn't saying anything, wasn't moving. What was he thinking, sitting there so close to her, his lean body tense—so tense she felt as if he was some animal lying along a tree in a dense jungle, hidden and secret and waiting to pounce, its still body vibrating with awful energy. His face was so quiet and grave, but his body . . .

She swallowed, and whispered. 'Say something.'

'What do you want me to say? What did you do?' His voice sounded weird, even stranger than her own. It had gravel in it; she felt he was talking through lava. He was angry. *He* was angry! She looked at him with her hands screwed up into fists and wanted to hit him and scream— why are *you* angry? Why should you be? I'm the only one here with the right to anger and it still erupts inside me every time I remember.

She didn't, though. She just laughed stupidly. 'Do? I didn't have a clue what to do. I was just seventeen, never been kissed . . .' she laughed and Keir's brows drew together at the high shrillness, so she swallowed again and made her mouth be still, made herself be very quiet before she went on calmly and coolly, because it was just a story about something that happened a long time ago to someone else. She wasn't that girl, not any more. That girl had died.

'I'd been chucked out of my home by then, you see,' she said and Keir made a funny, stifled noise, incredulous, shocked.

She laughed, although she didn't think it was funny, but it helped to get the words out if she pretended it hadn't happened to her at all, but only to some other girl.

'It was like one of those scenes in a Victorian

melodrama—I didn't believe my father meant it. I hadn't understood at first, what was wrong with me, I mean, and I went to the doctor because I felt ill, and of course he told my father, he was a family friend. My father said, "Get out of my house." I didn't think anybody really said things like that, but he was a very conservative man, my father. He was a lawyer, a country solicitor. His reputation mattered to him, he said I'd ruined his life. So I went—and I caught a train to London to find my lover—I thought he'd welcome me with open arms and it would be happy ever after. Pure soap opera, isn't it?'

'Don't,' Keir said harshly, looking white and grim.

There was a silence for a moment and she felt so tired, but she said wearily, 'And that was when I found out he was married, and I walked around for hours, trying to think. I didn't know what the hell to do. I had nowhere to go, no money, no friends in London. That was probably why I walked in front of the car . . .'

'Car?' Keir broke out and she frowned, wishing he wouldn't keep interrupting her story. Did he think she *wanted* to tell him all this?

'I didn't deliberately try to get killed, I was just so exhausted. Anyway, it solved my problems—I lost the baby and was in hospital for ages, which was a roof over my head, and I had food and time to think.'

'And your parents? Did they . . .?'

'I gave a false name; in fact, Liza Thurston isn't my real name. I made it up for the police and I refused to give an address. They kept coming back, but in the end they gave up because I was obviously old enough to leave home. By the time I left hospital at last I felt about forty years old, and I probably looked it.'

There was along silence and she felt him watching her. He was pale and she was afraid he was going to touch her, try to comfort her. She didn't want that. She didn't want him near her.

'Now, please go,' she said in a low, angry voice. 'Leave me alone! I've had enough, I can't take much more.' She almost ran to the front door and heard him following more slowly. He paused before leaving and she said harshly. 'No! Don't say a word.'

He went and she shut the door and leaned on it, her eyes closed. It still hurt, but it wasn't the pain of losing the man who had wrecked her life—it was the shame and humiliation of what he had done to her. She had flung herself into his arms because she had felt such a deep attraction, such passionate feeling. They should teach you not to let emotion run away with you. You shouldn't be allowed to reach adolescence without being warned about love, and taught never to lose control of yourself. Ever since, she had been very careful. She had locked up her heart and thrown away the key. It was a paler, colder world without that urgent feeling, but it was safer, too. You couldn't get hurt if you never took any risks, now could you?

She yawned, heavy-eyed. She was very sleepy now. Emotion and fear and champagne were taking their toll, and she could hardly keep her eyes open, so she just curled up on the bed and a few moments later was fast asleep. She kept waking up all night; the dreams were agonising. Her face was wet with tears several times when she broke out of the dream, but she was so tired that she always went slowly back to sleep, although in the morning she felt as if she hadn't slept at all.

She was in the bathroom brushing her teeth when the phone rang. She walked reluctantly to answer it. 'Mmm?'

'Liza, can we have lunch? I have to talk to you,' Keir said.

'Sorry, I'm all tied up today,' she said remotely and before she could hang up he quickly said, 'Tomorrow, then?'

'Same, I'm afraid. In fact, I'm busy most days. I don't have time for a private life. Goodbye, Mr Gifford.'

She hung up, but she hadn't reached the bathroom again before the phone began to ring. Liza turned and lifted it and it was Keir again, as she had expected.

'Liza, sooner or later you're going to talk to me,' he said curtly.

'Mr Gifford, I'm not,' she assured him. 'I'll say it one more time so that we both know where we stand. I do not want to see you. I do not want to have an affair with you. I cannot be bought and I haven't got time for this sort of hassle, so please just accept what I say and get out of my life.' She said the last words on a rising scale; higher and higher, with more and more anger until she was shouting. She didn't give him a chance to answer her. She just slammed the phone down, then took it off the hook and left it off.

CHAPTER EIGHT

LUCKILY, the office was very busy over the next few days and Liza was able to keep her mind occupied with Nicky Wallis's big advertising campaign. Nicky was a trial at times, but she was grateful to him for keeping her too busy to think about Keir Gifford, and for once was always available when he rang or popped in to her agency. She didn't mind if he smirked complacently or thought that at last he was getting somewhere with her. He would soon find out how wrong he was!

She knew very well who he had in mind for the campaign. He hadn't said as much, but from the minute he'd mentioned the project both of them had known he was thinking of Liza's protégée; a girl she had been grooming and training for over three months, and was almost ready to launch on a career Liza felt certain was going to be wildly successful.

The girl was just seventeen and had the fragile mix of rich, glowing sensuality and wide-eyed innocence that made a photographer like Nicky Wallis vibrate with excitement. Liza hadn't mentioned her to Nicky, but one day she had got Pamela to walk through the outer office while she knew Nicky was waiting there. Maddie had discreetly observed his face and had told Liza later, 'You should have seen his eyes! Big as saucers!'

When he'd walked into Liza's office, though, he'd spent ten minutes trying not to mention the girl; he didn't want to seem too eager. Liza had anticipated that because she knew Nicky well, and sat smiling, keeping up a bland unawareness. She hadn't mentioned Pam-

Pam either, knowing that that would bother Nicky. He would start wondering if he had already come too late, if Pam-Pam was under contract to someone.

In the end, it was Nicky who had cracked first and asked, 'Who's the little redhead with the green eyes?' and then Liza had said, 'Pam-Pam? Oh, she's going to be our top name within six months—isn't she fabulous? Ken Doyle was in here yesterday, raving about her. I think she'll be exactly what he's looking for this year.'

'Has he used her?' Nicky had asked urgently and Liza had looked vague and said no, he hadn't, not yet, but he was going to, and then Nicky had said, 'I want her exclusively for three months.' Liza had laughed, shaking her head. 'I couldn't do that. Three months? Her earnings in that time could be fantastic.'

She had known then that Nicky had something very special on his mind, and the minute he came out with the news about the cosmetics contract she knew why he had wanted Pam-Pam exclusively. It would mean no other work for Pam-Pam during the lifetime of the campaign, but if the company paid the right price Liza was ready to discuss the offer.

Pam-Pam was happy, too, when Liza explained it to her. She had met Liza in a park. Pamela Jones, just left a London comprehensive school and already unemployed with no prospect of getting a job, had been chasing a barking dog, a fluffy, scruffy mongrel. She had been laughing, flushed, skimpily dressed in a low-necked cotton top and a pair of very brief black shorts. Liza had stopped, assessing her with swift, professional interest, then she had handed Pamela her business card and said, 'If you're interested in a possible job, come up and see me some time.'

Pamela had giggled. 'Mae West, right?' Then she

looked warily at the card and even more warily at Liza. 'What sort of job?'

'Can't you read? Modelling,' Liza had said briskly. 'Don't take my word for it, check me out, and then call at that office and my staff will test you to see if you're as photogenic as I think you are. If they think you've got the makings of a model, then we'll put you to school and train you.'

Pamela had given her a cynical smile. 'And how much does all that cost me?'

'If we accept you on our books, nothing. I'm not running a modelling school; ours is a professional agency, but occasionally we do take a new model and train her, if we think she's worth the effort.' She had looked at her watch and given Pamela a nod. 'Think about it.' Walking on, she had felt the girl staring after her, one hand on the dog's collar. Liza had known nothing about Pam-Pam that first morning, yet she had felt she knew almost everything. Something in the girl reminded her of herself at that age; dewy and eager and painfully vulnerable. It was dangerous to be that wide-open to life. She sensed that Pam-Pam hadn't yet been hurt, but it was only a matter of time because the girl was so reckless.

'Keep a close eye on her,' she had told Maddie and the ex-model, Gabrielle, who had trained Pam-Pam—it had been Gabrielle who came up with the professional name after she heard that Pamela's little niece called her Auntie Pam-Pam. It was different, striking; it suited the girl.

Gabrielle had left modelling to get married, but the marriage had failed and Gabi had got divorced several years ago. She had had two children by then and was past the age when she could model, but she had taken on the job of 'governessing' the agency models. She made sure that they arrived on time, worked hard, behaved themselves, didn't drink too much or smoke or take drugs—generally acted sensibly.

Gabi was motherly but strict; the girls were fond of her, but they respected her and Pam-Pam was quite happy to move into Gabi's large Chelsea flat for a while so that Gabi could tutor her and keep a close eye on her private and professional life.

They had all been hoping for something exciting to turn up to launch Pam-Pam on her career, and Nicky Wallis's cosmetics campaign was undoubtedly big league stuff. The company, Oliviera, were a new firm in that field—they had been involved in medicines and herbal remedies for years and had only just branched out into 'natural' cosmetics as a sideline. The minute Liza heard about the campaign she realised that someone as young and vibrantly healthy as Pam-Pam would be perfect for the project.

'My only reservation is about Nicky Wallis,' she confided to Gabi and Maddie over coffee a few days after first hearing about the contract. 'You know what he's like.'

They both laughed wryly. 'Don't we just? More hands than an octopus, and Pam's his idea of a light snack—he'd gobble her up.' Gabi frowned uneasily. 'I'll talk to her about him, shall I? Give her the gypsy's warning?'

'I'm not sure that that's the right approach. With a kid her age, it might have the opposite effect—tell her Nicky's mad, bad and dangerous to know and she'll be at his feet!' The other two laughed and said they took Liza's point.

'So what do we do?'

'I'll have a casual chat,' Liza promised.

That evening Bruno rang. 'I'm leaving tomorrow. I'll miss you.'

'I'll miss you, too,' she said lightly, but feeling rather melancholy.

'We had fun, didn't we?' Bruno sounded mournful, too, and she forced a laugh.

'We will again, don't sound so blue!' she said, teasing him.

'If you're ever in New York, give me a buzz and we'll paint the town red,' he said before he rang off, and she said she'd do just that.

She was tempted to ask, 'How's your uncle?' but was afraid he might repeat it to Keir and she didn't want Keir to think she cared. If she never saw him again, it would be too soon for her. The rapid inroads he had made into her defences bothered her. She had thought she was man-proof, but he'd showed her she wasn't. She could fall for him in a big way if she wasn't careful, and she meant to be very careful from now on! A man like Keir Gifford was exactly what she wanted to avoid—he liked his women like his cars—fast, glossy and not intended to last.

She made a face at herself. That wasn't true! She just wanted to believe he was that much of a heel because it made it easier to stay away from him.

When the deal with Nicky was firm, Liza delicately began to give Pamela a casual warning about the sort of men she was likely to meet.

'I wasn't born yesterday, you know,' Pam said, cheerfully grinning at her. 'If you're hinting at Nicky Wallis, don't bother. He's so obvious it's embarrassing. Dressed like a kid my age, but with more tramlines than a city centre. I can take care of myself, you know. You grow up streetwise in my part of London.'

Liza laughed, very relieved. 'And I'm just a country mouse who still hasn't quite caught on to big city ways? Maybe you're right.' Perhaps she had underestimated

Pam's ability to cope with whatever life threw at her, because from the minute they'd met in that park she had seen Pam as an echo of herself, but that wasn't really true. Pam was a very different person with a very different background.

'Oh, I wouldn't call you a mouse—town or country,' Pam said, very amused. 'You're so elegant and you're far too shrewd to be any sort of mouse.'

'Once you get into the big time you're going to get rushed off your feet by a lot of men,' Liza warned, though. 'If you're in the public eye you get attention you wouldn't get otherwise, but they're . . .'

'Only after one thing; I know! You and my mum ought to get together—you have a lot in common!'

'You're lucky to have a stable home background. Cling to it as long as you can,' Liza said with a sigh and Pam watched her sympathetically.

'You haven't got any family, have you?'

'Not any more,' Liza said, making sure her face betrayed nothing of what she was feeling. That was a habit now. She was accustomed to her polite, blank mask. Sometimes she hated it, of course; she felt so lonely, keeping everyone at a distance. She had never wanted to end up living that way.

She was careful to insist on being with Pam at her first lunch with Nicky Wallis and the head of the advertising agency who had dreamed up the cosmetics campaign. Liza meant to make it crystal clear to both men that Pam-Pam had protection.

They arrived early, before the men had got to the Mayfair restaurant, and sat in the small bar waiting; both sipping a Perrier with ice and lemon, although Pam had plaintively read the cocktail list and turned pleading eyes on Liza, only to get a firm shake of the head.

'No alcohol! It ruins the complexion. When you stop

modelling, that's up to you, but while you work for me the rule stands. No smoking, no alcohol, no drugs.'

'And no sex,' Pam chuckled and heads swung from the bar counter; men stared at them, riveted.

Liza didn't turn a hair. 'There's no hard and fast rule about that, except that we ban late nights and wild parties, especially the night before you work. You can get away with burning the candle at both ends for a little while, but it soon begins to tell and the camera shows up every tiny line, every spot, every flaw in your face.'

'There aren't any,' said a cool male voice and Liza felt her whole body jerk to life as she looked round.

She hadn't seen him come into the bar; she had somehow imagined that when he was anywhere around she would sense it, but there had been no warning. He just appeared, and Liza couldn't stop the dark flush rising in her face, even though she felt Pam staring curiously.

She was too taken aback to come up with a snappy answer, but at that moment Nicky and the head of the advertising agency arrived, full of apologies for being late.

'Couldn't get a taxi, never is one when you want one! Darling Liza!' Nicky bent to kiss her cheek and she bore it without a flicker of expression, although he did not normally kiss her. She recognised it for a piece of window dressing; showing off for his client. That surprised her, because Terry Lexington knew both of them pretty well; why should Nicky suddenly want to impress him?

She nodded to Terry and said, 'Hi, there. How are you?'

'Fine, Liza,' he said, taking both her hands and smiling with that unfailing charm and sincerity, which was as thin as silver-plating on a cheap fork. He was a little older than Nicky, and far more conservatively dressed. Terry had to impress businessmen, money men, who were alarmed by panache and street-smart men like Nicky—so Terry was wearing a smooth, quiet suit, a discreetly fashionable shirt, a decorous tie. His face matched; his hair was sleek and silver, so was his tongue. Terry could sell anything. His face had two expressions—grave and loving. Neither of them meant a thing. Liza wouldn't trust him further than she could throw him.

Today she matched his smile and his warm sincerity. Usually she wouldn't bother, but she was so conscious of Keir Gifford standing there, watching, listening. Why didn't he go? If he was waiting to be asked to join them he could wait for ever. Liza wasn't even going to look in his direction.

'I don't have to introduce Mr Gifford, do I?' Nicky said and Liza's head swung in shock.

'What?'

Nicky looked startled; so she hurriedly dragged a smile over the ferocity of her stare.

'Mr Gifford?' she asked in a lighter voice and then her eyes met Keir's and her stomach plunged at something in his glinting blue eyes.

'I thought you knew each other,' Nicky was saying, staring at them both with shrewd, probing little eyes, and Keir smiled lazily, his expression bland.

'So we do, don't we, Liza? I'm her landlord, after all. We have more than one thing in common.'

Nicky chuckled, curious, fascinated. He had read all about Bruno; he was intrigued, but Liza had herself under control again and she wasn't giving anything else away.

'But you didn't realise Mr Gifford is our client?' Nicky asked, and at this second shock she had to fight like a wildcat to keep her face blank.

'Our client?' She looked at Terry Lexington, who was smiling easily, nodding. He glanced at Keir, waiting for instructions.

'That's right,' Keir said drily, ignoring him. 'The Lexington agency is handling the campaign for Oliviera, which is one of my companies.'

Liza's brows met and her nerves prickled uneasily. 'I thought it was an independent company!'

'It was! I bought it two days ago,' he said softly and then Terry bustled about, getting them all seated, calling over the waiter, asking for menus and ordering drinks. Liza had time to think and time to feel distinctly worried—why had he bought Oliviera? Why was he taking a personal interest in this campaign? Terry Lexington and Nicky Wallis were obviously on edge, overwhelmed at finding themselves actually having lunch with this man who was so far outside their usual orbit. Keir Gifford wasn't on their level at all; he was a legend; a name to conjure with, and the other two men were working hard to seem relaxed and unflurried in his company.

Pam was the only one who wasn't unnerved; she was talking to him now with a friendly grin, obviously without a clue who he was! Terry had carefully seated Keir next to her.

Did he think Keir was interested in Pam? Liza dropped her lashes and sipped her drink, watching the two of them secretly. She had given strict instructions about what the girl was to wear today, how she was to do her face and hair. Pam looked very young, very natural, her skin dewy and glowing, her eyes wide and clear; as though she had never used make-up in her life, and didn't need to! It was the look Terry had said he wanted for the campaign—from the indulgent smile Keir wore as he talked to Pam he approved, anyway, and Pam chatted exuberantly.

She looked down at her menu and decided on melon followed by a chef's salad while she pretended to be listening to Terry Lexington's outline of the way they were going to run the campaign. He would be putting it on paper for her, anyway; this lunch was a polite formality.

As they went into the restaurant to start eating Terry gave her a sideways wink, whispering, 'Think he fancies her? I couldn't believe it when his assistant rang to say he would be joining us for lunch. There has to be an ulterior motive. Gifford doesn't usually interest himself in the day-to-day running of his companies. I hadn't heard he was a womaniser, but what else would explain it?'

Liza shrugged and didn't answer. She had been thinking along those lines herself, but not quite in the same way as Terry, because she knew something he didn't know and hoped he would never know.

'How on earth did he get to hear about her, anyway?' Terry asked in that hasty whisper. 'I thought she was totally new?'

He was beginning to suspect something, to sense a mystery here, but his eyes were hard with suspicion of Liza, not of Keir. He wondered if she had lied to them, if Pam was more experienced and better known than they had been told. If the girl wasn't an advertising virgin she wouldn't be worth so much to them. They had to have a totally new face, they'd made that very clear, and Liza had assured them that Pam had never modelled for anyone before.

'She is,' Liza said shortly, then as Terry still stared narrowly at her added, 'He has the reputation of checking out everything about a company before he decides to buy, so maybe he found out about this

campaign and got interested enough to come along to see
what we planned?'

'It doesn't add up,' Terry said, frowning.

It did to Liza, but she wasn't giving Terry the true
explanation for Keir Gifford's presence there. She meant
to keep well away from the man throughout the lunch;
she would only speak to him when she had to and she
wouldn't look at him if she could help it.

Her plan didn't have a chance of succeeding. When
she and Terry got to the table she found that Keir had
arranged the seating this time and she was sitting next to
him with Terry on her other side. Keir drew out her chair
and she reluctantly sat down, a shiver running down her
spine as his hands brushed her shoulders. He didn't
hurry, his fingertips moved lingeringly over the smooth
crêpe of her designer-styled dress. Liza had chosen it
deliberately because they were eating in a very good
restaurant; it was one of her favourite dresses, a vivid
violet-blue with a deep V-neck and a flowing, slim skirt.
She knew she looked good in it; her figure graceful,
slender, her neck bare below the immaculate chignon.
Keir had almost touched her skin and she sensed that he
had refrained from doing so solely to make her tense, to
put her on edge, expecting it any minute.

'Melba toast?' he asked, offering her the basket of very
thin slices of crisp, dry toast, and she took one and
nibbled it while Terry talked about what the agency
planned. Keir seemed interested; he had his first course
in front of him by now—smoked salmon and prawns—
which he ate slowly as he listened. Liza ate her melon and
contributed nothing to the discussion. Her table napkin
kept sliding down off her lap; the material of her dress
was slippery. Keir observed this with a sideways glance.

'Having trouble?' he murmured while Terry was

laughing noisily at some joke Keir had made a second earlier.

'None I can't handle!' she said and her eyes met his, making it plain that she wasn't just referring to her slippery napkin.

'Sure about that?' he drawled softly, mocking her.

'Just watch me,' Liza muttered, feeling like throwing her wine at him.

'I mean to,' he promised, and she felt her pulses beat a flurried tattoo.

'As I was saying,' Terry broke in on their brief exchange, and Keir turned a cool smile on him, all attention again. Liza watched the waiter removing the plates, filling their glasses. She was on tenterhooks now; wishing that this lunch would come to an end because she was finding it very hard to sit next to Keir, feel his long, lean body so close to her, his legs stretching next to hers, his shoulder almost touching her now and then, his brown-skinned hand on the table, crumbling a bread roll on a small plate absently as he listened—all the physical intimacies of everyday life which she knew she would never have noticed if he had been any other man. She wasn't aware of Terry Lexington's gestures and movements. Terry simply wasn't impinging on her, but Keir had all her attention, even when she tried to look in the other direction.

Nicky was talking now and they were all listening. He was a very good photographer and his face lit up with excitement as he explained his ideas for the side of the campaign he would be handling. Liza slowly ate her chef's salad, her eyes lowered. She reached for her wine glass and, as she stretched, her napkin slid down again. She reached for it but Keir had moved faster. He retrieved it before it fell, but his fingers had brushed her knee first; a cool, light contact which made her furious because she knew it was all part of his needling campaign against her. He was taking every opportunity to touch her, and the wicked glint of his eyes told her he didn't care if she knew it; he meant her to know it, in fact. That was part of the strategy.

She was going to have to out-think this man if he wasn't to drive her completely crazy. She had been sure that after hearing why she didn't want to get involved with any other man he would leave her well alone, but she had underestimated his tenacity. He hadn't given up or gone away, or written her off as a bad risk. He had bought his way into her life in secret, and was pleased with himself for taking her by surprise today.

She couldn't think of a way of blocking him. She couldn't break the contract; she and Pam-Pam had signed with the advertising agency, and for the girl's sake Liza had to go through with the deal. This was Pamela's big break, she couldn't wreck it for her.

'We need somewhere really special to shoot the first series of ads,' Nicky said, looking at Terry. 'I've been thinking . . . how about famous beauty spots? Outdoor locations—the Lake District, the Yorkshire fells, that sort of thing—still on the natural kick, you get it?'

'We'll shoot them at Hartwell,' Keir said and the other men looked round, totally startled by that.

'Hartwell?' Nicky's jaw had dropped. The house was a tourist dream, but people usually only saw the gardens; the house wasn't open to the public except on special days for charity.

'Hartwell?' Terry murmured, in a different voice, flushed with excitement at the thought of using such a prestigious background for one of his campaigns, and even Pam had sat up, huge-eyed, open-mouthed. She had heard of Hartwell, it seemed, she couldn't believe she was going down there to be photographed.

'I suggest you all come down next weekend to decide exactly where to take these pictures,' Keir said and his lashes flicked sideways; Liza felt the deep blue glitter of his glance for a second, saw the ironic, mocking curl of his mouth. 'I'm not having any other house guests this week so I'd be glad if you could all stay for the whole weekend, Friday to Monday.'

Nicky and Terry eagerly said they'd love to, naturally, they would look forward to it, and Pam beamed, nodding. Keir turned his head to survey Liza, waiting for what he knew would be coming.

She smiled coldly. 'Thank you for the invitation, and I'd have loved to come, but I'm afraid I have a prior engagement. Pam will be there, though, and I'll send one of my senior staff to chaperon her, if I may.'

'I don't deal with anyone but the boss,' Keir said brusquely. 'Either you come or the deal's off. I can't have some stranger running around my home. This isn't just business, you know. This is where I live, it's my own home. I didn't invite one of your senior staff, I invited you personally.'

His face was icy, hauteur in every line. The relaxed and friendly atmosphere had frozen over and Terry and Nicky threw Liza horrified, pleading glances across the table. What was she doing, rocking the boat like this? their agitated eyes said. Didn't she know what a big compliment this was, being asked to stay at Hartwell, the home of the wealthy Giffords? You didn't normally get past the high iron gates unless you were somebody important, a VIP with the same sort of life-style as the master of the house. They had been astonished when he had appeared at this lunch, but they were staggered at the invitation to stay at his country house. They couldn't believe their ears when Liza tried to turn it down. Was she crazy? they silently demanded. Any minute now Keir

Gifford was going to cancel the invitation, maybe even the whole deal. He was angry; they looked at him nervously, sweating. When a man as important as Keir Gifford got angry, everyone around him got tense and Liza saw that she had a difficult situation ahead of her whatever she decided to do.

If she didn't go to Hartwell for the weekend Keir might pull out of the whole project and then she would have to explain why she had done it to Terry and Nicky and Pam.

If she did go to Hartwell, she would have to cope with Keir Gifford at much closer quarters and she had butterflies at the very idea of that.

'Of course Liza will come! She can break her other date,' Nicky said hastily.

'It isn't every day you get an invitation to Hartwell, after all,' Terry chimed in, and both men glared at Liza, begging and demanding in one stare, while Pam sat in stunned, incredulous anguish, unable to speak.

Liza sighed and met Keir's ironic, watchful eyes. She had no choice at all, did she?

CHAPTER NINE

LIZA heard the girls in the outer office talking before she even set foot out of the lift. Their voices were excited and they were all apparently talking at once, but the name Hartwell rose out of the general uproar. Liza stopped in mid-step, scowling. Now how on earth had they heard about that so soon? She had only told Maddie the previous afternoon and had sworn her to secrecy—had Maddie leaked it?

As she pushed through the swing doors the voices stopped dead; the girls moved like greased lightning in all directions, one to a computer terminal, another to a filing cabinet, and Joan dived for the machine room where Liza could hear the chuntering of the photocopier. Maddie was at her desk looking as cheerful as someone who had just seen her doom prophesied. Liza walked briskly across the room, bending a peremptory finger in Maddie's direction as she went.

Maddie followed, pad in hand, and burst out as soon as they were in Liza's office, 'It wasn't me! I didn't tell them!'

'So who did?'

'Joan ran into Pam and Gabi in the coffee shop across the street.'

Liza closed her eyes. 'I see. I hope Pam hasn't told too many people.' She opened her eyes and groaned impatiently. 'I told her not to tell a living soul!'

Maddie giggled suddenly. 'Perhaps Pam didn't think Joan counted?'

145

Liza stared blankly. 'What?'

'As a living soul!' said Maddie, then gently pointed out, 'This is a publicity campaign we're involved in, remember? I don't see why anyone should mind if word gets out that you're filming at Hartwell.'

'Not filming—planning the locations for the first advertisement,' Liza said, but sighed. 'And you're right, of course. I'm being a little hysterical about this. I'm just nervous.'

'About going to Hartwell?' Maddie looked at her with disbelief. 'I wouldn't have expected you to be nervous about anything. You're so cool, you always seem to have got it all together.'

'Thanks,' Liza said, smiling at her. She couldn't explain to Maddie why she was so uptight about this visit to Hartwell. The palatial scale of the house didn't bother her; it wasn't Hartwell she found overpowering, it was the house's owner, the master of the whole estate. Whenever she remembered him as he'd seemed when they had first met she felt a surge of rage. He had looked so shabby, untidy, down to earth—that man she had felt at ease with; she had argued with him and been infuriated by him, but she hadn't been painfully on edge every time he came near her. Had he really cooked in the kitchen in her cottage? Liza found that hard to believe now.

Keir Gifford was a bewildering man, though, and he was a very influential one. He could do her agency a lot of damage if he decided to! He could raise her rent for the office, or refuse to renew her lease at the end of the three-year term for which she had signed. He had a lot of friends, and even more acquaintances, who would be anxious to please him by being hostile to her once the word was out that he wanted her out of business. It would be so easy for a man with his pull. She would suddenly be ignored by advertising agencies, fashion houses, magazines—her models wouldn't get work, she could be ruined in a few months.

What on earth's the matter with you? You're going mad, she thought impatiently. Why on earth should he do that? Pull yourself together.

'Let's get some work done, shall we?' she said to Maddie, who was watching her with a worried little frown, as if Liza's face had been as ferocious as her thoughts.

Liza dictated some letters and read through the report cards filed by the various people who had employed her girls the previous day. Any complaints were always dealt with at once, but this morning it was nothing but compliments, and Liza smiled more cheerfully as she gave the cards to Maddie to file. An agency depended on its reputation, and that was the basic reason why it alarmed her to have an enemy like Keir Gifford. He was powerful, he could do her a lot of harm.

Why should he, though? she thought after Maddie had gone. Bruno was out of the picture, safely away from her in the States—why should Keir Gifford hound her now?

A shiver ran down her spine. She knew why, he had said it bluntly. He wanted her, and a man like that was accustomed to getting what he wanted. He didn't like being told 'No'. He hadn't accepted it—or else why was he insisting that she visit Hartwell? Why had he turned up at that lunch with Nicky and Terry Lexington?

He hadn't given up, nor would he go away. He was still in close pursuit, at her heels, and Liza's nerves were fraying at the edges, especially whenever she thought about spending a whole weekend at his country house. There would be others there, she comforted herself; she could stay close to Pam and Nicky, but even if she did she had the strong suspicion that Keir would find an opportunity of getting her alone, and she was afraid of what might happen if he did.

Since she had come to London she had been armoured against men. Now and then she had met a man she found pleasant, a man she thought of as a friend, like Bruno. As long as a man didn't attract her strongly, as long as she wasn't tempted, she felt safe, but once her own sensual instincts were aroused she was terrified of losing control, and it was disturbing now to find herself spending so much time just sitting around thinking about Keir Gifford.

She knew he attracted her; when he touched her she felt every pulse in her body going crazy, but he was light years out of her world, he was dangerous to her, she *must* forget him, keep him at bay.

She ran her hands through her hair, groaning aloud. How could she forget him when he wouldn't leave her alone?

He rang her on the Friday morning. When Maddie said reverently, 'It's Mr Gifford on the line!' Liza sat at her desk pulling faces for a second and Maddie said, 'Hello? Did you hear me?'

Liza said that she had, her voice grating. 'Put him through,' she added, because what else was she to do? It would be childish to pretend she wasn't here, and anyway Maddie would start to wonder, to be curious; Liza didn't want that.

His voice was deeper than she remembered; she felt a strange weakness inside her as she heard it, as if her insides had just turned to water.

'How are you getting down to Hartwell?' he asked

without preliminaries, and she was flustered, stammering.

'I—suppose by train.'

'Is your model coming with you?'

'Yes.' Maddie had made all the travel arrangements, as usual; Liza wasn't sure exactly what time the train was, but she knew it would be smoothly organised, Maddie would make sure of that. She would have a folder ready containing the tickets and anything else she might decide Liza needed—information about the destination, the name of the station and perhaps the telephone number of the hire-car firm who would meet the train and drive them to Hartwell. Liza didn't know all that; she didn't need to when she could rely so much on Maddie.

'I'm taking my plane,' he said coolly. 'Why don't the two of you come with me instead? Much quicker.'

Liza opened her mouth to refuse, but for some reason the words didn't come out the way she had intended.

'Thank you,' was what she said, stupidly.

He said in a brisk voice, 'I'll pick you up in the lobby at three-thirty, then,' and rang off.

She put the phone down, staring at it in stupefaction. He didn't waste time, did he? She buzzed for Maddie, re-arranging the files on her desk in an absent-minded way.

'Oh, Maddie, what arrangements did you make about picking Pam up? Is she coming here and what time?'

Maddie whisked away to get the folder and laid it open in front of her. 'You're picking Pam up on the way to the station.'

'From Gabi's place?'

'That's right. At three-forty-five. The train is four-fifteen; you should make it in plenty of time.'

'We aren't going by train—will you ring Pam and tell

her to get to the office by three-fifteen, instead? Mr
Gifford is taking us in his private jet.'

Maddie looked suitably impressed. 'Golly!'

'Shut your mouth, Maddie, and ring Pam,' Liza said
drily.

'Aren't you excited?' Maddie asked, but at Liza's
impatient glance she left the office to ring Pam, Liza
tried to concentrate on the work she had to get through
before she left that weekend.

Pam hadn't arrived by three-twenty and Maddie rang
her again, but Gabi's number was engaged for the next
five minutes. Maddie only got through just as Liza was
about to go down to the lobby to meet Keir Gifford. She
appeared in the doorway as Liza was checking her
reflection.

'She left rather late, but she should be here any
minute,' Maddie said breathlessly.

'Let's hope so,' Liza said with grim patience. 'Mr
Gifford isn't the type to enjoy being kept waiting.'

He was in the lobby when Liza stepped out of the lift
and she tensed immediately she saw him. Keir watched
her intently all the way across the marble floor between
them; she felt like hitting him, because he knew he was
making her nervous and it was amusing him.

Lifting her head, she consciously walked with a sway;
a model's trick, faintly arrogant, very cool. It erected a
shield for her; kept him at a distance.

'I'm sorry, I'm afraid Pam hasn't arrived yet. She may
have been delayed in traffic, but she is on her way and I
hope she won't be long.'

He raised his brows and looked at his watch. 'We'll
wait for a few minutes then.' Turning, he beckoned to the
doorman who shot over, all attention. 'We're going down

to the car park. When Miss Jones arrives, send her down, will you?'

'Why don't we wait for her here?' asked Liza as he took her arm to lead her back to the lift.

He didn't answer and she frowned as they shot downwards, suddenly afraid that she was going to find herself alone with him in his car, but as she stepped out of the lift she saw a uniformed chauffeur straighten and step on a cigarette before springing to open the passenger door of a long, black limousine.

'This is more comfortable than standing around in the lobby,' Keir said, sliding her into the rear seat and getting in beside her, and in one sense she had to admit he was right because the car was ultra-luxurious—the deep leather seats and air conditioning made it a very comfortable place to wait for Pam—but on the other hand Keir's presence was distinctly inhibiting.

Keir had told the chauffeur to wait by the lifts for the third member of their party, so they were alone once the man had put Liza's suitcase into the enormous boot of the car. Keir hadn't had a case; perhaps his was already in the boot?

'Will your family be at Hartwell this weekend?' she asked, smoothing down her straight blue linen skirt.

'My mother and sister will be,' he said, watching her brief gesture before his narrowed eyes slid down her long, sleek legs. Liza was watching him, angrily vibrating at the cool way he assessed her, and yet even angrier to find herself noticing the way his black hair sprang back from his forehead in a widow's peak, the moulding of that hard mouth, the line of his throat rising from a stiff, white collar. His suit was pure Savile Row today; very formal, very elegant. She had a flash of memory: Keir in his shabby tweeds and muddy boots. There was a funny little ache inside her. Why hadn't he been what he seemed that day?

He said softly, 'Missing Bruno?'

'Yes,' she told him with defiance in her voice, and their eyes met; Keir's sharp, searching, Liza's veiled by deliberate refusal to show what she thought. She did miss Bruno; she had enjoyed the free and easy nature of their relationship, the total absence of sexual awareness, any sexual hassle. It had made life so much more fun not to be challenged or disturbed the way she was every time she saw Keir.

'But you're not dating anyone else,' he said, his tone a cool statement.

'Who says?' she shrugged, tossing back her head.

'My detective.'

Liza's mouth opened wide and she drew in air sharply. 'You're kidding!'

He wasn't; he smiled.

'You've still been having me watched?' She had to make sure this wasn't one of his elaborate jokes, although his face wasn't teasing. It was amused, though, so she couldn't be sure.

'I'd put an agency on the job when I first heard about you and Bruno,' he told her calmly, 'I told you that. I had you checked out.'

'I didn't realise you meant . . .' She was slowly getting angry. 'You've really had me followed about by some little sneak in a dirty raincoat or something?'

'I've no idea who was doing the legwork,' he said and frowned as there was a purring sound in the car. Liza frowned, too, irritated by the distraction. 'Will you excuse me? That's the phone,' he said, and leaned forward. Liza had a start of surprise as she saw a telephone in his hand; where had that come from? With

Alice-in-Wonderland disbelief she heard him speaking.

'Hello? Yes? Oh, I see. When? See if you can get a better price, but if it looks as if it's climbing, buy immediately.' He firmly replaced the phone and said to Liza, 'The detective is off the job now, anyway—there's no need to get agitated.'

'You come from another planet!' Liza burst out furiously. 'What earthly right do you think you have to spy on me, just because I've been seeing your nephew socially?'

'Liza, you told me why you'd learnt to be wary of men,' Keir said flatly. 'Well, I have just as good reason for distrusting women. I told you we had more in common than you thought. Why do you think I've never married?'

'Why bother, when you can have all the fun without the wedding ring?' she said sourly and he eyed her with a sardonic smile.

'Who told you that? Bruno? My God, I'm a busy company executive—I work a twelve-hour day and I don't have time for a mad social whirl. You could count the women that I've dated on the fingers of one hand; dated for any length of time, I mean. Over the years there have been some women I hoped might mean something, but sooner or later I've always found out that they weren't what I was looking for, or that they cared more for my money than me, or even that there was someone else hidden away, some guy ready to step out of the picture until his lady had safely netted me. Since I was a schoolboy I've met them all, all types of women, and not one of them ever really made me happy.'

Liza listened soberly, watching the wry contours of his face as he talked, his mouth incisive, cynical. What Keir said didn't surprise her. She didn't doubt it, either. She could believe that he had been a target for some clever, ambitious, greedy women—a man as wealthy as Keir Gifford was bound to be!

'So when I heard that Bruno had started seeing a——'

'Blonde ex-model,' Liza supplied and he grinned at her.

'Exactly. When that news reached me, I rang the agency I use to check out my possible acquisitions and I told them to dig up everything they could on you.'

She frowned. 'I want to see that file.'

'One day,' he promised.

'Now, at once!' Liza said in spitting rage. 'I want to destroy it, and I want you to promise to destroy all the copies—it makes me sick to think of a file like that sitting about in your computers, all the data on me, my private life, my personal records . . .'

'Most of them were on a computer tape before my agency started looking!' Keir's mouth was hard with impatience. 'These days we're all on file, Liza; from the minute we take our first breath—no, before that, while we're in the womb. Somewhere there is always a computer record of your every movement, and as the years go by it gets worse, your privacy shrinks and shrinks.'

'You have a computer company, of course,' Liza said and he pulled a face.

'Of course. They're money spinners, even now.'

Liza looked at him with horror and alarm. 'You're a dangerous man, Mr Gifford. You're too powerful, you have too much money and too many tentacles; you can go anywhere, do anything. Someone like me has no chance against you, do I?'

'I'm just a man, Liza.' His hand came out and touched her cheek—lightly, almost imperceptibly, with a delicate uncertainty. 'If you cut me, I bleed. If you shoot me, I may die. I'm flesh and blood, like you. I can be hurt, or be made happy.' His fingers caressed her skin and he watched her with blue, smouldering eyes. 'You can do that to me, Liza; hurt me or make me happy—so how powerful does that make you?'

She laughed angrily, breathing very fast, because the touch of his hand was like a magnet to her blood; she felt it flowing hotly where he brushed her skin, and she was so tense she could hardly breath. She must not let him undermine her like this! He couldn't mean it; he was seducing her with that deep, husky voice, those hungry eyes.

'I'm just an ordinary girl, Mr Gifford. I have no power.'

'You are as ordinary as spring,' he murmured. 'As powerless as sunlight.' He ran his fingertips down her neck. 'And when I touch you, I burn,' he said, making her heart stop and a flare of wild panic light inside her. He was too close; he was getting to her.

At that instant she heard the click of Pam's very high red heels on the concrete and she arrived, chattering, pink and breathless, seeming quite blind to the atmosphere between the two in the limousine.

'I'm sorry, I couldn't get a taxi and then it got stuck in a traffic jam and I was going spare, honest. I thought I'd never get here, I was leaning forward, yelling at the driver, and he yelled back at me and said what did I want him to do, get out and push it? I'm very sorry, Liza, Mr Gifford. I hope I haven't kept you waiting about too long—I mean, we haven't missed our plane, have we?'

'It will wait for us,' Keir said coolly as the limousine smoothly drove out of the underground car park.

Pam stared, goggle-eyed. 'Ooh!' she said, deeply impressed. 'Will it really wait? I've never had a plane wait for me before.'

Keir smiled at her indulgently. 'Well, today it will.'

The plane was waiting on the runway; a small, private
jet with very comfortable fittings. They took off at five
o'clock and were in Somerset within an hour, landing at a
private airfield just a few miles from Hartwell. Pam was
chattering most of the way, but Liza hardly spoke. Pam
was sympathetic, assuming she was airsick.

'Bad luck, Liza. I'm never sick when I travel, thank
heavens. My Mum says my stomach's made of cast iron!
Have some of this iced water; it's very refreshing with a
piece of lemon in it.' Pam had eaten a slice of water-
melon and a few strawberries, but the other two had
refused—Keir seemed silent, too. Was he regretting
having said so much to her about his private life?

She was thinking about him as she stared down at the
green and gold of a Somerset landscape while they were
descending into it. He led a strange life; full of luxury and
privilege but, from what Keir said, nevertheless empty.
Had he told her the truth? She didn't want to feel too
much sympathy for him, or seem too friendly—in case all
this was just another game, another trap for her.

They were met at the airfield by another limousine
which drove them through the warm, summer evening at
a smooth pace. They first saw Hartwell from a hilltop; it
rose out of the formal park and gardens half a mile away
and Liza heard Pam give a stifled gasp of admiration and
awe.

'Is that it?'

'That's Hartwell,' Keir admitted, watching her face
with a smile.

'It's . . . amazing,' Pam said, giving up a short struggle
to find a better word to describe the glory of the house in
the early evening sunlight. Bruno had called it a

barracks, damp and rambling—but Liza suspected he
had run it down the way a mother sometimes talks
offhandedly of a much-loved child—Bruno didn't want
to let anyone see how much he loved the place. Keir
suffered no such inhibitions. He was gazing at it with
glowing, possessive eyes and he talked to Pam about it
with unhidden pride.

'The main part of the house is classical Georgian; built
in the early part of the eighteenth century on a site once
occupied by a Tudor abbey which was pulled down
during the Reformation—demolished to make way for a
big Elizabethan place some years later. That burnt down
in 1712 and that was when the present house was
started—it's been added to since then, but basically it's
the house designed by the owner of the time, with a little
help from a succession of architects who all left in high
dudgeon because he wouldn't take their advice.' Keir
grinned at them and Pam giggled.

'Was he an ancestor of yours, by any chance?'
enquired Liza coolly. 'I seem to recognise certain
characteristics.'

'Very funny, Miss Thurston,' he said, as they drove
towards the portico in the front of the house. Rhododen-
drons and thorn trees grew close to the drive, forming a
dark green tunnel through which they drove.

The limousine drew up right outside the portico, and a
butler in a dark suit opened the door and bowed them
past him into a great, echoing eighteenth-century hall.
Liza's eyes skated around in fascination at the worn
wood-block flooring, the dark gold of oak everywhere;
on walls and high rafters and the floor. The sunlight
made the wood gleam with a deep warmth, but Liza
could see why Bruno had called it a draughty house—the
ancient fireplace was so enormous that half a dozen men

could have stood up in it, and the wind must whistle down there on winter nights.

'Oh, suits of armour!' Pam said, standing close to Liza in awe of the butler's splendid presence, and nudging her secretly, her eyes on the man's haughty face. Keir was talking to him and Pam whispered to Liza, 'Imagine having a butler!'

'What would *I* do with a butler?' Liza whispered back, which made Pam start to giggle and drew Keir's eyes to them again.

'Norton will show you to your room,' he said and the butler picked up Pam's case from the floor and inclined his head with a faint smile.

'This way, miss.'

'When are the others arriving?' Liza asked Keir, who had told them that Nicky Wallis and his crew would make their own way by road, bringing their heavy equipment, and that Terry Lexington was coming with them.

'Later tonight, in time for dinner.'

Pam was following the butler, but glancing back at Liza, a little alarmed at being left alone with the awe-inspiring figure in the plain black suit.

'I'd better catch her up or she'll be struck dumb with horror,' Liza said, smiling and Keir smiled back.

'She's charming.'

'Yes, very unspoilt—I'm hoping to keep her that way.' Her eyes held a spark of aggression and he eyed her drily.

'Don't look at me like that; I won't try to change her. I like her the way she is.'

'She's far too young to cope with you,' Liza said and his brows met, black and angry.

'Are you hinting that I might make a pass at that child? For God's sake!' He talked through his teeth, looking down at Liza with menace. 'She's not even half my age!'

'I'm responsible for her, I have to look after her,' Liza said, watching Pam taking a turn in the wide, stone staircase leading up from the Georgian hall. The sound of her footsteps on the creamy, weathered stone was very loud, drowning the murmur of their voices.

'It isn't me you should be worrying about, then,' Keir said angrily. 'I don't cradle-snatch, but I wouldn't be so sure about your friends Wallis and Lexington. They both fancy her, I'd say, and they wouldn't have any scruples about age even though they're both older than me.'

'Really?' Liza said in pretended incredulity, turning wide green eyes on him.

He glared at her for a second; then suddenly laughed. 'Very funny, Miss Thurston, but frankly I'm not too flattered that you take me for the sort of guy who tries to seduce teenagers.'

Liza flushed and started to walk away towards the stairs. He caught her arm and held it, looking down at her probingly, with apology. 'That wasn't any sort of dig, Liza. I'd forgotten for the moment . . . was he much older than you? If he was married, I suppose he must have been. It was bad luck, Liza, meeting someone like that first time around, but we aren't all bastards, you know. I won't chase little Pam.'

She believed him and managed a rueful smile. 'I feel responsible for her, you see.'

'She reminds you of yourself at that age?' he guessed shrewdly, his eyes gentle, and she gave him a startled glance, then laughed.

'I suppose so, yes.'

'I must take a closer look at her,' drawled Keir. 'I'd like to know what you were like then.'

For some inexplicable reason that sent another stab of panic through Liza, and she headed for the stairs again with more determination. Keir let her go this time and followed with her suitcase, talking calmly.

'My mother must be in her room, changing for dinner, I expect. Would you like some help with your unpacking? I'll send someone . . .'

'Certainly not!' she said, startled at the very idea, laughing. 'I've only brought a few things—it won't take five minutes to unpack them all.'

'Well, when you've had time to settle in, put on a pretty dress and come down to meet my mother.' He flung open a door leading off the landing on the first floor. 'I picked this room for you myself.' He smiled. 'I hope you like it.'

She walked into the room and stood, amazed and delighted, staring with pleasure around the cool elegance of a green and ivory room furnished in the graceful style of the mid-eighteenth century. A four-poster bed, hung with silk striped curtains which matched those at the two windows, a deep white carpet, watered silk on the walls which had a green shimmering the late sunlight, rosewood dressing-table, chairs, chest of drawers. There seemed to be no wardrobe, but Keir walked across the room and opened a white door, gesturing.

'Bathroom through there—dressing-room through there.'

Liza joined him and stared at the two doors. 'A dressing-room? How useful,' she said and glanced in at the room which had a full-length mirror on one wall, rows of empty coat-hangers along another and shelves running vertically on the wall behind the door.

'I'll see you later, then,' Keir murmured, putting her case down and smiling at her with the charm she was rapidly coming to find irresistible. 'Thank you for coming, Liza. I've been waiting for a long time to see you here at Hartwell.'

He had gone before she had taken in what he had said. She heard her bedroom door close quietly and stumbled back from the dressing-room to stare at the empty bedroom, feeling almost dizzy.

What had he meant by that? Had it been a meaningless courtesy? Or . . . she broke off, biting her lip. Keir couldn't have meant it seriously, and anyway they had only met such a short time ago! Of course he hadn't meant it.

CHAPTER TEN

KEIR'S mother bore a strong resemblance to her children; she had the same beautiful, bony face as Pippa and eyes of the vivid blue she had handed on to her son. Her direct stare reminded Liza of Keir, too, and although his mother's hair was absolutely white Liza didn't need to guess that it had once been jet-black, because there was a large oil painting of Mrs Gifford over the fireplace in the drawing-room, painted in her girlhood, in the elegant clothes of the First World War era; cream silk and lace which she wore with style. She had been painted in a garden; lilies and roses around her. You could almost smell them, and she held flowers in her long, white hands, the shadow of their colour on her skin.

Fifty years later you could still trace that girl in the upright, graceful old woman who shook hands with Liza.

'Is your name really Elizabeth?' Mrs Gifford asked in a deep voice which reminded Liza of Keir, the timbre was so similiar.

Nodding, Liza agreed. 'But I was always called Liza because I had an aunt Elizabeth—I was named after her, I suppose, although I'd forgotten that.'

'Elizabeth is my name, too,' Mrs Gifford said, and Liza gave Keir a surprised, flushed look. He hadn't told her that. He was smiling, watching them both intently, but she couldn't read that expression and didn't trust his charm. It might mean anything, that was the whole trouble with charm—it was all things to all people and never personal, never special, just for you.

'Keir didn't tell you that?' His mother looked amused.
'He didn't mention it.'

'He likes to have secrets,' his mother said with wry
affection and Keir made a protesting sound.

'Don't give me away, Mother, please!'

'Was I? We won't talk about you, then—I wouldn't
want to spoil anything.'

Spoil what? thought Liza, her eyes flashing from one
to the other. They had a silent rapport; she read the
intimacy, the smiling understanding in their glances and
knew they were very close, needed no words.

'Sit by me and tell me all about yourself,' Mrs Gifford
said, patting the footstool next to her. 'Keir, get Liza a
sherry.'

'Sweet or dry?' he asked and Liza said she would prefer
dry. She didn't like sherry, but she didn't quite like to say
so and held the small glass, sipping gingerly while she
talked to Mrs Gifford about her modelling and her
agency business.

'Where do you come from, Liza? Now and then you
seem to have a West Country accent—were you born
around here?'

Startled, Liza flushed. 'Not quite, but it's clever of you
to pick up the accent—I haven't been back for years. I'd
forgotten I ever had an accent, I thought I'd lost it.'

'One never quite loses the intonation learnt in
childhood,' Mrs Gifford said, her chin resting on one
hand. She was wearing a white silk evening blouse, high-
necked and long-sleeved, almost Edwardian in style. Her
long black skirt rustled every time she moved—Liza
suspected she had a few layers of stiff petticoats under it.

'Where were you born?' Mrs Gifford asked and Liza
hesitated, aware of Keir listening, leaning against the
Adams fireplace, a glass in his hand and his lean body

graceful in evening dress.

'Wiltshire,' he murmured suddenly and Liza stiffened, turning incredulous, horrified eyes on him. She hadn't told him—how could he have known that? She had never told anyone at all and she had changed her name when she had come to London so he couldn't have traced her by checking on her birth certificate.

'What part of Wiltshire?' asked his mother, unaware of the undercurrents flowing between the other two.

That was when Pippa Morris joined them, and in the uneasy conversation following her arrival Mrs Gifford forgot what they had been talking about, to Liza's deep relief. Bruno's mother shook hands with Liza politely, but coolly; she wasn't welcoming her to Hartwell, but her manners were too good for her to be rude, especially while her family were watching.

Liza decided to be direct and ask about Bruno; there seemed no point in avoiding the subject. 'How's Bruno settling down in New York?' she asked, and his mother said curtly that he had now moved into an apartment and was finding his feet, it seemed. 'You haven't heard from him?' she asked then, watching Liza closely, and looked relieved when Liza shook her head.

'No, but I expect he'll remember to send me a postcard one day!'

Mrs Morris laughed. 'Bruno isn't very good at writing letters.'

'Nor am I,' said Pam, who had been very quiet since she and Liza came downstairs, perhaps overwhelmed by the grandeur of the house, or just the ambience surrounding the Giffords.

'Young people have lost the art,' said Mrs Gifford.

'Oh, I don't know,' Pippa Morris disagreed. 'I've never had the patience to write long letters, either, and I'm hardly young now.'

'You are to me,' her mother said and Pam giggled.

'That's what my Mum always says. She says that even when I'm going grey I'll still be her little girl. She's real soft, my Mum, at times.'

Mrs Morris smiled at her with a warmth she had never shown Liza, and in that smile Liza learnt more about Bruno's mother than she had done before. She understood why Bruno had said that once she got to know his mother she would like her; she hadn't believed it possible, but suddenly she thought she might come to like Keir's sister, after all.

They had a delicious meal that evening; a summer dinner party in a Victorian conservatory adjoining the back of the house. Candles on the table, the shadows of vine leaves giving a green and underwater gloom on the white damask tablecloth; a scent of exotic flowers heady in the air.

The food matched the suroundings—a chilled summer soup, followed by melon delicately flavoured with mint, and after that salmon hollandaise: the fish perfectly cooked and flaking as a fork touched it, the salad served with it crisp and unusual. By the time the dessert was served Liza was replete and yawning secretly; good food, good wine, had been too much for her after a very long day.

Pam looked greedily at the rum and chocolate mousse. 'It looks terrific! What is it?'

She had a large helping; Liza shook her head, smiling, and so did Pippa Morris, but Keir and his mother both ate some, and then they all moved back into the drawing-room to have coffee. Liza was having a problem hiding her yawns by then, and Keir noticed.

'Why don't you go up to bed? You look as if you're

half-asleep already. We'll look after Pam, won't we, Pam?'

Pam grinned cheerfully, helping herself to a chocolate mint. Liza eyed her sternly.

'You'll put on pounds at this rate!'

'You know I never do,' Pam said, and it was true. Liza made a face at Keir as he raised his brows enquiringly.

'She's one of those lucky people whose metabolism seems able to cope with any amount of food. Mind you, that may change as she gets older. At the moment she's always running around, exercising, working hard, burning up all those calories. When she stops living at that pace, she may not be able to eat anything she fancies.'

Pam took another mint, defiance in her eyes. 'Pooh,' she said, eating it.

Liza said goodnight amid laughter, and made her way into the great hall. She had one foot on the bottom stair when she heard the sound of cars pulling up outside on the drive, and the butler came slowly out of some back part of the house and moved to open the front door as someone crashed down the brass lion door-knocker.

Nicky Wallis and his team had arrived with Terry Lexington and a drowsy young secretary, who looked a little bemused as she followed the others into the oak-lined, vaulted hall.

'It's the House of Usher,' she said to Terry who grimaced at her.

'Ssh . . . our host may hear you.'

Liza turned to greet them a little reluctantly and Nicky looked her up and down, half in admiration, half in malice.

'You look very chic, lovie,' he said, his mouth curling. The rest of the arrivals stared at Liza, too—from her smooth blonde head, over her aquamarine silk dress, to her silver sandals. She had been clever in picking a Georgian-style dress, Nicky told her. 'It suits the house exactly—or did you know that? Have you been here before? You said you hadn't, but maybe Bruno did bring you down?'

'No, he didn't,' Liza said coolly. 'But I knew the house was eighteenth century, after all. It wasn't guesswork.'

'I'm starving,' the secretary wailed. 'They had drinks and sandwiches, but I can't eat in cars, it makes me sick.'

Keir appeared in time to hear that and smiled at the girl, who looked far too young to be working for Terry Lexington. Liza suspected her role in Terry's life was not entirely secretarial, but Keir, if he suspected that too, looked kindly at the girl.

'I've made arrangements for a cold buffet—it's laid out in the dining-room. My butler will show you the way after you've been up to your room.'

The girl looked completely knocked for six, pink and stammering. 'Oh, thanks, I . . . thanks.'

They all trooped up stairs, except Nicky's brawny young assistant who was ferrying heavy equipment into the house and asking, 'Where can I stack this safely, sir?'

The hall echoed with the tramp of feet, loud voices, clattering and bangs. Liza yawned and quietly went to bed, leaving them all to it. Their arrival had broken something; the gentle spell of the house, the warm summer evening, the candles in the old conservatory, the lazy voices and the lingering taste of white wine. Nicky and Terry and their crew were from another world altogether; they had crashed in on the deceptive idyll and made Liza remember she did not belong here, any more than they did.

She washed, undressed and was just getting into bed

when there was a tap on her door. Warily she put on her négligé and tied her belt tightly, then opened the door.

'Oh, I'm glad you hadn't had time to get to bed yet, my dear,' Keir's mother said, smiling warmly at her. 'I just wanted to check that you had everything you needed, that you were comfortable.'

'Oh—yes, thank you,' Liza said, her green eyes wide and startled, but warming with pleasure at the smile Keir's mother gave her.

'I've been looking forward to meeting you, Liza.'

'Have you?' Liza was bewildered by that. Did Mrs Gifford mean it, or was she just being polite? Keir had made it crystal clear that his family didn't think her suitable for Bruno, so why should Mrs Gifford have looked forward to meeting her?

'Ever since Keir talked to me about you,' Mrs Gifford nodded. 'Tomorrow we must manage to have some time alone, to talk without anyone else around. Maybe we could have tea together? I'll see what I can arrange. Goodnight, Liza, sleep well on your first night under Hartwell's roof.'

She was gone and Liza stood there, completely numb—what had all that been about? What had Keir said to his mother about her? A flush ran up her face— surely he hadn't told his mother how he had been pursuing her? Did men confide such things to their mothers? Even today, in these broad-minded times, Liza couldn't believe any man would cheerfully tell his mother he had tried to seduce some girl. And if it wasn't the truth Keir had told Mrs Gifford, what had he said?

She got into bed, sure she wouldn't sleep because she was so on edge, but she did. Outside the grounds and gardens were very quiet, almost silent except for the occasional sound of a bird or a rustling among undergrowth—a fox, perhaps, or a hedgehog or mouse. It was pitch-black out there tonight and very warm, humid—as if a storm was on the way. If it came, Liza would sleep through it.

She woke up very early next morning; the sky was mistily blue and the birds calling sleepily among the trees. After leaning on her window-sill for some time, Liza decided to go for a walk. She showered, put on lemon cotton slacks and a matching sleeveless top with a white and lemon overblouse, and quietly made her way out of the house. All was silent; nobody was about. They must all be sleeping late, including the servants, Liza thought, until she heard faint muffled sounds from the rear of the house later and realised that there were people working in the kitchens.

It was cooler than it had been; perhaps that storm had broken last night while she had slept? The immaculate lawns glistened with dew, and so did the formal rose-beds; red and white and full-hearted glossy pink. Liza wandered slowly, admiring the velvety flowers, watching a sleepy bumble-bee blundering from one to another on his first run of the day. He was the only bee out gathering pollen; like her he was an early riser, she thought, smilingly watching him.

A gate creaked behind her. She turned, startled, to see Keir coming from another garden. He halted, seeing her, his black brows lifting.

'You're up early!'

'So are you.'

He smiled wryly. 'A boring habit of mine, I'm afraid—picked up when I was a boy. I've never been able to stay in bed once I'm awake, and I'm always woken up by the first light. Napoleon had the same problem; he hated any light in his bedroom, even a candle outside in the corridor could wake him up.'

'Oh, something *else* you have in common with him!' commented Liza, fondling the soft, long ears of the black spaniels with him and, watching her, Keir looked amused.

'Other than what, or shouldn't I ask?'

'Megalomania?' she suggested demurely and he laughed.

'I knew it would be something like that, but you can't make me angry—not this morning, it's far too lovely.' His eyes slid over her with unhidden enjoyment. 'And so are you.'

She felt her colour heighten and hurriedly turned back towards the house, which stood among its gardens glowing in the early-morning light, the stone given a creamy gold warmth.

'Don't go in yet,' Keir said, catching her hand. 'Come for a walk with me. I haven't had a chance to get you alone yet.'

The back of her neck prickled tensely; he was using that voice which disturbed her, deep, warm, intimate. It made her edgy because she knew it aroused her, and she supected he knew it too.

'I don't think that would be a good idea,' she said, pulling free and walking quickly across the lawn, but Keir kept up with her and suddenly steered her sideways towards some stone steps leading to a lower terrace.

'Come and see the topiary,' he urged and Liza glanced downwards and was delighted by the yew trees clipped into the shapes of chessmen, peacocks, pyramids.

'How marvellous!' she said, moving towards them, and Keir told her that his mother had been very keen on topiary at one time, but she found it too tiring now and the gardeners kept the yews clipped into shape for her.

He was wearing very casual summer clothes this morning—an open-necked cream shirt without a tie, light blue trousers and some slip-on cream leather shoes that looked hand-made, they were so elegant. He talked about the topiary and his mother, and she listened, but her eyes were busy absorbing everything about him. His black hair gleamed in sunlight like a bird's wing, she thought, dreamily, and her mouth went dry because she knew she was falling in love and she couldn't stop herself. It was like falling down a deep, dark cavern towards the sound of the sea—a dreamlike, inevitable fate which she felt she had expected from the minute they had first met, although she had fought it off with angry reluctance.

'My mother has taken a liking to you,' he said, turning back to look at her after a glance at the dark green chessmen, and he saw that look in her face and bent towards her with a harshly indrawn breath. 'Liza!'

She pulled away and started walking back towards the house, saying unsteadily, 'I'm glad, I like your mother, too.'

'Don't run away,' he said, catching hold of her shoulders and holding her there, against his body, his head resting on her shoulder and his low voice close to her ear. 'Don't be scared of it, Liza. I'm not going to hurt you. You'll never be hurt through me, I promise you!'

'Men always make promises they don't mean to keep,' she said tightly.

'Are you going to waste the whole of your life because one man was a bastard?' he asked and she felt the bitter tension in the body pressing behind her, his angry breathing as if he had been running. He tightened his hold and whirled her to face him and looking up Liza saw a face which was white and drawn in lines of rage, or was it pain?

'Did you love him that much?' he asked, his blue eyes dark with violence, and she couldn't speak because he terrified her when he looked like that. 'What was his name?' Keir asked thickly. 'I'll find him and he'll pay—I promise you, he'll pay for what he did, Liza.'

She stared at him, stricken dumb, incredulous because she couldn't tell herself any more that Keir was only playing, chasing her for amusement, that he didn't really care about her. There was a fierce emotion in his face and she started shaking as if she was in shock. She was icy cold, convulsively shivering.

'Let me go,' she half sobbed, and Keir's hands released her slowly while he stared down at her pallor and distress.

'What . . .' he began and she didn't wait for him to finish the sentence, she turned and ran across the dew-wet grass, up the stone steps, towards the dreaming house trapped in a sunny web of summer.

She got back to her room without anyone seeing her and sat down on her bed, still trembling and still seeing inside her head Keir's face, the barbaric lines of jealousy and rage bitten into it.

She should not have come to his home; she couldn't keep him at arm's length while she was here, there were too many opportunities for them to meet. And she was rapidly becoming her own worst enemy, because she had begun to care for him; she was in love and constantly betraying herself. Her eyes, her body, were the traitors—she had begun to want him and Keir was far too clever to miss those telltale symptoms. He had seen them at once just now; either reading them in her face or intuitively picking up the vibrations in her body, and he hadn't hesitated in following up that advantage. All men were . . .

She broke off, groaning, burying her face in her shaky

hands. No, Keir wasn't like all men. She had felt the depth of feeling in his body just as he had felt it in hers. Their senses answered each other; her skin clung to his when they touched, her blood beat to the same rhythm. She must not lie to herself. Keir wasn't lying or deceiving her; it was real for him, too, and that was making her feel weak, helpless, hollow inside. Outside in the sunlit garden she had wanted to surrender to that feeling, to him, but she couldn't. She mustn't.

If she got hurt again she didn't know how she would survive it; she was no longer young enough to have the resilience of the first time. She had thought then that she would never get over it; but she had in time, scarred and embittered, but at last free of the pain and the longing.

Now she was safe, on a calm, happy plateau where day succeeded day in the same mood and no violent emotions swept her, there was no pain or fear. She had no highs and lows, but she had sanity, reason, a sense of contentment. She didn't want to be swept away by love again; she wanted her feet on the ground.

She stood up and walked to the window to stare out at the sunny garden—it looked so lovely out there, so peaceful, but the garden was full of predators and dangers; she must not stray into it alone again.

CHAPTER ELEVEN

It was another half an hour before Pam tapped on her door, and by then Liza had herself under control again and was able to smile and talk normally.

'I'm glad you're awake,' Pam said eagerly. 'I've been sitting in my room wondering what to do—I didn't like to go downstairs too early in case nobody was about, but I'm starving!'

Liza laughed. 'So am I, so we'll go and find some breakfast, shall we?'

There was no sign of Keir, but there was a lady in a blue dress carrying a tray of coffee and toast through the hall, so they followed her into a sunny morning-room overlooking the terraced lawns and found a number of the men sitting at a table, eating breakfast already. The woman was placing toast in front of Nicky Wallis, who was reading a newspaper. His assistant was eating bacon and egg, and Terry Lexington was drinking black coffee. They all looked up and greeted Liza and Pam.

'Sleep well? I slept like one of the dead,' said Nicky.

'It's so quiet here!' Pam said, sounding appalled. 'I couldn't hear a sound and I got real nervous; I kept listening, waiting for something, then I dropped off, I guess.'

'I wasn't expecting to see you up so early,' Liza said to the men, after telling the woman in blue that she didn't want a cooked breakfast, a slice of toast would do.

'We've got a lot to do today,' Nicky informed her briskly, folding his paper. 'We're going to walk around and find some locations. Want to come?'

'Oh, yes, please,' Pam said breathlessly and Liza nodded. She had no intention of being left behind. She was going to keep out of Keir's way while she was here, and staying close to the other men would be the best protection.

Just as they all left the table, Keir arrived with his sister and there was a brief chat, although Liza took no part in that, wandering into the hall and hovering there, waiting for the others. She hoped Keir wouldn't join them and was relieved to see that he wasn't among the group who headed towards the garden a few moments later. He was, it seemed, having breakfast with his sister.

He joined them an hour later and listened with intent interest to the discussions between Nicky and Terry. As those became more involved and technical, Liza discreetly slid away back to the house and found Pippa Morris arranging roses in a bowl in the hall, the deep, rich red of the petals reflected in the polished silver of the bowl. She worked slowly and methodically, her movements graceful, and Lisa watched her for a moment before walking towards her.

Looking up, Pippa said, 'Oh, hello—I thought you were all out in the gardens.'

'The others still are, but I got bored with all the technical details. I always did find them tedious.' Liza admired the roses, 'They're lovely, aren't they? Do you enjoy arranging flowers? I once read a book on doing that; it isn't as easy as it looks, is it?'

'Like modelling, then,' Pippa said drily and Liza laughed.

'I suppose that applies to all skills; whatever you do you have to practise and learn all the tricks of the trade, and it's never as glamorous as it looks.'

'Is it hot out there?' Pippa asked, gathering up the leaves and twigs she had discarded and pushing them into a wicker trug she had ready. 'I think I may sunbathe later, but first I'm going to have coffee with my mother. Why don't you join us?'

She was being much more friendly and Liza followed her into a small room full of neatly stacked boots and raincoats and sticks. Pippa emptied the trug's contents into a metal bin and stacked the trug among some others, then washed her hands in a basin on the wall opposite the door.

'This is a handy room,' she said and Liza blankly said she supposed it must be, which made Pippa laugh.

'No, I mean that that is what we call it. The handy room—we put all sorts of things in here, mostly to do with the garden. If you don't have somewhere special for them they get everywhere and litter up the place. My mother has a very tidy mind; it was her idea to use this old butler's pantry for all these things. Years ago this was where the butler kept his decanters and decanted the port and stuff like that—there's an old bell up above the door, in case he was urgently wanted while he was in here, which probably means he spent a lot of time in this room. He probably drank the port as well as decanting it, got a little drunk and slept it off! There was once an old armchair in here, but all the old stuff went when my mother had the room redecorated as a handy room.'

She loved the house; Liza heard it in her voice. How had she felt when her family had disowned her because of her marriage? Did she still nurse a lingering bitterness, or had time wiped it out?

They found Mrs Gifford in her private sitting-room, drinking coffee and listening to the radio. She leaned forward to turn it off as they arrived, smiling.

'I was beginning to think you had forgotten, Pippa. Hello, Liza, did you sleep well?' She patted a small, pink velvet chair. 'Sit down. Do you like your coffee with cream or black?'

Pippa relaxed in another chair and took her own coffee, nursing the bone china cup as she told her mother what a lovely day it was, adding, 'Our guests are all outside, exploring the gardens—except Miss Thurston, of course.'

'Liza,' Mrs Gifford said gently.

'Liza,' Pippa accepted, as though she still found it difficult to relax with Liza; she hadn't yet quite forgiven her for Bruno's dismissal to the States. Liza could understand that—mother and son were very close.

'What were you listening to?' Liza asked Mrs Gifford, who said it had been a music programme.

'You're fond of music?'

'Very fond—are you, Liza?' Mrs Gifford watched her with smiling interest as Liza nodded. They all talked of music for quite a while; then Pippa looked at her watch and said she had to fly, she had to meet somebody for lunch and must change.

'See you later, Liza,' she said, in quite a friendly voice, and as she left Liza stirred in her chair, realising that she ought to go too, but Mrs Gifford leaned forward and patted her hand, shaking her head.

'No, don't go, stay and talk to me, Liza. We may not get another chance!' Her smile was mischievous, amused. She had a criss-cross of fine lines in her face; yet her skin had a soft warmth which from a distance contradicted the fact of her age, and her smile was spontaneous, charming. Liza felt her heart contract as she admitted that she liked in Mrs Gifford what she recognised in Keir: the human warmth, the cool, calm intelligence, the charm, the humour. All Keir's qualities were there in the old woman's face; he was very much her son.

'Tell me about your childhood,' Mrs Gifford said, taking her by surprise.

'My childhood?' Liza repeated, eyes incredulous.

Mrs Gifford laughed. 'Don't you think a childhood makes an adult? When anyone talks about their childhood they tell me so much about themselves!'

'How unnerving! I think I'd be wiser not to tell you a thing!' Liza made a joke of it, laughing, but she was half serious—she did not want to betray anything to Keir's mother.

'Are you very secretive?' Mrs Gifford thought aloud, watching her. 'Or just wary of anyone knowing you too well?'

Liza smiled without answering, realising that the other woman was thinking aloud; it was a rhetorical question which needed no reply.

'You never told me which part of Wiltshire you came from?' Keir's mother asked.

'You probably wouldn't know it, it's just a small country town, half an hour away from Bath. Lovely country around there, very hilly; of course Bath is ringed with hills, it's that sort of countryside. You can see for miles from a hill just outside my old home, I used to walk up there on summer days with a few sandwiches and stay all day, lie on the grass and stare out over the woods and fields. They were such different colours; dark green trees and yellow corn and here and there splashes of scarlet poppies—like an enormous patchwork quilt.' She was talking very fast, burying the subject beneath a tidal wave of words, her voice restless, distressed. She hated remembering; she didn't want to think about her home, her family, the past.

'Which do you prefer, living in the town or the country?' asked Mrs Gifford quietly and Liza relaxed a little.

'Oh, the country, every time—that's why I have a cottage down on the estuary in Essex. I have a flat in town, too, but my *home* is in the countryside and I love it there. I sail and walk and ride whenever I'm at the cottage, but in town the most I can manage is an hour or two in the gym or the swimming pool.'

'Keir says you've been very successful with your agency. Are you still ambitious? Do you want to achieve other things?'

'I haven't really thought about it,' Liza said casually, then got up. 'I'd better go and find the others again, they'll be wondering where I am. Thank you for the coffee and the chat, Mrs Gifford. I enjoyed both very much.'

Keir's mother smiled a little ruefully, quite aware that Liza was fleeing from her questions. She said nothing, however, merely nodded.

'I'll see you later, Liza.' Her voice was gentle, but Liza was glad to get away. She liked Keir's mother very much, but that firm, insistent questioning was disturbing, and Liza found it hard to be offhand or downright rude to a woman of Mrs Gifford's age. Her instincts were to be courteous and tolerant, but Mrs Gifford had her son's tenacity and his belief that he knew best, and Liza had had to struggle with a desire to tell her to mind her own business several times that morning.

The day was growing very warm now. Liza was delighted to hear that Hartwell had its own swimming pool, and that afternoon, after a light salad lunch, they all swam and then sunbathed around the pool. It was an indoor one, but had a sun roof which electronically slid back when required so that you could have the best of both worlds. Keir had vanished, but his sister joined them in the pool and while they were lying on the striped red and white loungers the butler brought them iced drinks and some nuts, and a bowl of summer fruit: peaches and nectarines and strawberries.

'Pinch me, I'm dreaming,' Pam whispered, sitting up as the man departed and reaching for a strawberry which she slowly slid into her mouth with a beatific expression.

Liza turned her head to smile; she had been lying on her front for half an hour to get her shoulders brown, but the sun was so hot that she decided she ought to get up soon and adjust the striped umbrella to give her body a little more shade. The trouble was, she was too tired to move.

'Now I know how the idle rich live,' Pam said cheerfully, eating more strawberries. 'And I think it's great!'

Pippa Morris looked faintly offended, as if she thought Pam was talking about her.

Nicky was watching Pam and looking thoughtful. 'I think we could have a shot or two in here—the statuary and the plants are nice.' His eyes wandered around the long, tiled pool room; the water had an unreal blue shimmer, there were white statues elegantly placed on one side among a flurry of dark green tropical plants. The place did have the appearance of an advertisement in some glossy magazine, Liza thought drily, her mouth cynical. The house itself was absolutely real, but this place was an odd addition, although she was very glad of it this afternoon.

'I talked my mother into having this pool room built,' Pippa Morris said, slowly rubbing oil into her tanned skin. 'She can still swim, even if other exercise is difficult for her. She used to ride a lot, and walk and play golf, but she finds it hard now.'

'Oh, does this house belong to your mother, then?' asked Pam ingenuously. 'I thought your brother owned it.'

Pippa looked down her long nose. 'He does,' she said shortly.

'And he didn't mind having the pool built?' Pam pressed.

'If it was what my mother wanted, no,' Pippa said with obvious hauteur, and Liza suspected that she had talked her mother into asking Keir to have the pool room built. Did Keir realise that? Pippa was clearly sensitive on the point, but Pam was cheerfully unaware of that.

Liza heard a sound and turned over to see Keir walking towards them. He had changed into black swimming trunks and her pulses flickered with angry fire at the way he looked. He looked fantastic—it simply wasn't fair how sexy he looked, those long, long legs bare and tanned a warm gold, his hips lean and tapering, his chest a darker shade of brown except where the black coils of hair grew. Liza shut her eyes, but could still see him in her imagination, her body restless on the padded lounger.

The others greeted him, laughing. There was a splash and Liza felt a spray of cold water hit her hot skin, making her jump. Keir had dived into the pool and began to swim. Liza opened her eyes to watch his body sliding through the blue water, but when he came to the side and heaved himself out she got up and muttered that she was too hot, she was going to have a shower and go back to her bedroom.

Keir stood there, watching her, his stare wandering

over her slender body in the white bikini, and her breasts ached with aroused tension until she could get away from him.

She showered in one of the narrow changing rooms and towelled herself, then put on her cotton slacks and overblouse. She didn't know how much more of this she could stand—even when they weren't alone she felt the intensity of awareness between herself and Keir, and she couldn't help being afraid that the others would feel it too, soon.

She rested on her bed for a while later and drifted off to sleep, to be woken when the others came upstairs, talking and laughing after their afternoon by the pool, to change for dinner.

Pam tapped on her door and grinned at her, sun-flushed. 'I'm having a terrific time, are you, Liza?'

'Terrific,' Liza said brightly, her teeth aching from the effort of looking happy.

Pam vanished to dress and Liza slowly got ready, putting on a full-skirted white dress with a low, scooped neckline and a tiny waist. She trod into white high heels and sat at the dressing-table to put on her make-up and do her hair, listening to the sounds in the other rooms; running water, the slam of wardrobe doors, the bang of drawers. She felt oddly isolated; as though her troubled emotions set her apart, cut her off from the others in the party. She felt like someone on a desert island watching the busy waves running up and down on the sands, yet knowing there was no way of escaping.

She should never have accepted the invitation; she shouldn't have come here.

Keir would be changing for dinner now, so she felt it would be safe to go downstairs and drifted around the great hall, admiring the burnished armour and the bowls of roses; a strange pairing which was oddly poignant, especially where a few crimson petals had fallen and lay on the glowing wood of the floor, like spilt blood. Liza thought, staring, from some battle long ago.

That was when she heard music; familiar, haunting music from some old Fred Astaire film. She followed the sound and pushed open a double door to find herself on the threshold of a wide ballroom: parquet floor, pale eau-de-Nil walls, a chandelier and white curtains through which the late afternoon sun shafted poignantly. The music came from an old phonograph with a brass horn; an antique which had to be wound up with a large handle every so often.

Fascinated, Liza walked into the ballroom which seemed to be quite empty, but as her heels clicked on the parquet she heard a movement by the window and looked round with a start to see Keir turn to look at her. He was leaning on the deep bay window, the curtains blowing softly around him, hiding him from her until he turned.

'What a marvellous old gramophone,' she said huskily and he nodded, coming towards her.

He had a flower in his hand, she saw; a long-stemmed red rose, one of those from his sister's bowls of flowers in the great hall. He held it out and Liza took it wordlessly.

Keir put his arm out, staring into her eyes, and she didn't back away as he encircled her waist and drew her close. The music beat in her blood and she felt faint with pleasure and desire. She wanted to cry because it was so beautiful; the music, the sunlight, the empty room, the crimson rose and Keir holding her, moving against her with such fire and gentleness.

'I love you,' he said and the words had a finality which reached through her defences and made her weak. She couldn't think for the moment, she could only feel, and so she put her head down on his strong shoulder and let her body sway in his arms, surrendered to him.

Later, she would remember her fear, her need to protect herself, but at that instant nothing mattered but Keir's arms around her and the sweetness and rightness of loving him.

She never knew how long they danced; it must have been a matter of a moment because the record was slowing, dragging out the music, needing to be rewound, but for that brief spell they flowed in each other's arms around the sunlit room, in and out of shadows, with the white curtains blowing and their cheeks pressing against each other.

Then Keir stopped and leaned over to wind the gramophone and she had that time to think, her face paling, her heart beating far too fast.

'I can't,' she said and Keir looked quickly at her, his brows a black line above his vivid blue eyes.

'Stop running, darling. Start trusting me, you *can* trust me, Liza. You'll see. I'll never hurt you, never knowingly. I love you.'

'You don't understand!' she cried in anguish, remembering the past, and he held her very tightly, both arms round her.

'I do. You got badly burnt, but it's over, Liza. It's done with, and you have got to forget it or you'll never live fully again. You know I'm right, don't you? It's only common sense.'

'Perhaps,' she said, holding him at arm's length, fighting his arms, her blonde head flung back in agitation. 'But not with you, Keir. It wouldn't work.'

'Why not?' he frowned, watching her. His eyes saw far too much and she looked down, colour flowing up her face. 'Why not me?' Keir insisted harshly. 'I thought . . . are you saying you don't care? I was sure you did.' He suddenly caught her face in both hands and bent to kiss her urgently, his mouth hungry, fierce and hot, forcing down her weak attempt to resist him, wringing a reluctant response from her parted lips, until she stopped fighting altogether and her arms went round his neck as she kissed him back with the same need and passion. Once she had given in, she couldn't stop kissing him, she had been dying to all day, for ages, it seemed to have been for ever.

'Why not me?' Keir whispered at last, lifting his head and looking drowsily at her, his pupils huge and very black. His mouth was smiling in triumph, elation; he glittered with it and she groaned.

'Oh, Keir, listen . . . I have a hundred reasons, can't you see?'

'Name one.'

'I can't,' she wailed. 'I mean, I can't get involved with a man like you, I don't belong with all this, or with someone like you.'

'You belong to me and with me,' Keir said, kissing her neck deeply, his mouth pressed deep into her flesh. 'And I belong with you and to you. It's mutual, isn't it? You just told me, your mouth told me, you don't need words! We don't, Liza—we can kiss and know everything, can't we?'

Puzzled, she listened—know everything? she thought. *What* do I know about him? She had met him such a short time ago, and already she had known a dozen different Keir Giffords: the shabby, teasing man she met that first night in the mist, the elegant one in polo gear and knee-length polished boots, the formal city magnate in his pin-stripes and dark-windowed limousine, and this man, holding her in his arms, kissing her throat, whispering in that deep, husky voice which made her go hot and cold with passion.

But what was he, who was he—the man behind all the faces, the images, those bewildering, changing images of power and vitality?

'Only one thing matters,' Keir said and she was intent, needing to know—*what* mattered? He looked into her eyes and her body melted. He smiled and she shivered. He slowly brushed her mouth with his and she shut her eyes and moaned.

She was out of control; she had been for a long time now, even while she tried to pretend it wouldn't happen, couldn't happen.

'This matters,' Keir said softly. 'Just this—you and me.'

She was holding the rose he had given her; twisting the green stem in restless, tormented fingers. The thorns ran into her flesh, but she didn't even feel them then.

'But if it doesn't last?' she said. 'What if it all comes apart in our hands? I couldn't bear it, not again.' And she thought with wild helplessness: out of control, I'm out of control—must he look at me like that? He's turning my very bones to water. I wish he'd kiss me, I need to feel his mouth—I'd feel stronger if he would kiss me. Or weaker—but did it matter which?

'Liza, what do you want me to say? We can only try, like everybody else,' he said. 'Every other human being in the world who falls in love has to take the same risks. We're all in the same boat, we all want it to last for ever, but we can never know—we can only do our best, hang on and hope.' He was talking calmly, but his eyes weren't calm. Keir was fighting now, fighting for her; she saw the strain and urgency he was trying to hide and was shaken. Was Keir uncertain, after all? It wasn't like the Keir she had imagined, for she had never seen him on edge or distraught, as she suddenly sensed he could be now, behind that taut face.

'Your family will hate the idea of me . . . and you,' she muttered, frowning, confused and unsure.

'My mother likes you—she knows how I feel and she's happy about the idea.' Keir was watching her coaxingly, wanting her to believe him.

'You told her?' Liza had guessed, though; his mother had dropped more than one hint, and Liza instinctively knew that Mrs Gifford liked her. 'But it's more than that,' she said. 'There's your sister and . . . oh, everyone! I don't know if I could face all the fuss and the newspaper gossip and . . .'

'Liza,' Keir said, his voice harsh. 'None of this means a damn, you know that. I love you, that's the only thing that matters.'

She tore her eyes away and looked down at the rose she still held. That was when she saw the tiny spots of blood on her fingers and she started to smile, she didn't know why. Keir was right; even if it hurt, love was all that mattered. She slowly held the rose out to him and said huskily, laughingly, 'Mind the thorns!' and Keir threaded the rose through the lapel buttonhole on his jacket, and then he took her in his arms and held her for a long, long time, in total silence. They understood each other without needing to say a word, thought Liza. Why had she ever been afraid of losing control? Her instincts were wiser than she was.

BARBARY WHARF

THE BEGINNING...

Sir George Tyrrell, owner of the *Sentinel* newspaper, had brought his company close to bankruptcy with his over-ambitious plans to build a huge new complex at Barbary Wharf, an old dockland site on the Thames. Newspaper tycoon Nick Caspian stepped in, planning to buy the *Sentinel*. He approached Gina Tyrrell, the young widow of Sir George's dead grandson, James, to ask her to persuade Sir George to accept his terms.

Though Gina's best friend, foreign correspondent Roz Amery, warned her not to underestimate Nick, Gina could not help finding him disturbingly attractive, but, having a deep sense of loyalty to her dead husband and to Sir George, she continued to keep Nick at a distance.

Things seemed to be sorting themselves out when Sir George made a deal with Nick by which they would share the control of the company fifty-fifty. This left Gina free to admit that she had fallen in love with Nick, who seemed serious about her, but when Sir George discovered that Nick had made a secret bid for shares owned by another director, which would give Nick an overall majority and wrest control from Sir George's hands, his anger at Nick's apparent betrayal was such that he had a fatal heart attack and died. Hurt and confused, Gina bitterly told Nick that she would never forgive him, and that a day would come when she would make him pay for what he had done to Sir George, and to the *Sentinel*.

Book One:
BESIEGED

Gina Tyrrell knew Nick Caspian was trouble the moment she met him. Despite his good looks, he was a ruthless and dangerous man. Everyone thought so, even Hazel, who had a good word to say about everyone. Well, almost. She just couldn't stand Piet Van Leyden—Nick's chief architect and one of the most arrogant know-alls she had ever met! As far as Gina and Hazel were concerned, these men were twentieth-century warriors, and they were the ones being besieged.

AVAILABLE NOW!
£2.99

WORLDWIDE

Book Three:
TOO CLOSE FOR COMFORT

Irena Olivero was the talk of the *Sentinel*. Shy, demure, and very beautiful, she was extremely sought after, so why should Esteban Sebastian, the dashing marketing director with the fiery temper, always be trying to pick a fight with her? They were almost as bad as Nick and Gina, whose never-ending arguments were legendary. In both cases, however, though they sometimes appeared too close for comfort, it was soon becoming obvious that things were not quite what they seemed.

AVAILABLE NOW!

£2.99

WORLDWIDE

Book Four:
PLAYING HARD TO GET

Gib Collingwood, the charming but cheeky Finance Editor, had been after Valerie Knight for ages, but despite her obvious enjoyment in his company, the witty feature writer seemed determined to have nothing serious to do with him. Was she playing hard to get, or just following in the footsteps of her admired employer, Gina Tyrrell, whose rejection of *Sentinel* boss Nick Caspian appeared equally unjustified, equally cruel...

AVAILABLE NOW!
£2.99

WORLDWIDE

Book Five:
A SWEET ADDICTION

Both Guy Faulkner and Sophie Watson had been abandoned by the people they loved. But Sophie at least was determined that she would not allow her rejection to be the springboard for falling in love with a man like Guy—however sweet and nice he was. The same could be said for Gina Tyrrell, who was becoming increasingly confused over how she felt about Nick Caspian. Love him or leave him—the man just would not go away…

AVAILABLE NOW!

£2.99

WORLDWIDE

RELENTLESS AMBITIONS, SHOCKING SECRETS AND POWERFUL DESIRES

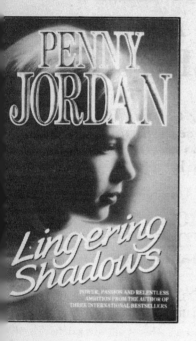

Penny Jordan's stunning new novel is not to be missed!

The dramatic story of six very different people—irrevocably linked by ambition and desire, each must face private demons in a riveting struggle for power. Together they must find the strength to emerge from the lingering shadows of the past, into the dawning promise of the future.

WORLDWIDE

AVAILABLE AUGUST 1993   PRICED £4.99

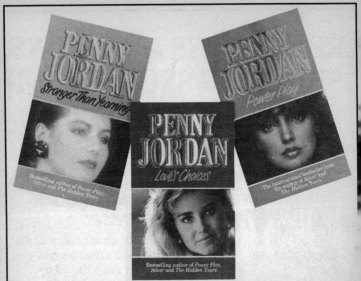

BETRAYALS, INTRIGUE
AND REVENGE . . .

LOVE'S CHOICES   £3.99

A sensitive story of a young girl's passionate journey into
womanhood. Hope Stanford quickly realised she was no
match for the ruthless Comte Alexei Serivace, but is nevertheless drawn into his subtle plan for revenge.

STRONGER THAN YEARNING   £3.99

With nothing in common but their hatred for the Deveril
family, both Jenna Stevens and James Allingham needed to
buy the Old Hall in recompense. Allingham was a determined
opponent, but Jenna would not allow him to stand in her way.

POWER PLAY   £3.99

Pepper Minesse had paid dearly for her success. For ten years
her thirst for revenge had fuelled her ambition and made her
rich. But now it was time for the four men who had raped her as
a teenager to pay too – their futures for her past.

WORLDWIDE

*Available from W. H. Smith, John Menzies, Martins, Forbuoys,
most supermarkets and other paperback stockists.
Also available from Worldwide Reader Service, FREEPOST, PO Box 236,
Thornton Road, Croydon, Surrey CR9 9EL. (UK Postage & Packing free)*

BY THE SAME AUTHOR

ANTIGUA KISS £3.99

Ash Lambard offered Christiana escape with a life in the sun on a lovely Caribbean island. He also offered her marriage. Christiana agreed to become his wife – but on certain conditions. Ash accepted her terms, until their wedding night when she found he'd no intention of keeping his word.

FLORA £3.99

A delicate Eurasian beauty who moved between two worlds, but was shunned by both. An innocent whose awakened fires could be ignited by only one man. This sensuous tale sweeps from remotest China to the decadence of old Shanghai, reaching its heart-stirring conclusion in the opulent Longwarden mansion and lush estates of Edwardian England.

SUMMER'S AWAKENING £3.99

A life-long battle had kept Summer Roberts isolated and insecure. Computer tycoon James Gardiner's entry into her sheltered world was devastating in more ways than one. Through his kindness and unintentional cruelty she emerged a slender, beautiful woman – sure of herself, and sure of her love.

WORLDWIDE